Best Wishes,

Tom Atchinson.

Many thanks for all your
hard work + support for
the city

Dald.

EDINBURGH

Biographies and Acknowledgements

Photographs by Dennis Hardley and Douglas Corrance

Photographer **Dennis Hardley** was born in 1940, in a Blitz-sieged Liverpool. His teenage years were spent doing odd jobs for The Beatles before becoming a Concorde engineer. In 1972, as an RAF civilian, Dennis began photography, supplying pictures to *Scots Magazine*. In 1974, he moved to Oban. Dennis has driven over 1,000,000 miles while photographing all aspects of Scotland.

Photographer **Douglas Corrance** was brought up in Inverness where he started as a photographer on the local newspaper. After 11 years with the Scottish Tourist Board he went freelance and subsequently produced guides on India, Japan, France and New York, along with several books on Scotland.

For Claudia and Paul
Author **Sonya Newland** is a full time editor and has written books on Ireland and England, she has a particular fascination with all aspects of history and tradition.

With thanks to David Bradley-Bird, Keith Irvine and Rebecca Gilfedder for their help and hospitality.

With grateful thanks to Helen Courtney who designed this book.

Dennis Hardley 14, 15, 18, 19, 21, 23, 24, 25, 51, 59, 87, 92, 93, 95, 99, 106, 111, 119, 121, 126, 127, 131, 133, 135, 139, 141, 147, 148, 149, 151, 153, 155, 156, 157, 162, 181, 183, 185, 187, 188, 191, 193, 194, 195. **The Bridgeman Art Library** 197. The following pictures are all courtesy of **The Still Moving Picture Co.** and: **Douglas Corrance** 17, 20, 30, 31, 32, 33, 34, 35, 38, 39, 40, 41, 42, 43, 46, 47, 48, 49, 52, 53, 54, 55, 57, 60, 61, 62, 63, 67, 68, 69, 70, 72, 75, 76, 77, 78, 80, 81, 82, 86, 89, 90, 96, 97, 98, 100, 101, 102, 103, 107, 108, 109, 112, 113, 114, 115, 116, 117, 120, 122, 132, 134, 138, 144, 145, 146, 152, 154, 160, 161, 163, 164, 165, 167, 170, 172, 174, 175, 176, 177, 180, 182, 186, 192. Ken Paterson 28. STB 29, 71, 73, 171, 173. Derek Laird 37, 66, 83, 128, 129, 137. Derek Braid 56. S. J. Taylor 79, 88, 91, 123, 140, 169. Paul Tomkins/STB 166. Michael Good 189.

ISBN 1 84204034 0

This edition published by Lomond Books 2001

First published by
Parragon
Queen Street House
4 Queen Street
Bath BA1 1HE, UK

Copyright © Parragon 1999

Produced by Foundry Design and Production.

Printed in Korea

EDINBURGH

PHOTOGRAPHS BY DENNIS HARDLEY & DOUGLAS CORRANCE

Text by Sonya Newland

LOMOND BOOKS

Contents

INTRODUCTION 8

THE MAGIC OF EDINBURGH 13
Edinburgh Castle by Night 14
Silhouette of Edinburgh from Calton Hill 15
Arthur's Seat 16
The Pentland Hills 18
Bass Rock 19
Fireworks 20
Statues in Waverley Market 21
Clock Tower 22
Fidra Lighthouse 24
Poppy Fields, Dunbar 25

TRADITION & ENTERTAINMENT 26
Ghost Tours 28
Ross Open Air Theatre 29
Edinburgh Festival Fringe 30
Edinburgh International Festival 31
Military Tattoo 32
Scots Guard 33
Traverse Theatre 34
Festival Theatre 35
Usher Hall 36
Royal Highland Show 38
Edinburgh Zoo 39
One O'Clock Gun, Edinburgh Castle 40
Procession, Royal Mile 41
Playhouse Theatre 42
Museum of Childhood 43

KIRKS & CATHEDRALS 44
St Mary's Episcopalian Cathedral 46
Aerial View, St Mary's Episcopalian Cathedral 47
St John's Kirk 48
Dalmeny Kirk 49
St Mary's Church, Haddington 50
St Andrew and St George's 52

Tron Kirk 53
St Margaret's Chapel, Edinburgh Castle 54
Canongate Kirk 55
Apprentice Pillar, Rosslyn Chapel 56
St Anthony's Chapel 57
St Cuthbert's Kirk 58
Corstorphine Church 60
Greyfriars Kirkyard 61
High Kirk of St Giles 62
Thistle Chapel, High Kirk of St Giles 63

LIFE & CULTURE 64
Scotch Whisky Heritage Centre 66
Royal Museum of Scotland 67
Parliament Square 68
Waverley Station 69
Old Observatory, Calton Hill 70
Camera Obscura 71
The City Chambers 72
Register House 73
Edinburgh International Conference Centre 74
Royal Bank of Scotland 76
West Register House 77
National Gallery of Scotland 78
Divinity College, Edinburgh University 79
Murrayfield Stadium 80
Meadowbank Stadium 81
Braid Hill Golf Course 82
Balmoral Hotel 83

THE OLD & THE NEW 84
The New Town 86
The Old Town 87
Victoria Street 88
White Horse Close 89
Moray Place 90
St Andrew's Square 91
Castlehill, The Royal Mile 92
The Mound 93
North Bridge 94
Tenement Housing, Marchmont 95
Fan Window, The New Town 97

The Royal Mile 98
Princes Street 99
Mylne's Court 100
Charlotte Square 101
Ramsay Garden 102
Ann Street 103

PARKS & WATERS 104
Princes Street Gardens 106
The Floral Clock 107
Dunsapie Loch 108
Newhaven Fishmarket 109
The Firth of Forth 110
Royal Botanic Garden 112
The Glasshouse, Royal Botanic Garden 113
Duddingston Loch 114
Holyrood Park 115
St Bernard's Well 116
The Meadows 117
Smug Anchorage, Cramond 118
St Margaret's Loch 120
Musselburgh Harbour 121
The Port of Leith 122
Union Canal 123

STATUES & MONUMENTS 124
National Monument, Calton Hill 126
Memorial to the Royal Scots Greys 127
Nelson Monument, Calton Hill 128
The Mercat Cross 129
Dugald Stewart Monument, Calton Hill 130
Greyfriars Bobby 132
Ross Fountain 133
Sherlock Holmes Statue 134
The Scott Monument 135
Burns Monument 136
Statue of George IV 138
Memorial Cannon, Calton Hill 139
Statue of Allan Ramsay 140
Statue of Field Marshal Haig 141

CASTLES & STATELY HOMES 142
The Palace of Holyroodhouse 144
Carving, Palace of Holyroodhouse 145
Lauriston Castle 146
Stevenson House 147
Tantallon Castle 148
Dirleton Castle 149
Blackness Castle 150
Craigmillar Castle 152
Dalmeny House 153
Edinburgh Castle, Spring 154
Penicuik House 155
Hopetoun House 156
Linlithgow Palace 157

HISTORIC EDINBURGH 158
Gladstone's Land 160
Holyrood Abbey 161
Edinburgh Castle, Late Afternoon 162
The Honours of Scotland, Edinburgh Castle 163
Roman Fort, Cramond 164
Old Royal High School 165
Grassmarket 166
Robert Louis Stevenson's House, Heriot Row 167
The Heart of Midlothian 168
Waterloo Bridge 170
John Knox's House 171
Canongate Tolbooth (The People's Story) 172
Inchcolm Abbey 173
Lady Stair's House (The Writer's Museum) 174
Deacon Brodie's Tavern 175
Gillespie Plaque 176
Huntly House Museum 177

AROUND EDINBURGH 178
Swanston Village 180
Inveresk Village 181
Dean Village 182
Stenton Village 183
Preston Mill, East Linton 184
Portobello Beach 186
Gifford Village 187
Dirleton Village 188
The Colonies, Stockbridge 189
Inn at Cramond 190
Hawes Inn, South Queensferry 192
Culross Village 193
Forth Road Bridge 194
Forth Rail Bridge 195

EDINBURGH PAST & PRESENT 196

INDEX 198

Contents by Region

The Royal Mile

Edinburgh Castle by Night	14
Fireworks	20
Ghost Tours	28
Edinburgh Festival Fringe	30
Edinburgh International Festival	31
Military Tattoo	32
Scots Guard	33
One O'Clock Gun, Edinburgh Castle	40
Procession, Royal Mile	41
Museum of Childhood	43
Tron Kirk	53
St Margaret's Chapel, Edinburgh Castle	54
Canongate Kirk	55
High Kirk of St Giles	62
Thistle Chapel, High Kirk of St Giles	63
Scotch Whisky Heritage Centre	66
Parliament Square	68
Camera Obscura	71
City Chambers	72
The Old Town	87
White Horse Close	89
Castlehill, The Royal Mile	92
The Royal Mile	98
Ramsay Garden	102

Mylne's Court	100
The Mercat Cross	129
Statue of Field Marshal Haig	141
The Palace of Holyroodhouse	144
Carving, Palace of Holyroodhouse	145
Edinburgh Castle, Spring	154
Holyrood Abbey	161
Lady Stair's House (The Writer's Museum)	174
Gladstone's Land	160
Gillespie Plaque	176
John Knox's House	171
Edinburgh Castle, Late Afternoon	162
The Honours of Scotland, Edinburgh Castle	163
Huntly House Museum	177
Canongate Tolbooth (The People's Story)	172
Deacon Brodie's Tavern	175
The Heart of Midlothian	168

Southern Edinburgh

Traverse Theatre	34
Festival Theatre	35
Usher Hall	36
Greyfriars Kirkyard	61
Royal Museum of Scotland	67
Edinburgh International Conference Centre	74
Divinity College, Edinburgh University	79
Victoria Street	88
Tenement Housing, Marchmont	96
The Meadows	117
Greyfriars Bobby	132
Grassmarket	166

The New Town

Edinburgh from Calton Hill	15
Statues in Waverley Market	21
Clock Tower, Princes Street	22
Ross Open Air Theatre	29
Playhouse Theatre	42
St Mary's Episcopal Cathedral	46
Aerial View, St Mary's Episcopal Cathedral	47
St John's Kirk	48
St Andrew and St George's	52
St Cuthbert's Kirk	58
Waverley Station	69
Old Observatory, Calton Hill	70
Register House	73
Royal Bank of Scotland	76
West Register House	77
National Gallery of Scotland	78
Balmoral Hotel	83
The New Town	86
Moray Place	90
St Andrew's Square	91
North Bridge	94
Fan Window, New Town	97
Princes Street	99
Charlotte Square	101

The Mound	93
Princes Street Gardens	106
The Floral Clock	107
National Monument, Calton Hill	126
Memorial to the Royal Scots Greys	127
Nelson Monument, Calton Hill	128
Dugald Stewart Monument, Calton Hill	130
Ross Fountain	133
Sherlock Holmes Statue	134
The Scott Monument	135
Burns Monument	136
Statue of George IV	138
Memorial Cannon, Calton Hill	139
Statue of Allan Ramsay	140
Old Royal High School	165
Robert Louis Stevenson's House, Heriot Row	167
Waterloo Bridge	170

The Suburbs

Arthur's Seat	16
Edinburgh Zoo	39
Royal Highland Show	38
Dalmeny Kirk	49
Corstorphine Church	60
St Anthony's Chapel, Holyrood Park	57
Murrayfield Stadium	80
Meadowbank Stadium	81
Ann Street, Stockbridge	103
Dunsapie Loch, Holyrood Park	108
Newhaven Fishmarket	109
Royal Botanic Garden	112
Glasshouse, Royal Botanic Garden	113
Duddingston Loch, Holyrood Park	114
Holyrood Park	115
St Bernard's Well, Dean Village	116
Smug Anchorage, Cramond	118
St Margaret's Loch, Holyrood Park	120
Musselburgh Harbour	121

The Port of Leith	122
Lauriston Castle	146
Craigmillar Castle	152
Dalmeny House	153
Hopetoun House	156
Roman Fort, Cramond	164
Inchcolm Abbey	173
Dean Village	182
Portobello Beach	186
The Colonies, Stockbridge	189
Inn at Cramond	190
Hawes Inn, South Queensferry	192
Forth Road Bridge	194
Forth Rail Bridge	195

Edinburgh Environs

The Pentland Hills	18
Bass Rock	19
Fidra Lighthouse	24
Poppy Fields, Dunbar	25
St Mary's Church, Haddington	50
Apprentice Pillar, Rosslyn Chapel	56
Braid Hill Golf Course	82
The Firth of Forth	110
Union Canal	123
Stevenson House	147
Tantallon Castle	148
Dirleton Castle	149
Blackness Castle	150
Penicuik House	155
Linlithgow Palace	157
Swanston Village	180
Inveresk Village	181
Stenton Village	183
Preston Mill, East Linton	184
Gifford Village	187
Dirleton Village	188
Culross Village	193

INTRODUCTION

E dinburgh is a city of contrasts: its diversity of character, landscape, architecture and history combine to make it a truly magical and unique place. The city's origins are ancient: archaeological evidence suggests that settlements existed on the formidable Castle Rock thousands of years BC, and since this time, Edinburgh has slowly expanded its boundaries, embracing a variety of characteristics that reflect every age which has contributed to the capital's rich and dramatic history.

The name 'Edinburgh' is believed to derive from the sixth-century settlement name 'Dun Eidyn', meaning 'Fort of Edin', and in its time this settlement marked the boundary between Scotland and England. The most significant moment in Edinburgh's history, however, really lies in the foundation of the castle in the eleventh century, for it was around this time that the city began to grow and prosper. Since its first stones were laid the castle has been the main focus of the city. Its importance has not diminished in nearly 900 years, and the castle's significance is as strong today as it was in ancient times – it is the symbol of Scotland's capital.

Like most capital cities, Edinburgh's fortunes have fluctuated over the centuries, and the city has witnessed some of Scotland's finest hours and darkest days. During the twelfth century, as the castle expanded and the abbey was founded at Holyrood, a town began to develop along what is now known as the Royal Mile, and by the mid-fifteenth century, the town had been granted a charter and was surrounded by its own walls. These would be needed, for Edinburgh became the focus of numerous attacks – political, religious and territorial – largely from the ever-present enemy to the south: England.

The English victory at the Battle of Flodden in 1513 was the start of hard times for Edinburgh. Determined to gain permanent rule over the Scots, the English monarchs sought unions with the Scottish royals. Mary, Queen of Scots, fled to France in an attempt to escape a union with the young Prince Edward, Henry VIII's only son. She returned in 1561 to a country rife with religious dissension and turmoil. A devout Catholic herself, Mary came into conflict on a number of occasions with the minister of

St Giles, John Knox – a Protestant reformer who, having spent some time exiled in Europe, had been strongly influenced by Calvinist ideals, and was now preaching these reforms to a responsive Edinburgh population. The tide of reform was too strong for Mary to turn back, and her downfall was tragic, but absolute. Her overthrow led eventually to a change in Edinburgh's role as capital, when her son James VI became James I of England on the death of Elizabeth I, uniting the thrones of the former enemies and moving the seat of the monarchy to London.

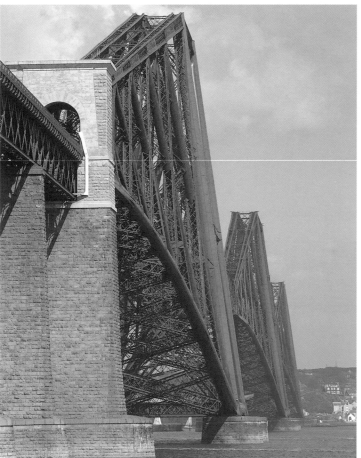

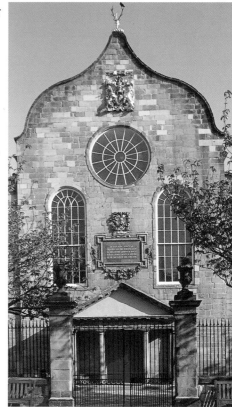

The century that followed was characterised by a series of religious struggles initiated by the introduction of Episcopacy to Scotland. This move, instigated by Charles I, was vastly unpopular in the north, and the aptly named 'killing times' ensued. It was at this time that the signing of the National Covenant took place at Greyfriars, and the subsequent rebellions meant persecution, imprisonment and death for many. Episcopacy was eventually overthrown – and the king executed – and the Presbyterian sect began to gain momentum. To this day it remains the main

religious following in Scotland. Edinburgh subsequently survived Oliver Cromwell and his armies and the Restoration, but with the Act of Union in 1707, the city's importance once again declined.

The tide of the Industrial Revolution brought about a turn in Edinburgh's fortunes, and although the city itself avoided succumbing completely to industry, in the way many northern cities did, the arrival of the railroads and other conveniences enhanced and broadened the professional opportunities that had previously been limited. The Age of Enlightenment burned bright in Scotland's capital city, as huge steps were taken in scientific and medical research, helped by the old and well-renowned university. The changes in art, architecture and literature manifested themselves in the very heart and soul of the city and the eighteenth and nineteenth centuries were acknowledged as Edinburgh's heyday. Some of the city's pre-eminent citizens hail from this period – architects, designers, sculptors, novelists and poets. The conception, and eventual creation, of the New Town epitomises the prosperity and magnificence of this era.

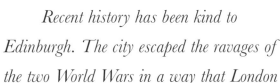

Recent history has been kind to Edinburgh. The city escaped the ravages of the two World Wars in a way that London did not. As a result, the architecture – from the Old Town tenements to the gracious New Town façades – has remained untouched, and the essential character of the capital is undiminished. After the Second World War there arose the newest of Edinburgh's traditions, one for which the city is best known – the Edinburgh International Festival. Today, thousands upon thousands of people flood to the city during the summer months to take in the spectacle of every conceivable form of entertainment.

Every step one takes through the streets of Edinburgh echoes this rich and fascinating history. The slabs of the Grassmarket cry out with the blood of the martyred Covenanters; the crowded closes along the Royal Mile reverberate with the hubbub of the densely populated seventeenth-century Old Town; the sweeping avenues and carefully planned squares of James Craig's New Town reek of Georgian elegance and luxury. The people – rich and poor, kings and paupers, merchants and criminals – who have

each played their part in the capital's story – walk the streets still. Tales of ghosts and spirits, mystery and magic are an integral feature of Edinburgh, and the city's evocative atmosphere, particularly in the Old Town, makes it easy to believe such tales.

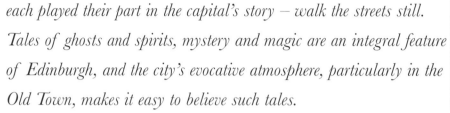

Edinburgh has many attractions, and a visitor can spend weeks experiencing them all: admiring the careful preservation of so many fine buildings; marvelling at the craftsmanship of the many monuments, carvings and interiors; enjoying the variety of entertainments, theatres and museums; basking in the beauty of the parks and gardens; and soaking up the history of this ancient city. But the real joy of Edinburgh lies in the breathtaking mixture of all these attractions, and the unique and marvellous atmosphere

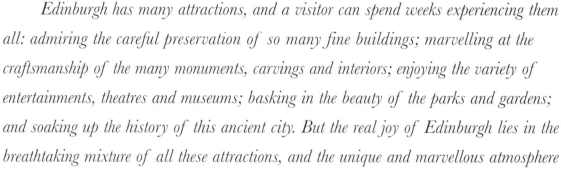

they combine to create here. Somehow, despite the diversity of style and structure, the city maintains a harmonious feel. The city has grown from small and humble roots, spread out geographically and boomed in terms of population. The modern and the ancient are embraced in Edinburgh in a welcoming and unconcerned manner. Nothing seems out of place. Even the sprawling Old Town has its own peculiar symmetry. There is a tale to tell on every corner and there is a welcome at every turn. The pleasure that can be gained from a visit to Scotland's magical capital, an exploration of its beautiful suburbs or a trip out into the beauty of the surrounding Lothian countryside, is inescapable and intoxicating.

THE MAGIC OF EDINBURGH

The magic of Edinburgh is evident at every turn: its great history, its diversity of architecture, its verdant parks and tranquil waters, all combine to create the unique and enchanting atmosphere that embraces this breathtaking city.

Edinburgh Castle
CASTLEHILL

The castle is the most impressive and mysterious feature of this ancient city. There have been settlements on Castle Rock – a craggy outcrop from an extinct volcano – from the earliest times. It is even possible that Stone Age men gathered here up to 8,000 years ago, hunting in the dense woods that long ago covered the whole of Edinburgh. Archaeological evidence dating from the Bronze Age – around 1000 BC – has been found, when it is believed people first lived on the rock.

Over the centuries the castle has grown, been fortified, destroyed and rebuilt on numerous occasions, but has remained the focal point of the city since it was first built. From the highest points of the castle, the rich and varied Scottish landscape stretches out for miles, encompassing rolling hills and dark crags, busy towns and quiet hamlets, valleys and rivers. From here, the threat of enemy attack could be spotted many miles distant and prepared for – its situation on the peak of the sheer cliff face being its most reliable defence. From anywhere in the city, the castle can be seen in all its ancient mystery and glory.

Silhouette of Edinburgh
FROM CALTON HILL

The views from the top of Calton Hill are more all-encompassing than from anywhere else, especially if one climbs to the highest viewpoint –the top of the Nelson Monument. The Firth of Forth stretches away to the north and east; to the south lies the dark roofs of the Old Town, the verdant Holyrood Park and the un-mistakable outcrop of the Salisbury Crags; in the west the lively bustle of the New Town is visible, and high on the ridge the castle, dark and brooding, surveys its kingdom.

Like the other hills in the area, Calton is part of Edinburgh's volcanic legacy, and long ago its associations were dark and mysterious. Many illegal executions took place here, away from the prying eyes of the law, and it was a popular place for duels to be fought, as well as secret romantic meetings. In its time it was also a haunt for Ladies of the Night (it is known that Robert Louis Stevenson had a great interest in the evening trade on Calton Hill). Today the hill is a veritable mausoleum of monuments and had Edinburgh's best architects tried to conceive a suitable building for these pieces, they could not have come up with a more perfect setting than the one nature has provided.

Arthur's Seat
HOLYROOD PARK

Arthur's Seat is Edinburgh's most famous natural landmark. Rising dramatically to 251 metres (823 ft) above sea level, this impressive volcanic crag gives off an air of ancient calm. It has seen the area's first people settle at its foot; it has seen the building of the castle on the rock to the west and the growth of the city around it; it has stood silent sentry while battles raged below, and the history of a nation unfolded.

It is believed its name derives from the ancient Gaelic phrase 'Ard-na-Said', or 'Height of Arrows', a reference either to its previous use as an old hunting ground, or to its lofty position. Arthur's Seat is reached by a roadway that starts in Holyrood Park, and it is well worth the climb. From the summit of the crag a panorama of a typical Scottish landscape can be seen – truly one of the finest in the Lothians. On a clear day, it is even possible to see the southernmost peaks of the Highlands. It is a local tradition to greet the summer solstice from the top of Arthur's Seat and, despite the crowds, is one of this beautiful city's loveliest customs.

The Pentland Hills
SOUTH-WEST EDINBURGH

It has been said that the Pentland Hills are a miniature version of the Highlands, and they are just as beautiful, if slightly less dramatic. They run south-westwards from Edinburgh in a rolling green stretch nearly 8 km (5 miles) wide.

The village of Swanston (see page 180) is nestled at the foot of the Pentlands. The writer Robert Louis Stevenson spent some time here, and he is said to have had a great love of the area, particularly the hills surrounding the village. This is perfect walking country, and there are a number of routes that can be followed through the hills. It is even possible to follow the old paths made by the cattle drovers in centuries past. All the walks provide an abundance of spectacular views, and the landscape is truly magical. Higher up in the hills, the moorland is carpeted with heather and bracken, and small streams and rivers wend their way through the high grasses. This is one of the best places to escape to from the bustle and noise of the city centre.

Bass Rock
FIRTH OF FORTH

The strange lump of basalt known as 'Bass Rock' lies 2½ km (1½ miles) out in the Firth of Forth, and for centuries has been a landmark for sailors, because of the lighthouse that stands on it, and because of its distinctive size and shape. Bass Rock, another of Edinburgh's volcanic legacies, is 1 mile in circumference and 107 metres (350 ft) high.

This rock has been made use of over the years – from early times a castle stood here, evidence of which can still be seen. It is also said that the seventh-century hermit St Baldred made his home on Bass Rock and later died here. The young James I stopped on the rock on his way to seek sanctuary in France in 1406. Both Covenanters and Jacobite rebels have been imprisoned on the rock.

Today, like many other islands in the Forth, Bass Rock is a harsh and uninhabited place, haunted by seabirds, particularly gannets, whose cries echo through this relic of Scotland's history.

Fireworks
THE OLD TOWN

For three weeks in August each year, during the Edinburgh International Festival, the city comes alive with drama and spectacle, culminating in the Military Tattoo on the castle esplanade. Breathtaking firework displays, such as the one pictured here, have become a common feature. Full of pomp and circumstance against the magnificent backdrop of the floodlit castle, they light up the impressive Edinburgh skyline for miles around, a fitting end to the celebrations.

It is not only at Festival time that the city plays host to such displays, though. All year round, Edinburgh is haven of lively activity and entertainment. Street performers and bagpipers can be found on every corner and in every open area across the city; the theatres, of which Edinburgh has an abundance, provide a surprising variety of shows, from West End musicals to the very latest in alternative drama. Opera, comedy, film, professional and amateur alike, are all catered for here. It cannot be denied that Edinburgh is the social and cultural heart of Scotland.

Statues in Waverley Market
PRINCES STREET

The Waverley Shopping Centre is one of Edinburgh's most successful modern developments. Situated in the heart of the city's commercial area, at the east end of Princes Street, the underground centre is much admired for its tasteful interior design, replete with plants and water.

Its roof serves as a popular stage for street performers, a wide open piazza made of pale grey granite – a striking contrast to the honey-coloured sandstone that characterises the majority of the New Town. The curious collection of statues that adorn this roof-top enhance the modern feel of the area. They were created by the English sculptor Crispin Guest and erected in 1991. As the sun rises in the east these eerie figures are silhouetted against the backdrop of Princes Street and the nearby Waverley Station, creating a dramatic spectacle. Despite the predominance of classical statues and monuments all around Edinburgh, there are a also number of modern sculptures like these to be found, indicating the old city's willingness to embrace the new.

Clock Tower
PRINCES STREET

The clock tower at the east end of Princes Street is one of the most dramatic and dominant features of Edinburgh's impressive evening skyline. As night falls over the New Town, an astonishing array of illuminations – on shops, monuments, public buildings and especially the North Bridge – set the whole area aglow with their light and colour. The richness of many of the old buildings is shown off to its best advantage by this modern enhancement.

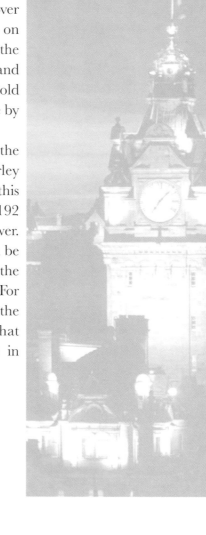

The clock tower is actually part of the Balmoral Hotel, situated near Waverley Station, and it is the *pièce de résistance* of this magnificent building: it stands 59 metres (192 ft) high on the top of a bold, square tower. The clock's face is floodlit at night and can be seen for many miles around. Surmounting the clock itself is a wrought-iron lantern. For many years it has been a tradition to keep the clock running two minutes fast, so that travellers using Waverley Station will be in time for their trains.

Fidra Lighthouse
FIDRA ISLAND

This lighthouse stands on Fidra Island, one of four small islands off the coast of North Berwick. The other three islands are Craigleith, Lamb and Eyebroughty. Robert Louis Stevenson spent a few years of his childhood here, and it is said that Fidra was the early inspiration for his best-loved novel *Treasure Island*. Despite his later travels across the world, eventually making his home in Samoa, Stevenson was to remain profoundly affected by the people and the places he experienced during his youth in Scotland. Fidra is now a wild and forlorn-looking place, rocky and dark – a perfect place to let the imagination run wild. As well as the lighthouse, Fidra is home to the ruins of an ancient Celtic monastery, some of the oldest such remains in the Edinburgh area.

This photograph was taken from the shores of Yellowcraig, a beautiful, sandy, dune-scattered beach surrounded by picturesque woodland, wild grasses and flowers. Stevenson also spent much time here in his youth, and Yellowcraig's influence can also be seen in his novel.

Poppy Fields
DUNBAR

Poppy fields are frequently associated with battle sites, and these fields, a short distance from the town of Dunbar, are no exception. Dunbar has been the site of some of the most notorious battles in Scotland's history. In 1295 the Battle of Dunbar saw Edward I of England defeat the Scots. This disastrous turn of events eventually led to the English seizing Edinburgh Castle – an advantage they retained for some years. Some centuries later Oliver Cromwell and his army of Roundheads beat the supporters of Charles II in a decisive battle near Dunbar, that claimed the lives of 3,000 Cavaliers.

Dunbar has two main features that have enhanced its strategic importance throughout the centuries: its harbour and its castle. The harbour saved Edward II from certain death as he made his escape from here after the Scots' victory at the famous Battle of Bannockburn. Mary, Queen of Scots was brought to Dunbar Castle after her abduction by Bothwell, and later they sought sanctuary here during the turmoil that preceded Mary's downfall in 1567. The castle was destroyed by Mary's half-brother shortly afterwards, but this emotive ruin still echoes with the voices of Scotland's past.

TRADITION & ENTERTAINMENT

From its plethora of theatres, hosting every conceivable entertainment, through traditions such as the One O'Clock Gun, to the spectacle of the famous International Festival, Edinburgh is a city whose vitality is evident at every turn.

Ghost Tours
THE OLD TOWN

Edinburgh's history abounds with tales of mystery and murder. The ghosts of tormented souls walk the streets and closes of the Old Town relentlessly – or so Edinburgh locals would like to make one believe. Although many of these chilling tales are likely to be the result of generations of vivid imaginations, there are also many that are indeed true: the history of Deacon Brodie (the real Dr Jekyll and Mr Hyde), Burke and Hare (Grassmarket's notorious murderers and body snatchers) and many other Edinburgh citizens are rooted in fact.

The ghost tours are some of Edinburgh's most popular tourist attractions, and despite their obvious commercialism, should not be missed. A costumed guide will walk you round the streets of the city, telling tales of bloody executions, murderous revenge, ghosts, ghouls and witches. There are a number of different tours to choose from, ranging from the light-hearted to the truly spine-chilling, but most end up in the recently discovered vaults beneath the Old Town and the cold, damp and dark caverns heighten the atmosphere of mystery and horror.

Ross Open Air Theatre
PRINCES STREET GARDENS

In the summer months, one of the main attractions in the Princes Street Gardens is the Ross Theatre. This huge open-air venue, often sheltered by a vast canopy, provides many distractions and a whole series of varied events. It is especially popular with children, for whom talent contests and other targeted entertainments are provided. But it is a place for all the family, and other shows such as traditional Scottish dancing draw crowds every day, with people hovering around the edges, participating as much or as little as they like. The informal atmosphere it encourages is one of its greatest attractions.

Its other great asset, though, is its situation: the Gardens lie just to the east of the flamboyant Ross fountain, under the watchful eye of the castle, and all around, the verdant lawns and bright colours of the Gardens stretch out to form a peaceful and beautiful cultivated landscape.

Edinburgh Festival Fringe

Although the original Festival was intended to be essentially an operatic event, it excited the interest of a number of theatre groups, which turned up in 1947 and played out their performances wherever they could find the space and the audience. This sowed the seeds of what was to become the Festival Fringe.

The Fringe was officially established in 1951, and had a small party of organisers independent of the Festival proper. It has always encouraged a wide variety of performers and maintains a broad-minded attitude to the definition of entertainment. As a result, the Fringe has incorporated eclectic artistic styles and abilities right from its outset. It has proved to be the launch pad to the big-time for many individuals and shows.

Although they are two separate events, the International and Fringe Festivals have become mutually dependent. Together they provide the widest variety of entertainment found in any one city. Numerous other festivals have grown up around them and now Edinburgh in summer provides something for everyone; all tastes, ages and nationalities.

Edinburgh International Festival

Established in 1947, in an effort to relieve the darkness of the post-war era, the Edinburgh International Festival found so much success that its lavishness, experimentalism and world-wide renown has grown every year since.

The original concept was based around a massive operatic gathering, organised by Rudolf Bing, administrator for the Glyndebourne Opera. For the first few years of the Festival, opera was its main focus. Eventually, the spectrum of entertainment broadened to encompass almost every genre imaginable: dance, theatre, musical, ballet, comedy. Classical and contemporary, amateur and professional, the good, the bad and the downright bizarre were all welcomed.

Today, thousands of people from all over the world flock to Edinburgh in August and September to witness this spectacular event. Every conceivable space is turned into a stage for all manner of performances. Parties, parades, the traditional and the unexpected all meet on the streets of Scotland's capital to make up what is now the largest festival of arts in the world.

MILITARY TATTOO
EDINBURGH CASTLE

For all the hundreds of different entertainments to come out of the Edinburgh International Festival, there is one that has become a major focal point and the single most enduring and popular event to take place at this time – the Military Tattoo.

Since the Festival began in 1947, thousands of people have taken their places on summer evenings on high-rising scaffolding seats constructed either side of the Castle Esplanade to watch perhaps the world's most famous military tattoo. The Scottish regiments, all in full military uniform and regaled by the inescapably Scottish music of the pipes and drums, perform precision marches and military movements and recreate historical events. The show is gloriously Scottish – although

regiments from all over the world frequently guest in the Tattoo – over-poweringly emotive and, climaxing with fireworks and a lone piper playing the Last Post from the ramparts of the floodlit castle, it is one of the highlights of the Festival calendar, and a true celebration of Scottish history and tradition.

Scots Guard
EDINBURGH CASTLE

The Scottish Division of the British Army is made up of seven regiments, and each of these has played its own part in Scotland's glorious military history. Born of war-like peoples, the Scots have an unprecedented reputation for courage and military prowess. This is more than likely due to the continued attacks from their marauding southern enemy, as Scottish history from the earliest times will testify.

Edinburgh's main regiment is the Royal Scots, or the Royal Regiment. It is the oldest of the seven Scottish regiments, and was founded in 1633 by Sir John Hepburn, while attempting to raise an army to fight under Louis XIII of France. The new group of men he gathered together distinguished themselves in this service amongst the ancient French regiments. A member of the Picardy Regiment, no doubt somewhat slighted by the achievements of the Scots, boasted that the Picardys had been on duty the night of Christ's Crucifixion, drawing the famous retort from the Royal Scots' colonel: 'if we had been on guard, we should not have slept at our posts' – earning the Scots the nickname 'Pontius Pilate's Bodyguard'.

Guards like this can be seen in and around the castle, which, even today, works as a military operation.

Traverse Theatre
CAMBRIDGE STREET

As one would expect from the city that spawned the Festival Fringe, Edinburgh has, particularly in recent years, become one of the leading lights in experimental drama. The free-for-all nature of the Fringe means that anyone with any inclination to perform is able to do so, and this has uncovered some major talents on the alternative scene.

The Traverse Theatre is the focal point in Edinburgh for this genre. The theatre was first built in the early 1960s in an effort to maintain a year-round interest in the avant-garde, rather than just having a burst of fascinated enthusiasm for three weeks of the year. The original theatre was housed in St James's Court and could house only 60 spectators, and by 1969 was forced to set up anew in the Grassmarket. Here, it slowly gathered a good reputation and in 1991 it moved to its new, prestigious home in Cambridge Street. A far cry from its humble origins, the new theatre was purpose-built with a magnificent auditorium and stage, all reflecting the unusual nature of its repertoire. The theatre continues to draw the crowds, all coming to witness new, unusual and often *risqué* drama in surroundings that mirror the theatre's success.

Festival Theatre
NICOLSON STREET

The dramatic glass-fronted Festival Theatre seems strikingly out of place amongst the typical grey and sandstone buildings on the south side of the city, near the University Old Quad.

It began its life in 1892 as the Empire Theatre, burning down less than 20 years later, and it stayed a shell for some time. Reconstruction work was completed in 1928 and for a while the theatre regained its former popularity. Eventually this began to wane and by the 1960s, its use as a home for the performing arts had been usurped by the somewhat less glamorous role of a bingo hall.

The magnificent modern structure standing here today is the result of a major redevelopment programme, completed just a few years ago, which aimed to restore the theatre to its former glory. Elements of the original Empire Theatre have been retained within the building, while other parts have been extended and modified to such an extent that the Festival is now the main home to opera in Edinburgh. The programme is not exclusive though, and a variety of performing arts can be enjoyed here. It is a part of Edinburgh's cultural history that has fortunately not been abandoned.

Usher Hall
LOTHIAN ROAD

The eye-catching structure of Usher Hall has a curiously contradictory air of old-fashioned opulence and timeless modernity. Its octagonal exterior is enhanced by columns and canopies, archways and stone carvings. Inside, the semi-circular auditorium is crowned with a domed copper roof and sprinkled with just enough gilding to lend it a sense of luxury, but not so much that it becomes overwhelming.

All in all, the Hall is an appropriately elegant building, drawing crowds of music and opera lovers every season. Constructed just before the outbreak of the First World War, the money for the Hall was bequeathed by one Andrew Usher – a strange legacy for a local brewer.

Like the many other purpose-built venues in Edinburgh, Usher Hall becomes the epicentre of musical life during the Festival, but it hardly lies dormant during the rest of the year. Throughout the winter, the Hall plays host to the Scottish National Orchestra, and a variety of musical extravaganzas can be seen here all year round.

Royal Highland Show
INGLISTON

Ingliston, situated near Edinburgh airport, is just a short drive out of the city centre. It is here that one of the area's best-loved annual events takes place – the Royal Highland Show. The show invades the area every June and provides a great family day out, with many different attractions, exhibitions and 'hands on' experiences.

Epitomising Scottish agricultural life from past to present, the fair hosts shows of the famous Highland cattle, sheepdog trials and show-jumping. There are demonstrations of forestry techniques and farming methods, but most spectacular are the motorcycle display teams and parachute jumps.

The Scottish Agricultural Museum, which can be visited all year round, has many different exhibitions explaining the rural way of life, the hardships and rewards, machinery and methods of Scottish agriculture. During the Highland Show, further exhibitions complete the picture of how people lived off the land in times past.

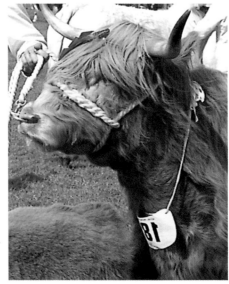

Edinburgh Zoo
COSTORPHINE HILL

No city's attractions are complete without a zoo, and Edinburgh boasts one of the finest. Spreading over 80 acres across Costorphine Hill on the outskirts of the city, the whole complex commands fine views of the city and surrounding countryside.

Opened just prior to the outbreak of the First World War, Edinburgh Zoo was remarkably modern in its design and planning. The animals are housed comfortably in spacious enclosures, and every effort has been made to recreate as natural an environment as possible for them.

Although the zoo has over 1,000 different species within its confines, it is best known for its penguins. Four different types are kept here, with nearly 200 altogether. Every day there is the famous 'Penguin Parade' through the zoo – a great tourist attraction, and immensely popular with children. Another of Edinburgh Zoo's magnificent sites is its free-flying Night Herons, which can be seen in the evenings, sweeping by overhead.

One O'Clock Gun
EDINBURGH CASTLE

This tradition is now so much a part of everyday life in Edinburgh that the residents of the city hardly hear the noise of the gun, let alone pay it any heed. The gun is situated on Mill's Mount Battery, one of the castle's loftiest sites, whose vantage points offered great protection and opportunities for defence in the city's turbulent past. For most of the day, the battery is simply one of the best places in the city to view the spectacular surroundings, which encompass Arthur's Seat and the Firth of Forth, but every day, except Sunday, crowds gather at the appointed hour to watch this old Edinburgh ritual being executed.

The tradition dates back to the days when ships sailing in and out of the Forth used the signal to check their chronometers. At exactly the same moment as the gun is fired, a time ball drops in the Nelson Monument on Calton Hill, at the east end of Princes Street. This too was a signal to sailors, and the accuracy of these two events occurring simultaneously every day was, in its day, considered to be a miracle of modern technology.

Procession
ROYAL MILE

For a long time after the construction of the New Town – and indeed for a while before – the Old Town was a place of dirt and slums, of poverty and disease, and the contrast between the two parts of the city was acute. It was only in the nineteenth century that efforts were made to clean up the Old Town, making it desirable and habitable once again. For a long time the rich tapestry of history that makes up the Royal Mile and the surrounding area was forgotten.

Today, of course, the historical sights in the Old Town are Edinburgh's main attraction, but a sense of competition between the old and the new still hovers in the air. The Old Town Renewal Trust organises a number of events every year that prove that, although the south side of the city may be old, it is still alive and kicking. These include numerous processions up and down the Royal Mile, such as the one pictured here, which are normally accompanied by drums and bagpipes, celebrating the Old Town's history. There is also 'Doors Open Day' every September when the many attractions along the Royal Mile – from the Outlook Tower to the plethora of museums – open their doors to the public free of charge.

Playhouse Theatre
GREENHOUSE PLACE

Perhaps in no city in Britain other than London is there such a concentration of theatres and entertainment venues as Edinburgh. But this is only to be expected from a city that every year hosts the largest festival of arts in the world. Like the International Festival in August, the city's theatres provide entertainment and attractions to suit every age and every taste – all year round.

The Playhouse Theatre is Edinburgh's answer to London's West End. It is a large venue, with an auditorium that can seat 3,000 people. The theatre suffered great damage in a fire in the early 1990s, but it has been carefully restored and is now bigger and better than ever. It is here that the most popular musicals play when touring, and the neon lights often advertise successful shows from the West End or Broadway. But the Playhouse is not reserved exclusively for musicals. It is the local indoor venue for pop concerts – even opera has been performed here. It gives the impression largely of being a young person's theatre though, even showing films occasionally. It is only during the Festival that the Playhouse gives itself up to more classical productions, when it plays host to large-scale ballet.

Museum of Childhood
HIGH STREET

It is a well-known irony that the Museum of Childhood was founded by a with a notorious dislike of children. Town Councillor Patrick Murray set up the museum from his own collection of toys and games, intending it to be seen as a social study rather than, as its name implies, a museum geared specifically towards children.

Five storeys, packed with childhood memorabilia, have a universal appeal for both old and young. The museum was the first of its type, and the founder's original collection has been much enhanced by gifts from all over the world, from people who liked the idea of a museum dedicated solely to such exhibits. Everything can be found here; from toys made of wood, metal and every other conceivable material to Britain's largest collection of dolls. Timeless classics like the train set are displayed alongside toys and games that have been the subject of brief but all-consuming trends over the past decades.

Children will love it and parents will sigh over it, but will also hopefully appreciate Murray's sardonic humour which permeates much of the museum, most obviously in the appropriately inappropriate window at the museum's entrance – a memorial to King Herod!

ARCHIBALD·CAMPBELL·MARQVESS·of·ARGYLL

BEHEADED · NEAR · THIS · CATHEDRAL · A·D·1661

LEADER·IN·COVNCIL·AND·IN·FIELD·FOR·THE·REFORMED·RELIGION

"I set the Crown on the King's Head
He hastens me to a better
Crown than his own"

ST. MARGARETS CHAPEL

BANK HOTEL

KIRKS &
CATHEDRALS

The magnificent spires of Edinburgh's kirks and cathedrals are the highlight of the city's famous skyline. The buildings, from many different ages and illustrating many different styles, tell the story of Edinburgh's turbulent religious history.

St Mary's Episcopalian Cathedral
PALMERSTON PLACE

The great entrance doors to St Mary's are embellished with fine ironwork, above which are carvings of Christ, John the Baptist and the Apostles. Walking around the outside of the building, one can only marvel at the skill with which these and the many other carvings have been executed – all around the gables and even high up on the triple spires, figures of various saints have been lovingly worked.

The interior of St Mary's has a lot to live up to and, although the magnificence of its outward appearance is not quite matched by its inner designs, it is none the less an impressive and atmospheric place: long aisles covered by grand, medieval-style interlinking arches stretch the length of the nave and unusual diagonally placed buttresses, centring on four main pillars, support the lofty height of the main spire.

In the north transept, near the pulpit, is the chapel dedicated to Charles I (Charles the Martyr), who founded the Edinburgh Episcopal Church in 1633. He was executed in 1649 and the chapel contains depictions of the king holding a crown of thorns, the symbol of his martyrdom.

Aerial View
St Mary's Episcopalian Cathedral
PALMERSTON PLACE

This photograph gives some idea of the immensity and grandeur of St Mary's Episcopalian Cathedral. Its main spire is one of the most instantly recognisable features of the Edinburgh skyline, and the cathedral building itself dominates the west end of the New Town. St Mary's is the largest church to have been built in Scotland after the Reformation.

Its relentlessly Gothic exterior belies its actual construction date of 1879, with the west tower and the twin spires dating from the early twentieth century. That the cathedral's dark and intricate appearance seems authentic is a tribute to its designer, Sir George Gilbert Scott. The funds to build such a magnificent cathedral came from Barbara and Mary Walker, whose initial plan was to commission a simple chapel dedicated to the memory of their mother. At the time, there was no Episcopalian cathedral in the diocese. St Giles – a short distance from the castle, on the Royal Mile – briefly enjoyed the status of cathedral twice during the seventeenth century, after which it was handed back to the Presbyterians and became a High Kirk once more. Thus, the projected chapel never materialised, and the architectural enormity that is St Mary's was born.

St John's Kirk
LOTHIAN ROAD

Standing unassumingly at the end of Princes Street, St John's Kirk is surrounded by the hub of Edinburgh's busy main shopping precinct andcan easily be over-looked. It is worth taking the time to investigate the church, though, as well as wandering through its overgrown yard.

Dating from the early nineteenth century, the design of St John's consists of just a nave and aisles, with no transepts. The eight bays that divide the nave are ornate with pinnacles and buttresses, and carvings of biblical figures abound in the shafts. There is a sense of harmony about the whole building, inside and out; even the chapel and vestry, both of which were added in the twentieth century, are absorbed easily into the whole.

Around the sides and back of the church, away from the busy street corners, gravestones and monuments lie in abundance on and around the small crumbling walls and overgrown pathways. From here, the sheer wall of St Cuthbert's Kirk blocks the view to the south and the visitor is tempted over the walls by the intriguing wilderness of neglected graves beyond.

Dalmeny Kirk
DALMENY

It is difficult to believe that Dalmeny Kirk actually dates from the twelfth century, so unaffected by time and progress does it appear. In almost every way, it is the finest example of its kind to be found in Scotland. Its perfectly ordered, complete exterior is enhanced by magnificent stonework and Romanesque carvings. These carvings are remarkable, but the strange figures of beasts adorning the south doorway, despite having endured nearly 800 years of wind and weather, are particularly notable.

The satisfaction gained from wandering around the kirk's exterior and ancient kirkyard is maintained inside. Its simple form is not marred by over-decoration – for example, the vaulting is confined to the small chancel and apse, with none to be found in the nave.

The quality of this kirk, its exquisitely preserved aspect and its situation as the focal point of the beautiful village of Dalmeny make this a fascinating and thought-provoking historical place.

St Mary's Church
HADDINGTON

The church of St Mary's in Haddington was completed in the mid-1400s, but it was to survive only a hundred years before invading English armies wreaked havoc on it, leaving it a roofless shell. Although some restoration work was done on the nave shortly afterwards, large parts were left to crumble and decay. Surprisingly, this large and beautiful building was left this way for four centuries, until the decision was made in the 1970s to restore the church to its former glory.

How glorious it now is. Its size is its most impressive feature; large, but not imposing. Inside, it is airy and spacious, bathed in a glow from the

stained-glass windows, which include one by the Pre-Raphaelite Edward Burne-Jones. Some of its other fascinating features are the 'Green Men'. These peculiar mythological creatures are carved in the fine stone, and depict strange human figures with foliage sprouting from their mouths, representing the association between man and nature. Green Men are quite common in Scottish churches and cathedrals, and those here at St Mary's are fine examples.

St Andrew and St George's
GEORGE STREET

When the plans for the New Town were drawn up, they included the two main squares, St Andrew's and Charlotte, each one with its own church. However, the site of the church in St Andrew's Square was quickly bought by Sir Laurence Dundas, who proceeded to build his own mansion house there – now the Royal Bank of Scotland headquarters (see page 76) – thus forcing the Town's planners to find a new site for their church. They settled upon the east end of George Street, and what is now known as the church of St Andrew and St George's was built.

This was the first of the New Town's many churches, designed by Major Andrew Frazer of the Royal Engineers and opened for worship in 1784. Best known for being the setting for the Great Disruption in 1843, when hundreds of clergy left to form the Free Church of Scotland, St Andrew and St George's has an unusual appearance. The theme of its oval exterior is continued inside, with a curving gallery and a rounded ceiling. Its simplicity is refreshing amongst the predominance of Gothic architecture that characterises much of Edinburgh.

Tron Kirk
HIGH STREET

Christ's Church at the Tron was built to take the influx of people from St Giles when it underwent one of its brief periods as an Episcopalian Cathedral in the mid-seventeenth century. Lacking in ornamentation, and some would say beauty, the Tron Kirk is still a fascinating reminder of Scottish religious and civic history.

Its original plan was T-shaped, but the south side was destroyed when the road bisecting the Royal Mile from the North Bridge was built in the 1780s. Half a century later, a fire further rendered the building's original shape unrecognisable and destroyed the old wood and iron tower and steeple.

It has not been used as a kirk since the 1950s and now houses the Old Town Information Centre: a humble end for such an historic place. Recent excavations have changed the focus of the building, and a visit here still brings surprises, for within the kirk walls, under its still-fine hammerbeam roof, one of Edinburgh's oldest roads, Marlin's Wynd, has been uncovered. This paved pathway is believed to have been named after Walter Merlion, the man responsible for first paving the Royal Mile in the sixteenth century. The archaeological look of the ground, enclosed in the severe kirk building, with its stained-glass windows still intact, provides a fascinating and unusual scene.

St Margaret's Chapel
EDINBURGH CASTLE

Although it is named after St Margaret, wife of King Malcolm, the first monarch to build a residence on Castle Rock, the chapel was actually built in the century after her death in 1093, perhaps by her son King David I. It is now the oldest surviving part of the castle, and throughout the centuries the chapel has seen many uses, most degradingly as a storeroom for gunpowder – its original purpose was at first neglected, then eventually forgotten, and it was not until the mid-1800s that its medieval role as a chapel was re-discovered and restoration work began.

It is not altogether surprising that the chapel's importance was over-looked for centuries, for it is a small, unadorned, rectangular building, no more than 9.1 metres (30 ft) long, with only five small windows. Today these windows are one of the chapel's focal points: the beautiful, brightly coloured stained glass standing out in the simple interior. Each window depicts an illustrious Scottish character or saint: William Wallace, St Andrew, St Columba, St Ninian and St Margaret herself. The windows are twentieth-century additions, but somehow enhance the religious and medieval atmosphere of the chapel.

Canongate Kirk
CANONGATE

It is quite possible to overlook the small Canongate Kirk, down towards the end of the Royal Mile. The whitewashed building, set back from the road and hidden behind a cluster of cherry trees, is as far removed in appearance from almost every other house of religion in Edinburgh as it could be.

Its origins lie with the nearby Holyrood Abbey. The Abbey served for many years as the parish church of the Canongate but, in 1687, King James II ordered that the chapel there be turned over for the use of the Knights of the Order of the Thistle. The new church was designed by James Smith (who was a Roman Catholic like the king – an unusual state of affairs amidst the warring Protestant factions of seventeenth-century Edinburgh – a fact which led to the monarch's deposition shortly after this time and which probably explains the anomaly of the kirk's cruciform structure).

Further surprises await inside the kirk, which is bright and spacious. Natural light floods through the clear glass windows – no stained glass here – illuminating the simple nave and aisles. Understated it may appear, but both the history and unexpected appearance of the Canongate Kirk make it worth a stop on the way to Holyrood.

Apprentice Pillar
ROSSLYN CHAPEL

Seven miles away from Edinburgh, on the outskirts of the Esk Valley, lies one of the most magical places in Scotland – Rosslyn Chapel. Built in the mid-1400s by William St Clair, this extraordinary place has the most marvellous collection of religious carving and sculpture anywhere in Britain.

It is this, the Apprentice Pillar, that is the finest and the most famous piece in the building. Encircled at the base by a series of winged serpents, four leafed vines climb from the bottom in a majestic swirl. The story surrounding this is a popular local legend. It is said that a master mason and his apprentice were working on the chapel, when the mason was called away. On his return he saw that the apprentice had carved this pillar and, in a fit of rage and jealousy, killed the boy. Elsewhere in the chapel, figures of the mason and his apprentice (depicted with a head wound) can be found. This is no more than a romantic tale, and nobody really knows the reason why Rosslyn Chapel is home to so much craftsmanship, but this only adds to its mystique.

St Anthony's Chapel
HOLYROOD PARK

High on a rocky crag in Holyrood Park sit the ancient ruins of St Anthony's Chapel. The chapel is a forlorn and mysterious site. No one has ever established exactly why, or for whom, the chapel was built on this isolated spot. It stands as the only mark of human life in this area, and there is no evidence of any other building or habitation around it.

What is known is that this building dates from the fifteenth century and was once made up of the small vaulted chapel with a room situated on the west side, presumably the priest's sleeping quarters.

A number of explanations for the chapel have been suggested. The most commonly accepted is that it was in some way associated with a hospital that had been established at Leith, which specialised in the care of people suffering from 'St Anthony's fire', a form of eye disease. The genuine purpose of this small chapel will probably never be confirmed, but it is a curious feature in this most spectacular landscape.

St Cuthbert's Kirk
LOTHIAN ROAD

The kirk that stands here now is mainly a late nineteenth-century reconstruction, but this relatively modern structure hides a long history. It is believed that St Margaret founded a church here in 1127, which altered gradually over the centuries until by the mid-seventeenth century it was a long, narrow building with just a tower and a south transept. The changes continued and evidence suggests that by the eighteenth century St Cuthbert's consisted of an eclectic mixture of buildings, a tower and the ruins of the older versions of the church.

It is not surprising then, that the present church has an odd, unidentifiable quality about it – a quality, it should be said, that givees it an added aspect of intrigue. From the outside, a visitor would not expect much from the interior of St Cuthbert's, but this is where the real pleasure of this kirk lies. Inside, wide, spacious transepts are offset by marvellous Corinthian pillars, intricately carved stalls and a beautiful mosaic floor.

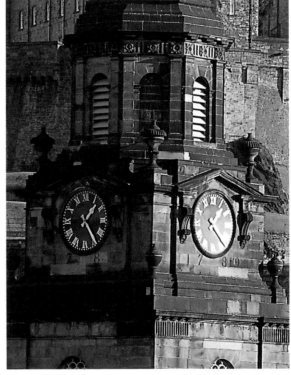

The rambling graveyard is another of St Cuthbert's curiosities; Alexander Nasmyth is buried here along with hundreds of others, whose memorials make for a fascinating afternoon's wandering.

Costorphine Church
COSTORPHINE

Costorphine manages to retain a medieval sense of peace and solitude despite its proximity to the city centre, a reflection of the ancient rural parish it once was. Like many old churches, Costorphine has been extended and rebuilt over the centuries so that today it is a curious mixture of architectural styles, and echoes the religious history of a number of different eras. Medieval in origin, a chapel was built next to the church at the turn of the fifteenth century, to which a chancel and a tower were added a few years later. Further renovations took place in the mid-1600s when the chapel had a porch added and the church itself was razed and rebuilt. Most of the present church is the result of further rebuilding in 1828, when the chapel was finally absorbed into the church building.

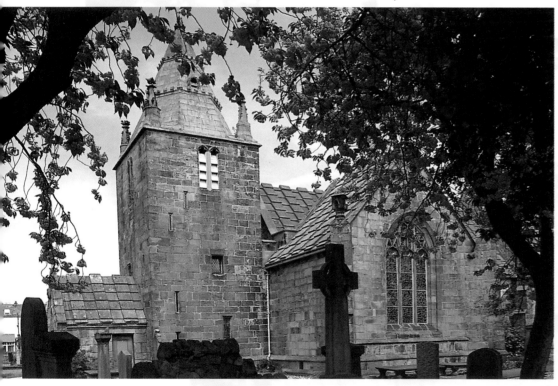

Despite its many changes, the medieval character of the church is predominant, even in the interior – a careful nineteenth-century renovation. The tombs set into recesses along the inside are particularly fine and include those of Sir Adam Forrester, the man responsible for building the original chapel, and his wife.

Greyfriars Kirkyard
GREYFRIARS

The historic Greyfriars Kirkyard sadly spends much time swamped with tourists, all clamouring to see the grave of the famous 'Greyfriars Bobby' (see page 132). But if you are fortunate enough to visit it at a quiet time, the impression it makes is truly breathtaking. The small but attractive kirk stands in the centre of the kirkyard and all around it grassy lawns spread out, with a small scattering of free-standing headstones; crooked, mossy and picturesque. Impressive funerary monuments and wall memorials cover every inch of the crumbling stone walls around the edge, the majority blackened and worn with age. The grandiose vaults are decaying and broken, but their magnificence is not diminished, for their essence remains. The list of people buried here is distinguished: the poet Allan Ramsay; James Craig, the man whose vision shaped the New Town; and the architect family the Adams, whose marble-carved vault stands out bright amidst the grey of the other monuments.

Here, in 1638, the National Covenant was signed – the beginning of the long struggle between the Scottish Presbyterians and the Episcopalians, followers of the new religion established by Charles I. Here, some 40 years later, over 1,000 Covenanters were imprisoned. An iron gate separates this prison from the kirkyard, and nearby the Martyr's Monument pays homage to all those who died in this fight for religious freedom.

High Kirk of St Giles
HIGH STREET

The High Kirk of St Giles has been the religious heart of the Old Town for centuries, and is now a majestic and impressive reminder of Edinburgh's turbulent religious history.

A church has stood on this spot since 854 AD, gradually being rebuilt and extended. Named after the Patron Saint of Cripples (a popular saint in medieval times!), the Norman kirk which replaced the original was destroyed in 1385 by the English. A Gothic replacement was built during the fifteenth century, and the church became once again the focal point of Old Edinburgh. It was not to last long – as the tide of the Reformation swept the country, St Giles suffered the loss of some of its finest fixtures and fittings.

The honorary title of 'Cathedral' is really a misnomer: it was officially a cathedral only twice, only then for brief periods. The first time was in 1633, when Charles I established Episcopacy in Scotland, and then later in the century during the Covenanters' Rebellion. Episcopacy was eventually abandoned and St Giles reverted to its old title of High Kirk.

The interior is breathtaking. Aisles – including this, the Argyll aisle – altars and chapels lie under the light of the rich stained-glass windows, which date from various periods, from Pre-Raphaelite to the modern west window commemorating Robbie Burns.

Thistle Chapel
High Kirk of St Giles
HIGH STREET

The Thistle Chapel is a relatively modern addition to this old kirk. Built between 1909 and 1911 by Sir Robert Lorimer, the chapel is dedicated to the Knights of the Order of the Thistle, one of the oldest chivalric orders in Scotland. The Order of the Thistle was established in 1687 by James VII, and since that time has consisted of a small group – the monarch and 16 others. The Knights of the Thistle still attend a special service annually in the chapel.

It is a tiny but breathtaking corner of the kirk. Extravagantly (some have said over-indulgently) carved, every inch of the chapel is a testimony to the workmanship of William and Alexander Clow, the two Edinburgh men responsible for the fantastic detail. The chapel was carefully designed to reflect the fifteenth-century origins of the present kirk, and the bossed roof, granite floor, ribbed vault and elaborate stalls successfully blend in with the Gothic style of the rest. The effect is overwhelmingly opulent and it is worth taking some time to sit and appreciate the handiwork, and to try to find the wee oak-carved angel playing bagpipes amongst the myriad of carvings.

LIFE & CULTURE

Modern life in Edinburgh has grown up from the city's cultural roots, and the old and the new survive harmoniously together, from the beautiful architecture of old to the very latest in sports stadiums and business centres.

Scotch Whisky Heritage Centre
CASTLEHILL

The production of whisky is one of the oldest industries in Scotland and it is a symbol that is inextricably linked with the country.

The Scotch Whisky Heritage Centre, just down the Royal Mile from the Castle, is one of the Old Town's premier tourist attractions, but while it is undoubtedly a highly commercial enterprise, it also offers a fascinating insight into Scotland's best-known export. Exhibitions illustrate the history of the product, complete with sights, sounds and smells from the various ages. The distilling process is explained, and the different whisky-producing regions and types of whisky are discussed. It charts the progress of the whisky industry, from its origins to its present-day success. Samples of the different whiskies are available to try, and for those with a taste for the liquor, just about every variety imaginable can be bought here.

Royal Museum of Scotland
CHAMBERS STREET

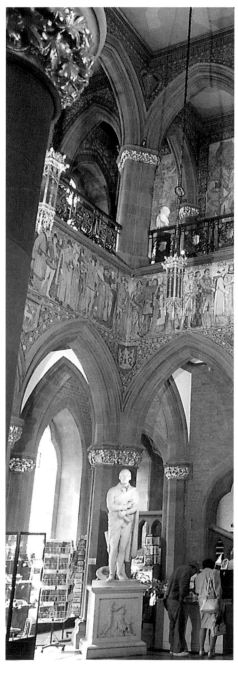

The building housing the Royal Museum of Scotland was designed by a captain of the Royal Engineers, Francis Fowke, in the mid-1800s. It is a large, low, quite imposing building, constructed from pink sandstone. The central block of the museum is only two storeys high, although the wings have three levels. The only obvious external ornamentations are the urns and balustrades adorning the façade over the entrance.

The interior is marvellously spacious, most obvious in the Great Hall, a magnificent and unusual room – all glass and cast iron – with a high ceiling supported by elegant iron columns. The inspiration for this design came from London's Crystal Palace, and it gives the whole museum a sense of modernity that is quite at odds with some of its collections.

The eclectic mixture of exhibits found here include art and sculpture, relics of ancient civilisations from around the world, dinosaurs, evidence of ancient industrial practices ... the list is endless: there is something here to please all visitors.

Parliament Square
HIGH STREET

Parliament Square, despite its name, is now the legal heart of the Old Town. Surrounding the High Kirk of St Giles, this area was once occupied by the kirkyard. Parliament House was built in the seventeenth century, but the frontage seen today is the result of later additions made to designs by Robert Reid in the early nineteenth century.

Parliament House was used as the seat of the Scottish Parliament until the Act of Union in 1707, after which it was rendered obsolete. Its purpose then changed and it became the Law Courts (Scotland's legal system remained independent from England's, even after the Union) and the Supreme Court of Scotland still holds session here. Today the two great attractions within Parliament Square are the Great Hall of Parliament House, which boasts a fine hammerbeam roof, and the extravagant Signet Library, designed by William Stark.

Waverley Station
PRINCES STREET

When the proposal to run a railway through Princes Street Gardens was first made in the 1830s, it was vehemently opposed by the residents. As Princes Street became less residential and more commercial, however, resistance lessened. This was, after all, the age of industry and Edinburgh, as Scotland's capital, felt the pressures of progress. In 1846, the railway was constructed.

The fact that the Gardens remain as beautiful today as they were when first laid out, is testament to the care and consideration that was made in the planning and building of this railway. By creating tunnels and building embankments, the railway was hardly noticeable. It did not – and still does not – encroach upon the beauty of this area.

Two stations sprang up, built by rival rail companies, Princes Street to the east and Waverley to the west. With these came the first two major building developments on the south side of the street: the great railway hotels, the Caledonian and the North British (now the Balmoral – see page 83). Today, just as in the nineteenth century, these two magnificent buildings serve the customers of the rail lines, and along with the station itself, they are fitting testimonies to the industrial age.

Old Observatory
CALTON HILL

The two observatories on Calton Hill were built within 30 years of each other. The first, pictured here, is the Old Observatory and was designed by the architect of the New Town, James Craig. This round-towered, three-storeyed building was the brainchild of a Leith man who was inspired by the marvel of a telescope owned by his brother, an optician. He decided to build an observatory that people could come and pay to use. Work began on the building in 1776, but the design was extravagant and ambitious and funds were slow to come in. Consequently, the observatory was not finished until 1792, by which time the impetus had waned somewhat, and it was never the success that the businessman envisaged.

The City Observatory is another of Calton Hill's testimonies to William Playfair, who built it for his uncle, an astronomer, in 1818. This observatory is open to the public, and is also host to the Edinburgh Astronomical Society. These were both eventually overtaken in popularity by the construction of the Royal Observatory at Blackford Hill, but their ideal hilltop situation ensures a continued interest in both their style and purpose.

Camera Obscura
CASTLEHILL

The building that now houses the camera obscura was once a tenement housing block, built in the seventeenth century. In 1853, its height was utilised by the installation of the camera obscura and since then has drawn thousands of visitors each year who come to marvel at this piece of nineteenth-century technology.

The original camera obscura was installed by Edinburgh optician, Maria Theresa Short, but this was replaced by Patrick Geddes' instrument when he bought the building in 1892. The device is situated in the building's distinctive black and white dome and is a marvellous cinematic extravaganza. A system of lenses and mirrors revolve to produce a telescopic view of the city that is projected on to a large, white table. Here one can watch everyday life going on below, as well as appreciate close-ups of the architecture of nearby buildings.

The building also houses a number of related exhibitions, including International Holography and Victorian Edinburgh, and makes for a fascinating journey through the city, past and present.

The City Chambers
HIGH STREET

The buildings that now house the City Chambers were designed by John Adam as a Royal Exchange. This was part of an attempt by the city council in the late eighteenth century to encourage the local merchants and traders to move their business from the streets into open offices. However, it soon became clear the merchants preferred to ply their various trades on the streets and, loath to see the building go to waste, the city council moved their head offices here.

The appearance of the Chambers is delightfully deceptive, for from the front the buildings appear to be only three storeys high. Built right on the ridge of the Old Town, however, the sheer drop is accommodated by up to 12 storeys at the back.

Beneath the foundations of the City Chambers lies Mary King's Close. This was one of the first places to experience the Plague when it reached the capital in 1645 and, in an attempt to contain the disease, the whole close was sealed off and the people left to die. Mary King's Close was eventually opened again, and the bodies cleared away, but the whole area was later completely covered by the City Chambers. It is said that the ghosts of those who died in the close still haunt this part of the Old Town.

Register House
PRINCES STREET

Walking north across the bridge from the Old Town brings you to one of Edinburgh's most stately buildings – Register House. Situated at the north-east corner of Princes Street, this was built from designs by Robert Adam in the 1770s, specifically to house Scotland's historical records. It has continued to serve this purpose ever since; the first place to be custom-built as a record office.

The building's exterior is not overly ornamented, featuring just a pedimented centrepiece and four columns. Extensions to the building were made in the 1830s, but fortunately these were to the rear of the building, so its smooth, neo-classical façade was not destroyed. It is simple, elegant and appropriately distinguished. Its interior is magnificent, the main feature being the domed ceiling, complete with detailed plasterwork and gilding.

Register House is open to the public, who can investigate the thousands of fascinating records here. Although certain collections of records have, by necessity, been housed elsewhere, this remains one of the most important, and beautiful, of Edinburgh's public buildings.

Edinburgh International Conference Centre
MORRISON STREET

As well as being a popular holiday destination, Edinburgh has also become one of Scotland's main thriving business centres. In order to cater for the ever-growing commercial and business side of the country's capital, a number of modern structures have been built, and today Edinburgh can keep up with the greatest European cities, boasting facilities of all kinds. It is an essential part of Edinburgh's modern culture and lifestyle.

Work began on the Edinburgh International Conference Centre in the early 1990s and it opened in 1995. Somehow the modern building does not look out of place in a city characterised by sixteenth-, seventeenth- and eighteenth-century structures; a testimony to the skill of its architects. Equipped with all the latest facilities, the Conference Centre has a unique, multi-purpose auditorium, that unusually, can be divided up into three separate auditoria, or used as one main one, which can seat up to 1,200 people.

Royal Bank of Scotland
ST ANDREW'S SQUARE

St Andrew's Square is now the financial heart of the city of Edinburgh, and many of the palatial former residences have been transformed into offices and company headquarters. While the outward appearance of the square has not changed much since it was built in the eighteenth century, the activity going on within the walls of the stately Georgian houses is very different.

The building housing the Royal Bank of Scotland headquarters is one of the most beautiful in the square. The site on which it stands was where Craig originally envisaged St Andrew's Church, but before these plans could get off the ground, the land was bought and developed by Sir Laurence Dundas. He commissioned Sir William Chambers to design him a suitable town house and the result was this marvellous mansion, completed in 1774.

After Sir Laurence's death, the building was acquired by the Excise offices and later, in 1825, by the Bank of Scotland. Much of the inside has been changed to accommodate its new purpose, but the main hall in particular, a mid-nineteenth-century addition characterised by star-shaped windows, makes a visit to the bank an unusual experience.

West Register House
CHARLOTTE SQUARE

The building that now houses a large part of the Scottish Record Office was once St George's Church. James Craig had planned to have a church in each of his two squares, Charlotte and St Andrew's, but his plans were foiled before they could get off the ground and St Andrew's Church had to be built instead in George Street (see page 52). Charlotte Square got its church, however, built by Robert Reid in 1824. The cost of realising Robert Adam's lavish designs proved prohibitive, and in the end the church only vaguely resembled them. The result is a noble but simple affair, with just four columns rather than Adam's original eight and no extraneous ornamentation. The dome remains one of the dominant features of Edinburgh's skyline, reaching a height of 46 metres (150 ft).

In the 1960s, the interior of the church was renovated to make way for the Public Record Office, and today it houses hundreds of government records, as well as a fascinating exhibition on Scottish history. The building has, since its construction, been the focal point of Charlotte Square, and it continues to be so, despite its change of use.

National Gallery of Scotland
PRINCES STREET

The National Gallery of Scotland is one of the finest pieces of architecture to grace the Princes Street area, and is a suitably sumptuous building for the fine works housed within it.

The Gallery was designed by William Playfair, whose original plans actually included a number of grand features which never made it off the drawing board, due to a restriction of funds. This, however, does not detract from the magnificence of the stately columned porticoes and the graceful exterior.

Inside, the design is as carefully planned as the outside. Two galleries are divided into ten octagonal rooms and later additions include an upper floor containing a further five galleries, and a basement that was cleverly built to provide more space within the Gallery without spoiling Playfair's marvellous exterior.

The National Gallery houses the finest collection of painting and sculpture to be found anywhere in Scotland. The exhibits include pieces from all ages, and works by numerous renowned international artists: Raphael, Van Dycke, Rembrandt, several of the Impressionists, as well as many by English and Scottish painters. The collections of work by Edinburgh's own Sir Henry Raeburn are the pride of the Gallery.

Divinity College
EDINBURGH UNIVERSITY

The foundations of the University of Edinburgh were set in the late sixteenth century. In 1580, Clement Little, a local man, donated his vast collection of books to the city in order to found a library, and from this grew the Town College, which received its Royal Charter in 1582 from King James VI.

The oldest surviving part of the University, and still the very soul of the establishment, is the Old Quad. This was designed largely by Robert Adam, but was built after his death, and the influence of William Playfair, who modified Adam's designs, can also be felt. The Old Quad was completed in 1789, and consisted of just one of Adam's projected quadrangles, as well as the spectacular Upper Library.

The University campus now spreads over a wide area in the city, and the Old College is no longer the central seat of learning. It is, however, the finest of all the university buildings. Over the years some of Britain's most brilliant scholars have passed through the University's gates, especially those in the field of medicine, in which Edinburgh has a world-wide reputation for excellence.

Murrayfield Stadium
WEST EDINBURGH

Edinburgh caters for sporting fanatics of all kinds, and sports stadia, grounds and courses can be found both in and around the city centre. The best-known and all-encompassing is the Meadowbank Stadium, situated near the breathtaking landscape of Holyrood Park. Smaller venues, pools, tennis courts and a plethora of other sites make indulging in a sporting life very easy in Scotland's capital.

To the west of the city lies the Murrayfield Stadium. This is the home of Scottish international rugby, and throughout the season it hosts Scotland's home games against the best in the sport. As is befitting an international sporting arena, Murrayfield is a fine modern stadium, and has recently been renovated to keep in line with the very latest in the sport's developments. It attracts thousands of rugby fans every year to watch the games – both international and domestic.

Meadowbank Stadium
NEAR HOLYROOD PARK

Meadowbank is Edinburgh's foremost sports stadium and the biggest arena in the city for sporting events of all kinds. Over 80 sports are hosted here throughout the year at both international and domestic levels.

The stadium is situated to the north-east of the striking landscape of Holyrood Park and caters for both indoor and outdoor activities. It has a huge, modern athletics track and a velodrome; inside all manner of sports can be indulged in, including the latest sporting trends such as rock-climbing.

Meadowbank was built in 1970 when Edinburgh was the host city for the Commonwealth Games. Its most impressive achievement is the stadium itself, in which 15,000 spectators can be seated around the track under its enormous cantilever roof. It was clearly a success as the Commonwealth Games returned to Meadowbank in 1986, placing Edinburgh amongst Europe's leading sporting cities.

Braid Hill Golf Course
BRAID HILLS

The natural plateau on the top of the Braid Hills made this the ideal place to build a golf course, but the topographical suitability was only one of the factors that encouraged golfing fanatics; the exceptional views from the Braids make this the perfect setting for a day's golfing. The City of Edinburgh acquired this land towards the end of the nineteenth century, and there are now two full courses here in the Braids, both publicly owned and offering more than just the opportunity for a little relaxation. Golfing is a popular pastime in Scotland, no doubt largely due to the great number of picturesque spots and open spaces throughout the country. There are six municipal courses in the Edinburgh area alone, but none could have a more stunning location than the Braid Hills.

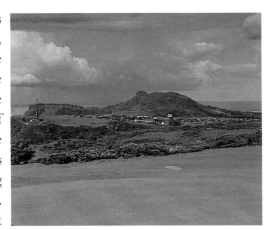

At an elevation of 206 metres (675 ft), the views from the Braids are unsurpassed. The visual spectacle must be a distraction even to the most dedicated of players, with the Firth of Forth stretching out to the horizon and the ancient wooded valleys of the Braid Burns spreading out mysteriously below.

Balmoral Hotel
PRINCES STREET

One of the most exclusive hotels in Edinburgh, the Balmoral is honoured to be one of the few constructions allowed on the south side of Princes Street, after an Act of Parliament forever preserved the Gardens and views of the Old Town. The rise of this awe-inspiring building came at the same time as the rise of the railway in the city. It was one of two grand hotels built by the companies that owned the railways in the early twentieth century. The other, the Caledonian, stands at the west end of the Gardens.

The Balmoral was originally named the Great British, but this was changed when objections were voiced (North Britain being another – not well-liked – name for Scotland). It is a massive square building, made from the same golden sandstone that is so popularly evident throughout Edinburgh. The hotel is highly ornamented, boasting bow and dormer windows, false balconies and a clock tower. It has recently been renovated and is now a high-class establishment with all the modern conveniences.

THE OLD &
THE NEW

From the crowded closes of the Royal Mile, through the splendid baronial tenement estates to the sweeping avenues of the Georgian New Town, each part of Edinburgh carries haunting echoes of the ages through which it developed.

THE ROYA
CASTLEH

The New Town
NORTH EDINBURGH

The development to the north of the Old Town could not be more different from the ancient part of the city. Beautifully designed residences line the straight, symmetrical streets, and everything fits into a careful plan: churches, houses, public buildings and avenues all complement one another. Some say it lacks the dynamic spirit of the Old Town, but the New Town has a character all of its own: stately, regal and unassumingly opulent.

The two men responsible for the success of the New Town were: George Drummond, Lord Provost, whose imagination and determination it was to develop a new town on the edge of the old one; and James Craig,

the chief architect, whose genius is evident in so much of the work. Craig's grid of streets and squares was organised around the main thoroughfare, George Street, with two squares, St Andrew's and George Square (later renamed Charlotte Square) on either side. Running parallel to George Street were two subsidiary streets, Princes Street and Queen Street. Little did Craig guess that it would be Princes Street, not George Street, that would eventually become the heart of the New Town. Work began on the New Town in 1767, after permission to extend the boundaries was finally granted, and the magnificent Georgian sweep of the town slowly began to take shape.

The Old Town
SOUTH EDINBURGH

The Old Town grew up around the rocky crag on which the castle sits, and by the eleventh century a track had been forged between the castle and Holyrood Abbey below: the beginnings of what is now known as the Royal Mile, the spine of the Old Town. Leading from this, many side streets – or wynds – and closes developed, and it is this intriguing network of ancient streets that characterise this part of the city. Although many disappeared beneath later developments, particularly during the nineteenth-century slum clearances, this street pattern is still very much in evidence.

It was neither a healthy nor particularly pleasant place in which to live: from medieval times people lived close together – packed into the high buildings – and disease spread easily. By the mid-1800s, an estimated 40,000 citizens lived in this small area. It was this overcrowding that finally sent people across the bridge to the north, where the New Town offered more spacious and less dangerous habitation. The exodus was large-scale though, and the Old Town suffered greatly as a result, the population eventually sinking to below 3,000. Recent restorations have ensured that the Old Town is now enjoying a revived popularity, without losing any of the mystique that gives it its character.

VICTORIA STREET
THE OLD TOWN

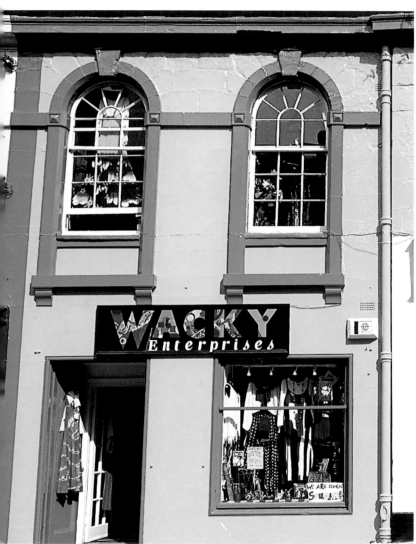

To the south of the Royal Mile, Victoria Street, part of an area formerly known as West Bow, rises up to George IV Bridge. Set back from the overcrowded closes of the Royal Mile this was one of the most desirable and fashionable places to live in the eighteenth century, helped by the founding of the first Assembly Rooms here in 1710. A few of these residences still stand on the north side of Victoria Street.

Towards the end of the century this part of the city, like much of the rest of the Old Town, began to experience a decline, and for 50 years the street deteriorated. Developments in the early part of the nineteenth century, which included the construction of George IV Bridge, saw a new rise in fortunes for Victoria Street, although many of the old buildings were pulled down in the name of progress.

Today, Victoria Street boasts an interesting medley of period houses and arcaded shops and, although it has not quite recaptured the vitality of its heyday, it makes for a captivating stroll through this part of town.

White Horse Close
CANONGATE

At the bottom of the Royal Mile, near the iron gates of Holyrood Palace, is one of the most picturesque of all Edinburgh's closes. Whitehorse Close was once of prime importance to travellers to and from Scotland's capital: it was here that the long and arduous journey to London by stage-coach began. The old coaching inn here is believed to be where Charles Edward Stuart's officers lodged in 1745, before the army embarked on their march to London.

The oldest buildings in the close date back to the early seventeenth century, but renovations and restorations over the years mean that many of them have been lost. The quaint whitewashed exteriors that characterise the close today set this apart from the dark and somewhat cramped closes further west. The typical Scots architecture is inescapable though, and the two-tiered houses with their gables and outside stairways add to the feeling of harmony and order that pervades the close.

Moray Place
THE NEW TOWN

When the New Town was completed in the nineteenth century, development of the north side of Edinburgh continued, until a third age of construction was accomplished. This became known as the Second New Town, spreading north and westwards.

Moray Place is one of the finest examples of the architectural style that characterises the newest phase. Designed by James Gillespie Graham, it was built on land owned by the Earl of Moray. Moray wanted the estates on his land to be completely different from the symmetrical, straight streets of Craig's plan, and so Graham devised an unusual series of streets, crescents and circuses. Moray Place is the pinnacle of his achievement. It is a massive, 12-sided block of high buildings, each one four storeys. Situated evenly around the perimeter of the circus are columned centrepieces and pilasters, enhancing the sense of upper-class luxury that pervades this area. So successful was the design that the Earl of Moray himself actually moved into this street (number 28).

St Andrew's Square
THE NEW TOWN

This was the first part of the New Town to be built – with the corresponding Charlotte Square on the other side of George Street. Unlike Charlotte Square, however, this has a fascinating mixture of architecture. Over two centuries, new and contrasting buildings have sprung up in St Andrew's Square, each one representing its own style and era. As well as the original Georgian houses that line the north side, there are structures from all ages, most notably the Guardian Royal Exchange building, a curiously individual black and white structure, erected in the 1930s.

The square is dominated by the statue which stands in the fenced-off central green. Commonly known as the 'Melville Monument' this is a memorial to Henry Dundas, the first Viscount Melville. A key political figure in the government of Pitt the Younger, it is now known that Melville's methods were somewhat dubious, but he none the less held great sway over the constituencies in Scotland in his time. The extent of his power is borne out in his nickname, 'Harry IX, uncrowned king of Scotland'.

Castlehill
THE ROYAL MILE

The beginning of the Royal Mile is the narrow street known as Castlehill which stretches from the castle Esplanade to where the road widens into the High Street. A plethora of buildings relate the history of this area, many of them to the castle itself.

Among the best-known buildings on Castlehill is the seventeenth-century Cannonball House. This is named after the cannonball that is lodged in the gables. Opinion is divided on exactly how it got there: local tales would have us believe it was fired from one of the great guns on the Mills Mount Battery during Bonnie Prince Charlie's brief occupation. The less romantic say it was put there in the nineteenth century in an effort to attract tourism. Either way, it is a talking point.

From Castlehill, cobbled steps lead down to the Grassmarket (see page 166), one of Edinburgh's most notorious places and the site of execution, murder and subterfuge. Other buildings of interest along this stretch include the Outlook Tower and Tolbooth St Johns, whose spire forms an unmistakable part of the Edinburgh skyline.

The Mound
THE NEW TOWN

The unromantically named Mound came into being shortly after construction of the New Town began. Before the boggy Nor' Loch was drained, there was no convenient way of travelling between the New Town and the Old. This became a problem for those who lived in the Old Town, but saw the opportunity for business in the New.

Such a man was George Boyd, an Old Town tailor who, with the rise in popularity of the north of the city, found trade somewhat scuppered by the lack of a direct route. He began to form a makeshift walkway with planks and stones that ran from the Lawnmarket on the Old Town ridge down to the eastern end of Princes Street. The idea caught on, and soon many people were contributing to 'Geordie Boyd's Mud Brig'. The excess of earth and mud that came about from the building of the New Town soon ensured that a permanent track was established here. In its early days it must have been an unattractive sight across the valley; time and landscaping have now turned it into one of Edinburgh's most picturesque roads.

North Bridge
THE NEW TOWN

When the plans for the New Town were accepted in the 1760s and the possibility of the city being extended to the north became a reality, it was realised instantly that the first step in this new plan was to build a bridge connecting the two parts of the city. Many metres below the Old Town ridge lay the marshy and unattractive Nor' Loch, creating a natural barrier between south and north. Almost immediately, work began on draining the loch and the first North Bridge was completed in 1772. The sturdy, three-arched structure was the first milestone in Edinburgh's New Town development.

The bridge that now spans the valley was built in the 1890s, an enforced reconstruction due to the arrival of the railway in Edinburgh, and it is a marvellous sight. It carries the road from the Royal Mile at the Tron Kirk over Waverley Station and the Princes Street Gardens to the thoroughfare at the east end. It is worth pausing to appreciate the vista from the bridge: to the east lies the sweep of Arthur's Seat and the Salisbury Crags, and to the west stretches Princes Street Gardens and the spires and buildings of the New Town.

Tenement Housing
MARCHMONT

The word 'tenement' tends to conjure up images of council estates and crumbling, closely packed buildings, but no vision could be more out of place with regard to Edinburgh's tenements. There is little sign of poverty here, and today estates like Marchmont are inhabited largely by the city's middle classes.

The first appealing feature of Marchmont is that it lies on the edge of the parkland commonly called the Meadows, wide open spaces of green lawns and woodland. But it is not only its situation that makes it a desirable habitat. The fine Baronial architecture is one of its main selling points, and the tenements are as rich in their own way as any of the marvellous Georgian buildings in the New Town.

The estate was built on land owned by Sir George Warrender, who saw a lucrative business opportunity in developing this land into housing estates. By the late 1860s, plans were on paper and construction was ready to begin. The rich architecture is largely thanks to Warrender's determination that sub-standard and ugly buildings would not grace his land. A network of extravagant Scottish Baronial structures arose, and Edinburgh's middle classes flocked to rent their properties, having found a more suitable niche than the overwhelming and expensive New Town or the slums of the Old.

Fan Window
THE NEW TOWN

A walk across the North Bridge from the Old Town to the New is like travelling to another city completely. In style, atmosphere, attitude and history, these two parts of Edinburgh could not be more different.

The most immediately noticeable, and striking, difference is the architecture. The Old Town is characterised by mysterious wynds and steep alleyways lined with high tenements and densely packed, ancient-looking grey buildings – every house seems huddled over its own closely guarded secrets. The New Town, in total contrast, is bright, open, neat and majestic. It was laid out in a grid-like network of streets and connecting avenues, and all the buildings had to conform to a standard of design and construction to keep the aesthetic whole harmonious. The golden sandstone buildings are enhanced by classical ornamentation: Corinthian pillars, carved panels, balustrades and pediments abound. Georgian windows and fanlights are found everywhere, adding to the orderly and unified aspect of the whole New Town. The finest works of some of Scotland's greatest architects and designers can be found here, including members of the Adam family, Sir William Chambers and James Craig, the father of the New Town.

The Royal Mile
THE OLD TOWN

Roughly following the ridge of the Old Town, the Royal Mile extends from the foot of the castle to the Palace of Holyroodhouse below. It is divided into four sections: Castlehill, the Lawnmarket, the High Street and Canongate, each with its own objects of interest and particular tales to tell.

Shops, historical buildings and museums combine in a fascinating mixture of the old and the new. To either side of the street, numerous closes and wynds offer an insight into Edinburgh's past. The Royal Mile has a dark and enclosed feeling, due to the great height of many of the buildings. This feature dates from when the city was surrounded by fortified walls and houses had to be built high so as to accommodate the huge population living within such a small area. This adds to the brooding atmosphere of mystery that abounds here, and as one walks down the street, through the ancient market places, past the place of public execution, past the Old Tolbooth that was once the prison, enjoying the varied churches and ancient winding alleyways, it is impossible not to feel awed by the history echoing from every step.

Princes Street
THE NEW TOWN

Now the busiest street in Edinburgh, Princes Street was originally a subsidiary road in the plans for the New Town. However, when the railway was built in the nineteenth century, Princes Street became an important thoroughfare and it has risen in prominence since then.

Lined on the north side by rows of shops, it is the south side that offers the most interest. Flanked by the magnificent Princes Street Gardens, dotted with memorials and statues, including the Scott Monument, and boasting some of the finest architecture in the city in the form of the galleries, the Balmoral Hotel and others, a walk along here is truly a journey of discovery. An Act of Parliament has forbidden any further development on this side of the street, so that the vast ridge of the Old Town, with the crag and the castle, will always be seen unobstructed, a reminder of Edinburgh's ancient past from the centre of its modern life.

Mylne's Court
LAWNMARKET

This is one of the oldest closes that remains in Edinburgh's Old Town, a large number having been destroyed during the large-scale clearance projects that helped rid the city of many of its slum areas, while causing numerous fine old buildings to be irretrievably lost. Mylne's Court dates from the late seventeenth century, and is named in honour of Robert Mylne, one of Edinburgh's pre-eminent architects and Charles II's master mason, who had a hand in the current design of the Palace of Holyroodhouse at the opposite end of the Royal Mile.

Only two of the tenements that Mylne designed are still standing and these have been converted into student houses (perhaps nowhere else in Britain do students have the honour of residing in such historical surroundings!). Despite this, they give a clear idea of how the whole close must once have looked. Rising to seven storeys, including an attic, the buildings have quite an austere appearance, but in their day were considered quite stately, and there is nowhere better to gain an idea of how life must have been lived in the seventeenth- and eighteenth-century Old Town.

Charlotte Square
THE NEW TOWN

Charlotte Square is the epitome of the New Town, its reality as perfect as its concept. One of two grand squares (the other being St Andrew's, see page 91) that were designed to flank the main thoroughfare of George Street, the plans for Charlotte Square were drawn up by Robert Adam. Although the initial design, consisting of classical palace façades, embellished by carved panels and balustrades never came to fruition, Adam's influence still pervades the glory of the square.

The north side is the closest example of Adam's vision for the square: 11 houses around a central section, characterised by eight large pillars and guarded at either end by stone sphinxes. These are not the only unusual ornamental features to be found here: amongst the fine architecture lurk stone-hewn Grecian urns, carved pediments and many other embellishments. To see the interiors of these houses, one must visit the National Trust-owned 'Georgian House', at number 7. This gives a good idea of the lifestyle and trends of upper-class culture in the eighteenth century.

Ramsay Garden
CASTLEHILL

Ramsay Garden was named after the poet Allan Ramsay who lived here in the mid-1700s in the octagonal 'Goose-Pie House'. A building of his own conception, the house has a view down to the foot of the Mound, where the poet's statue stands on the edge of Princes Street Gardens. This strange building is characteristic of Ramsay Garden's peculiar aspect, but despite this, it was this particular development that began the Old Town's revival.

The man responsible for this revival was town planner Patrick Geddes, who bought some land here towards the end of the nineteenth century and immediately set about constructing blocks of flats whose character made up for what they lacked in uniform design. In complete contrast to almost anything else in Edinburgh, the flats in Ramsay Garden were half-timbered with picturesque red roofs and a quaint, rambling character. They were an immediate success, drawing the more affluent members of Edinburgh society back into the arms of the Old Town. They are still some of the most desirable residences in the area.

Ann Street
STOCKBRIDGE

Ann Street is the most beautiful road in Stockbridge, and the pride of the suburb. Its design is attributed to the architect James Mylne, and it is both unusual and strikingly quaint.

The houses which rise up on both sides of Ann Street are at first hidden from view behind rows of trees and lilac bushes, and are set back, each with its own carefully planted and maintained gardens at the front. Further investigation, however, reveals rows of magnificent palace fronts, enhanced by pediments and pilasters, columns and balconies in a staged effect, each row set a little back from the others, and each row of varying heights. This abundance of classical architecture in the middle of this quiet, garden street is astonishing, and the architect would have been pleased with the effect that Ann Street still has on visitors. No detail has been left undone, and the overall effect is completed by iron railings and ornamental lamps. It is a truly exquisite achievement.

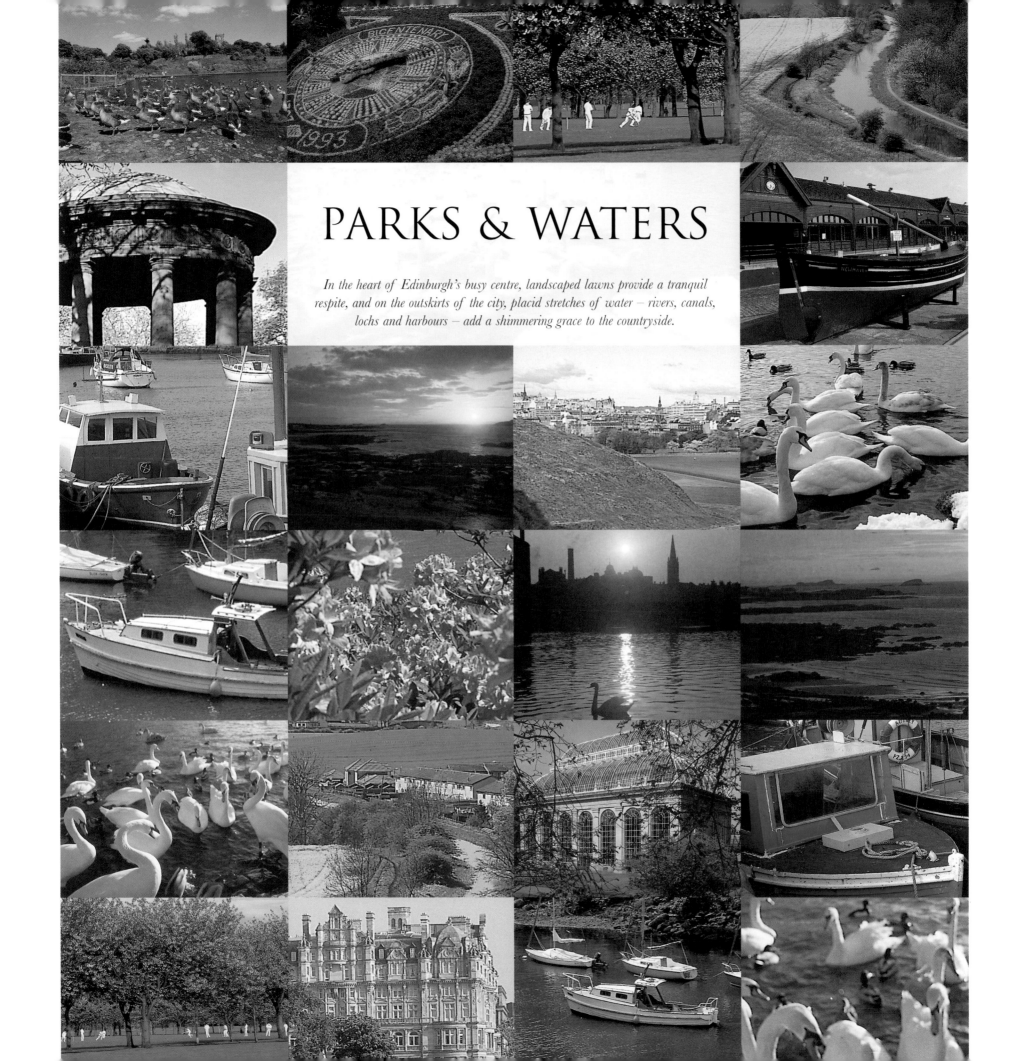

PARKS & WATERS

In the heart of Edinburgh's busy centre, landscaped lawns provide a tranquil respite, and on the outskirts of the city, placid stretches of water – rivers, canals, lochs and harbours – add a shimmering grace to the countryside.

Princes Street Gardens
PRINCES STREET

Where the beautifully land-scaped Princes Street Gardens now lie was once a bog, the Nor' Loch, which stretched across the valley from the rocky ridge of the Old Town to the north. The loch was drained in 1759 and the residents of Princes Street planned and planted the Gardens, reserving them for their own private use. By 1816, it was decided that the south side of the street be kept free from all further development, preserving the beauty of this open space. This agreement has largely been kept to, despite the proximity of the railway, and in the 1870s the Gardens became common ground, open to the public.

Today the park is divided into two parts: the West and East Gardens. These are separated by the National Gallery and the Royal Scottish Academy on the Mound. Within, the Gardens are not only large stretches of bordered grass, but also pathways that lead to smaller areas, such as the Heather Garden and the Peace Garden. Here is an escape from the frenetic activity of Princes Street and an atmosphere of calm and solitude.

The Floral Clock
PRINCES STREET GARDENS

Princes Street Gardens are full of pleasant surprises: statues, monuments and memorials are artlessly scattered amongst the carefully landscaped and lovingly tended parkland, and pathways lead to unexpected areas of enclosed tranquillity. One of the most unexpected features of the Gardens, however, is the Floral Clock.

Hidden just below the street where the West Gardens descend from the Gallery entrance and at the foot of the statue of poet Allan Ramsay, one of Edinburgh's most famous citizens, this working clock is constructed entirely from plants and flowers. It is fascinating to stand and watch the huge minute hand move around, and wait for the announcement of the hour, which comes from a wooden cuckoo in a wooden bird house to the left of the clock.

Planted in 1903, the Floral Clock is believed to be the oldest in the world, but it does not look its age. Each year, it is planted with new flowers, and in the summer, its vivid colours and unusual character draw hundreds of people, locals and tourists alike, to admire this marvellous piece of horticulture.

Dunsapie Loch
HOLYROOD PARK

Like St Margaret's Loch, also situated in the park, this is a man-made stretch of water, intended to enhance the park. This it certainly does, and is a popular attraction for tourists, who picnic before starting the ascent to Arthur's Seat which rises dramatically behind it. This is the easiest point from which to start the climb, which is 137 metres (450 ft) above the loch, ascending by way of the road that winds its way to the top.

The loch itself is 122 metres (400 ft) above sea level and commands magnificent views across the diverse park landscape and surrounding area. Many wild birds have made their homes here, including ducks and swans. The small island in the middle of the loch was created especially to provide a nesting place for these birds, encouraging them to stay, and they seem undisturbed by the constant toing and froing of human visitors.

Fishmarket
NEWHAVEN

The seafaring tradition that is still so evident in Newhaven began in the fifteenth century when James IV decided that this was the place to build his warship, the *Great Michael*. Legend has it that the ship needed all the trees in Fife to build, but it was never used: perhaps this is why Newhaven never really took off as a shipbuilding port. Instead, it turned its attentions to the fishing trade, and for many centuries the wealth of the village depended on the catches of herring and oysters that were to be found in the Firth of Forth.

By the nineteenth century, Newhaven oysters were famous world-wide and a huge oyster fishery thrived here. Sadly, the interference of the English again put the mockers on Scottish progress, this time not in the form of marauding armies, but by one George Clark, who leased the fishery, overshipped the area and left Newhaven all but bereft of its livelihood. Today, only echoes of the eminent fishing port that Newhaven once was remain. The lively fishmarket has gone and pleasure boats rather than fishing boats sit in the harbour. Newhaven's fortunes have been somewhat revived recently, with the establishment of Harry Ramsden's restaurant in what was the old fishmarket, and the port still offers a fascinating insight into the old seafaring traditions.

Sunset
THE FIRTH OF FORTH

Yonder the shores of Fife you saw;
Here Preston-Bay And Berwick Law;
And, broad between them rolled,
The gallant Firth the eye might note,
Whose islands on its bosom float,
Like emeralds in gold.

Sir Walter Scott

The Firth of Forth is the main natural landmark in the Edinburgh district. It is a magnificent stretch of water, and picturesque villages that once drew their living from it lie along its shores. Small harbours are remnants of once-thriving fishing and trading communities. More dramatically, the coastline is scattered with the haunting ruins of medieval castles and stately homes. The Forth Islands are largely uninhabited now, and play home to scores of wild birds and water creatures, such as otters and even the occasional seal. Fishing is a popular pastime in the Forth waters and tributaries, where trout and salmon can be found.

From the high points of Edinburgh, from the castle ramparts, from the top of Calton Hill and Arthur's Seat, the Forth can be seen stretching out, magical and shimmering, part of the life and culture of the city since earliest times.

Royal Botanic Garden
INVERLEITH

Just north of the New Town lies yet another surprisingly tranquil area of parkland – the Royal Botanic Garden. This rich and splendid garden was not always situated here, though, and as one of the oldest botanic gardens in Britain it has a long and fascinating history.

Its origins lie with the University, when one of the Royal College of Physicians' founders began a small physic garden near Holyrood. The interest this generated forced it to move to an area near what is now Princes Street and a few years later, it moved again to Leith Walk. Each time, the Garden grew in magnificence, encompassing a wider variety of plants and flowers than the medicinal herbs it originally grew.

Finally, in 1823, the Garden moved to its present site in Inverleith. It now stretches over 70 acres and includes areas of finely landscaped lawns and picturesque woodland. It is also home to some of the best collections of unusual and exotic plants to be found anywhere in the country. Most spectacular are the rhododendrons, which are a breathtaking site in the spring months, and these alone make the garden well worth a visit.

The Glasshouse
Royal Botanic Garden
INVERLEITH

In the heart of the Royal Botanic Garden stands a collection of variously aged greenhouses, known as the 'Glasshouse Experience'. These are home to fantastic collections of exotic plants and are one of the Garden's greatest assets.

There are 11 plant houses altogether, ranging from the Victorian Palm House to the New Glass Houses, built in the 1960s. The glasshouses alone are a point of interest, their differing architectural styles each a reflection of the age in which they were designed: the Palm House, built in 1858, is a medley of cast-iron columns and stairways, appropriately decorated; the New Glass Houses built on frames of tubular steel with modern elevated walkways and suspension cables.

Once inside, this fades into insignificance as one is enveloped by the hot, steamy atmosphere and the riot of colour and variety. Here, it seems, is every type of exotic plant imaginable, from orchids to palm trees. The man largely responsible for this fine collection was George Forrest, an avid traveller, who brought back hundreds of different plant types from his frequent trips abroad, especially to south-west China. The Glasshouse Experience is one not to be missed – it is a journey to foreign lands, in a world of its own.

Duddingston Loch
HOLYROOD PARK

The village of Duddingston is a curiosity. Although officially a suburb of Edinburgh, it is an independent place that has grown up through the centuries into a quaint and individual collection of buildings, all alive with history. They include the Sheeps Heid, reputedly once frequented by James VI; the twelfth-century church, set on a rocky outcrop above the loch, and the house where Bonnie Prince Charlie held a council of war before the Battle of Prestonpans.

The loch, one of three in Holyrood Park, is now a designated bird sanctuary, and flocks of geese, ducks and coots, among other varieties, have made their homes here. There used to be otters here too, gliding amongst the reeds, but these have now gone, making way for the increasing numbers of birds and other wildlife. In Victorian times, the loch was larger than it is now and was the focal point of the village, attracting people from the surrounding area to admire its tranquillity in the summer months, and to host ice-skating parties during winter.

View of Edinburgh
HOLYROOD PARK

Within the dramatic spread of Holyrood Park is contained a marvellous mixture of landscapes: large areas of wide open space are countered by small glens and woodlands; the harsh outcrops of the Salisbury Crags are scattered with marshlands and lochs. It is a microcosm of the Scottish landscape, represented in an area measuring only 6.4 km (4 miles), and startlingly close to Edinburgh's busy centre.

The whole area was once a great hunting lodge, and it was here that David I was miraculously saved from a charging stag, causing him to found Holyrood Abbey. Although much of it has now been landscaped, the park somehow maintains a wild and romantic air. In 1745, Prince Charles' entire army camped here before setting off on their fatal journey to London. Here too, many of Scotland's monarchs have walked, from the earliest leaders to the more recent royals, in particular Prince Albert, who instigated the creation of St Margaret's Loch, and George VI, who is reputed to have had a special fondness for the place, admiring the beauty of the park and the dramatic nature of the views that enclose it.

St Bernard's Well
DEAN VILLAGE

It is often said that Edinburgh lacks the one element all major cities should have – a river. Although the city and its environs are blessed with an abundance of water in the form of lochs, harbours and the ever-present Firth of Forth, the Water of Leith is its only true claim to a river. The Water, sourced in the Pentland Hills, is hardly a raging torrent – in certain places it is no more than a stream, hardly noticeable amongst the valleys and gorges.

In Dean Village, the old miller's community by the Water of Leith, stands St Bernard's Well. Local legend states that in the twelfth century, during a visit to Scotland, St Bernard of Clairvaux was led by birds to the healing waters of a spring on this spot. In reality, the well was discovered by three boys while fishing in the Water in 1760. The well-water was found to contain minerals and a pump room was soon constructed, with this small Doric temple over it. The statue in the middle portrays Hygieia, the Goddess of Health, and throughout the eighteenth and nineteenth centuries this spot became a popular attraction, not only because of the natural waters, but also because of its beautiful, secluded situation by the calm river waters.

The Meadows
SOUTH EDINBURGH

Hidden behind the University lies another of Edinburgh's many pleasant parks – the Meadows. Like Princes Street Gardens, the area over which the Meadows now stretches was once entirely under water. Known as the South Loch, it used to be the city's main source of water.

By the early eighteenth century, Edinburgh's water was supplied from elsewhere, and plans for a park in this part of town evolved. The loch was drained in 1740, trees were planted and stretches of open grass and woodland sprang up. Paths crossed through the Meadows, and by the late eighteenth century the area had become a fashionable promenade for Edinburgh citizens.

Today, the Meadows are pretty much as they were then, still popular with those seeking the pleasure of open space in the heart of a city. The greens have become common ground for friendly games of cricket and football; the woodland paths and avenues favourites with joggers or those just taking a stroll.

Smug Anchorage
CRAMOND

Cramond is situated at the mouth of the River Almond where it meets the Forth Estuary, and once this was a thriving iron-producing area and milling community, plying its trade via the harbour at the river mouth. At low tide, the whole area is a low, sandy bed and it is possible to walk to the island that lies in the middle, inhabited now only by seabirds. From here, the views across to Fife are spellbinding.

The harbour was also once used as a fishing port, and in its heyday during the eighteenth and nineteenth centuries the village, indeed the whole area, was extremely prosperous. Progress took its toll though, and after the harbour silted up, trading ceased. Now, like Newhaven and Leith, few vessels except pleasure boats anchor here. It remains a charming and historic place. Walks along the banks of the Almond provide the odd reminder of the old trades: remnants of the quarry wharves, relics of the old weirs, mills and cottages.

St Margaret's Loch

HOLYROOD PARK

St Margaret was the grand-niece of Edward the Confessor, but was born exiled in Hungary. In 1054, the Saxon monarchy was re-established and Margaret went to England with her father, to live at Edward's court. After her father died, Margaret's upbringing was left to the austere guidance of Edward, and she did not have a happy youth. With the ascension of King Harold, Margaret decided to return to Hungary, but she got no further than the Firth of Forth, where her ship was wrecked. The English Princess then met the King of Scotland, Malcolm III, whom she married. She died in 1093, three days after hearing of the deaths of her husband and eldest son in battle. The throne passed to her youngest son David I, who was responsible for founding the Abbey at Holyrood. She was canonised in 1249.

It is appropriate then, that this loch situated in Holyrood Park at the foot of Arthur's Seat should be named after her, and that it has royal origins: Prince Albert ordered the loch to be created in an attempt to enhance the beauty of the park. It is a lovely spot, overlooked by the romantic ruins of St Anthony's Chapel, and home to ducks, swans and the famous greylag geese.

Musselburgh Harbour
MUSSELBURGH

The town of Musselburgh takes its name from the many mussel beds that were once found in the River Esk, upon which the town is situated. This was its main source of income for centuries and proved extremely lucrative, causing the harbour to become one of the main fishing and trading ports in the Edinburgh area. It was only in the nineteenth century, when the harbour silted up, that trading diminished.

It is an ancient settlement, dating from Roman times, when a fort was established here to support their camp at Inveresk. The town has seen a victorious Cromwellian army, fresh from the Battle of Dunbar, settle here for a short time, and over the centuries has endured sacking and pillaging by English armies on the march to and from Edinburgh.

Its nickname, the 'Honest Toun', dates from 1332 when Thomas Randolph, Earl of Moray and nephew of Robert the Bruce, was taken ill nearby and was sheltered by the citizens of Musselburgh, away from the invading English, until his death. 'Honest Toun' pageants are still held here annually. Other attractions in Musselburgh include its ancient golf links and racecourse and Pinkie House, the earliest parts of which date from the fourteenth century.

The Port of Leith
LEITH

For many centuries, Leith was separate from Edinburgh, although it was not until 1833 that it became a royal burgh in its own right. The role it has played in Scottish history should not be undervalued, for it was once Scotland's major east coast port.

It was at Leith that Mary, Queen of Scots landed on her joyful return from France to take up her place as monarch of Scotland in 1561. By this time, the port had already suffered much at the hands of the English, having been burned twice in the preceding two decades. It was here also that Cromwell settled his armies for a time during the mid-seventeenth century.

The shipbuilding trade was one of Leith's major industries up until the 1980s, and the remains of this once-thriving port are still in evidence, albeit now in modern terms: the disused warehouses and offices have been turned into exclusive flats, and pubs and bars created from the old buildings abound on the dockside. From here, the ships that sail on a daily basis from the large harbour can be seen embarking on voyages to English and Scandinavian ports, just as they have done for centuries.

Union Canal
EDINBURGH ENVIRONS

In the late eighteenth century, canal-fever swept through Britain. Canals were the ideal method of transporting goods to and from all the major cities, increasing trading potential. In England, these man-made waterways sprung up throughout the country, but in Scotland they were faced with problems: topographically, the country did not invite direct routes and very few of the major cities were far enough away from the coast to warrant canal building.

However, after the construction of the Forth and Clyde Canal, it was decided an extension was needed to enable Lanarkshire coal to reach Scotland's capital and also to transport grain from Edinburgh's milling communities out to Glasgow and the surrounding area. Thus, the Union Canal was born. Stretching 50 km (31 miles) from the Forth and Clyde at Falkirk to a basin ½ mile west of Edinburgh, the Union Canal did not require the construction of any locks, although the valleyed regions needed several aqueducts, some of which survive today.

The Forth and Clyde and the Union Canals were rendered obsolete – like most others in Britain – with the advent of the railways. Today, pleasure cruises along its picturesque stretch are enjoyed, and anglers make the most of the solitude, all a far cry from the trading traffic that once filled the canal.

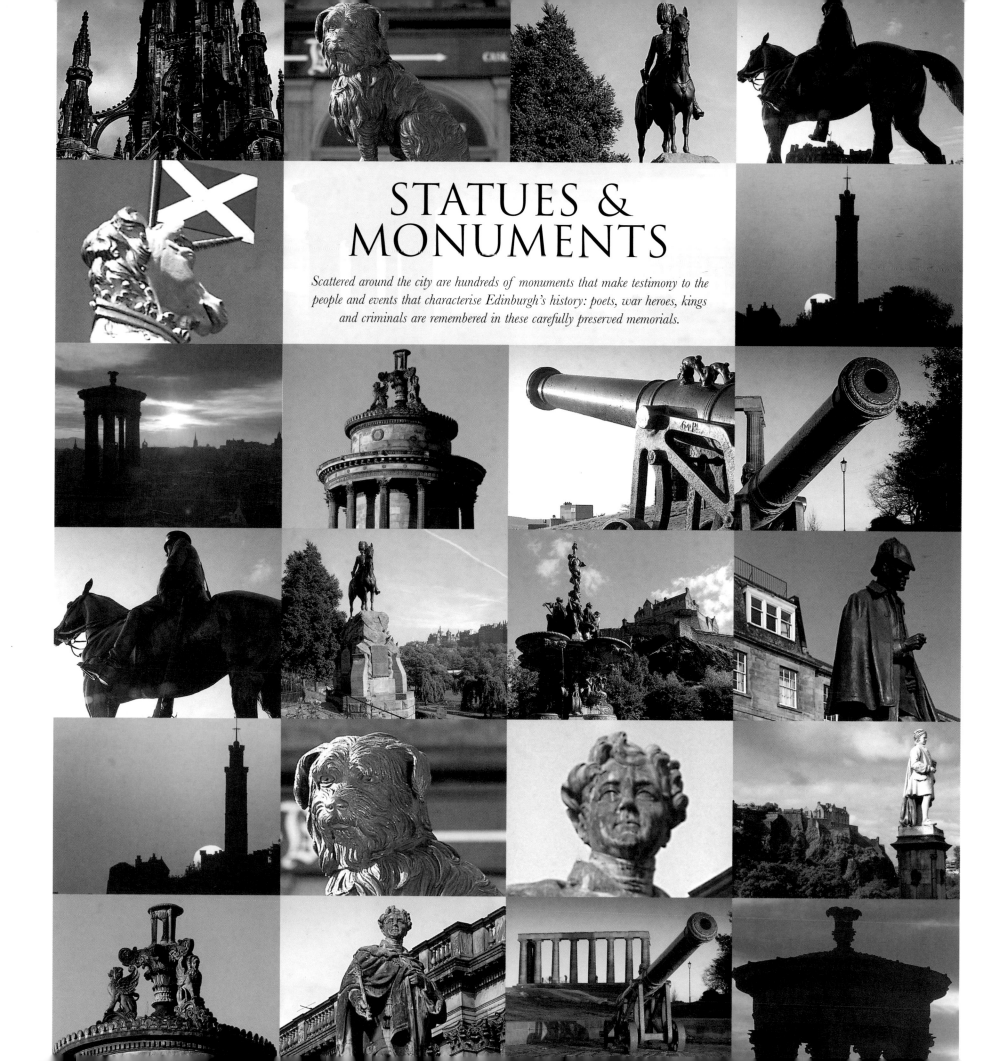

STATUES &
MONUMENTS

*Scattered around the city are hundreds of monuments that make testimony to the
people and events that characterise Edinburgh's history: poets, war heroes, kings
and criminals are remembered in these carefully preserved memorials.*

National Monument
CALTON HILL

The greatest and strangest of all the monuments scattered across Calton Hill is the National Monument; a half-built Greek temple that gives no indication of its meaning or symbolism. This grand and ambiguous structure was designed by William Playfair in 1822. Intended as a commemoration of the recently ended Napoleonic Wars, Playfair turned to the Scottish love of classical architecture for inspiration for his design, reproducing the Parthenon to Athena, Goddess of War.

Despite lacking sufficient funds to build the monument, work began. It was, needless to say, a difficult task – the huge blocks of stone had to be transported from the quarry outside the city all the way up Calton Hill. By 1829, the money ran out and building stopped. Over the next few years, many suggestions were made as to the uses to which the building could be put, including an art gallery and even the new home for Scottish Parliament. In the event, nothing was decided upon and the monument was left, a massive, half-finished and mysterious object, the purpose of which there appears to be no rhyme or reason.

Memorial to the Royal Scots Greys
PRINCES STREET GARDENS

Set on roughly hewn blocks of sandstone, this bronze equestrian statue is a memorial to the Royal Scots Greys, the oldest regiment in the British Army; one with a reputation for great courage in the face of adversity: the roll of honours listed here bears testimony to this. The statue was erected in 1906 and is the work of Birnie Rhind.

Situated at the east end of Princes Street Gardens, this is one of many monuments that can be found in the Gardens. Many statues line the north side of the boundaries, along the busy line of Princes Street, and scattered around the Gardens are numerous and varied testimonials to a diverse range of people. These include Allan Ramsay, the poet, and Dr James Simpson, the first person to use chloroform as an anaesthetic. Small and discreet, or large and flamboyant, the statues in the Gardens encapsulate the many facets of Edinburgh's intellectual and social history.

Nelson Monument
CALTON HILL

The Scottish have a talent for designing and building imaginative memorials. On Calton Hill alone there is a collection of monuments that seems to defy logic or explanation, and the five-storeyed circular tower that is the Nelson Monument is one of the most peculiar. Built in 1807 shortly after Nelson's death at the Battle of Trafalgar, this is one of the earlier of the hill's buildings and is a curious commemoration of the great naval hero.

The tower stretches over 30 metres (100 ft) high, and its most fascinating feature is the time ball at the top. Every day at one o'clock, this time ball drops in exact synchronisation with the one o'clock gun that is set off across the city at the castle battery. This was once used as a visual time signal to ships in the Firth of Forth, but is now a major tourist attraction. It is certainly worth the climb to the top of the monument, because from here the views over the Forth, the city and out to the horizon, enveloping the dramatic Salisbury Crags, are spectacular.

The Mercat Cross
HIGH STREET

The Mercat Cross on the Royal Mile marks the centre of Old Edinburgh, and has played a vital role in the city's official life. The old high Cross stood in the middle of the High Street in medieval times, and was rebuilt twice before being moved to its present position outside the west door of the High Kirk of St Giles in 1885. The most important ceremony carried out here is the Royal Proclamation: for centuries, royal announcements have been made from here and still are today, accompanied by a fanfare from the Lord Lyon King of Arms. Legend has it that the Cross flowed with wine when the return of Mary, Queen of Scots was declared. Civic proclamations are also made here, most recently the announcement of devolution.

The Cross has a darker history, too. For hundreds of years, executions took place nearby, including that of the great military hero the Marquis of Montrose. Just prior to the infamous Battle of Flodden in 1513, a ghost is said to have stood at the Cross and announced the names of those who would meet their doom in the ensuing fight.

Dugald Stewart Monument
CALTON HILL

The first of the many and varied monuments reached after ascending Calton Hill, this is a memorial to Dugald Stewart (1753 –1828). Like many of Edinburgh's other buildings and monuments, including the Burns Monument (see page 136) and the National Monument (see page 130), this has Grecian echoes, modelled on the Choragic Monument of Lysicrates in Athens.

But who was Dugald Stewart? All over Edinburgh, well-known historical figures – political, literary and royal – are paid tribute to in a marvellous assortment of statues and monuments, but this stately construction – by William Playfair – is something of a curiosity. A Professor of Philosophy at Edinburgh University, Dugald Stewart was a pioneer in his field and had a widespread reputation in his time, his lectures drawing crowds of students eager to hear him expound his latest theories. Unfortunately, time and the ever-changing trends in modern thought and philosophy have rendered his work and reputation obsolete, and he is now a little-known figure outside academic circles. Perhaps though, this attractive memorial will ensure that the he is never entirely forgotten and may one day revive the interest and appreciation of one of the pioneers of modern thought.

Greyfriars Bobby
GREYFRIARS

Amongst the most famous of Edinburgh's citizens is the small Skye terrier known as Greyfriars Bobby, whose life-size statue stands outside Greyfriars Kirkyard on the south side of the Royal Mile.

When his master, John Gray, died in 1858 Bobby followed the procession to the interment in Greyfriars and then refused to leave. At first he was fed by scraps from local kitchens, but soon his fame spread and people would travel to the kirkyard just to see the loyal little dog, ever vigilant at his master's grave. The local people even put up a special shelter for

him. He won the hearts not only of the people of Edinburgh, but also the hearts of people the world over as his story spread. Even the Lord Provost of the city at the time paid Bobby's license fee, so that he would not be taken away as a stray.

For 14 years Greyfriars Bobby was never far from John Gray's grave, and when the terrier himself died in 1872, he was laid to rest within the kirkyard near the master he loved so dearly. A year later, this bronze effigy of Bobby was unveiled in testimony to his loyalty and to the sentimental hold his story had – and still has – on visitors and locals.

Ross Fountain
PRINCES STREET GARDENS

The Ross Fountain is one of Princes Street Gardens' more controversial pieces of ornamentation. It is a glorious gilded and impressively large creation that stands in the middle of the park, somewhat out of place amidst the stately landscaped lawns and neat flower beds.

It was created for the 1862 Paris Exhibition and once the Exhibition was finished, the piece was bought by one Daniel Ross, an Edinburgh native, who presented it to the city. It was a noble gesture, but unfortunately not universally pleasing, and the fountain was placed in the Gardens, as hidden away as possible. Perhaps the extravagantly carved, voluptuous figures were rather too much for Victorian sensibilities; they certainly shocked some of the locals, causing the minister at nearby St John's Church to expound that the fountain was 'grossly indecent and disgusting'.

A century later it can be appreciated for what it is – a fine piece of flamboyant experimentation – and the talking point of the Princes Street Gardens!

Sherlock Holmes Statue
PICARDY PLACE

This fine statue of the fictional detective Sherlock Holmes may seem more at home in London's Baker Street than in an unassuming corner of Edinburgh, but its presence here is not altogether unwarranted. Holmes' creator Sir Arthur Conan Doyle was born here at number 11 Picardy Place, and studied medicine at the University of Edinburgh.

The statue was erected in 1991 and was commissioned by the Federation of Master Builders in Edinburgh as a celebration of their fiftieth anniversary. The man responsible for its creation was Gerald Ogilvie Laing, and surprisingly is the only statue of Sherlock Holmes to be found in Britain. Sadly, Conan Doyle's birthplace no longer exists, so it is especially appropriate that he is commemorated here in some way.

The statue is not the only sculpture in this part of the city. A short walk away are some less classical pieces sculpted by Sir Edouardo Paolozzi, Her Majesty's Sculptor-in-Ordinary in Scotland. These bronze pieces include a huge hand and foot, and it is worth a trip to cast a wondering eye over them.

The Scott Monument
PRINCES STREET

The Scott Monument is Edinburgh's most famous memorial, and it is dedicated to its most famous literary son – Sir Walter Scott.

Towering at the east end of Princes Street Gardens, the magnificent Gothic spire of the Scott Monument dominates the vista in this part of the city. Built in 1840 with funds drawn from public subscription, the 67 metre (220 ft) monument was the design of George Meikle Kemp, who sadly did not live to see his masterpiece – and only architectural work – completed. Much thought went into the design, however, and it is a fitting testimony. At every level of the age-blackened spire representations of Scottish writers and characters from Scott's novels are intricately carved. It is a complete three-dimensional résumé of the works of Scotland's best-loved writer.

At the base of the monument sits a Carrara marble statue of Scott himself, with his dog Maida. This is the inspiration of Sir John Steell, a perfect complement to the lofty spire. The Scott Monument, the largest and most ambitious memorial to a writer ever constructed, is the focus of the New Town and Edinburgh's pride in it echoes the nation's pride in the man to whom it is dedicated.

Burns Monument
REGENT ROAD

Is there a Bard of rustic song,
Who, noteless, steals the crouds among,
That weekly this area throng,
O, pass not by!
But with a frater-feeling strong,
Here, heave a sigh.

Although Robert Burns was not an Edinburgher by birth, his status as national bard undoubtedly earns him a memorial in his country's capital. Like the monument to Dugald Stewart on the nearby Calton Hill, the Burns Monument is a simplified replica of the Monument to Lysicrates in Athens, reflecting the Scots love of classical Greek architecture. A two-staged, cylindrical-columned structure, it was erected in 1830 at the foot of the Royal Mile in Regent Road.

The Burns Monument was once enhanced by a statue of the poet at its base. Sadly, this has been taken away, and although it can still be admired in the National Portrait Gallery, its loss somehow detracts from the significance of the small Corinthian temple erected in Burn's honour.

Statue of George IV
GEORGE STREET

George Street was intended to be one of the main thoroughfares in the New Town, running from St Andrew's Square and Charlotte Square, parallel to Princes Street. Craig, the chief designer and architect of the New Town, planned this stately avenue to be the city's residential heart. Today, there are no private residences along this stretch, the fine houses have all been turned into offices and the street is now the financial centre of Edinburgh, the equivalent of the City of London. The buildings, however, stand as a reminder of the way Edinburgh's wealthier residents once lived.

Standing tall on a granite pedestal, the regal statue of George IV, designed by Chantrey, was unveiled in 1831 – a year after the King's death – and stands at the crossing of Hanover Street. Here, the monarch surveys the architectural triumph of the Royal Scottish Academy and the picturesque rise of The Mound, looking south towards the Old Town. George IV paid a visit to Edinburgh in 1822, and certainly made an impression on the Scottish people by parading around the Palace of Holyroodhouse in his tartan kilt.

Memorial Cannon
CALTON HILL

The cannon on Calton Hill is one of the most photographed monuments in Edinburgh, yet it is also one of the most obscure and little of its history is readily accessible.

It is believed to have been built sometime before 1624, the date inscribed on the barrel, and is almost certainly Portuguese. It came to Edinburgh via Burma, where it must have seen some action – a Burmese inscription on the cannon reinforces this. It was captured by the British during the Conquest of Burma in 1886, and taken as a memento of the Mandalay Campaign. After being transported to Britain it was presented as a gift to the City of Edinburgh, and put on show at the Meadows International Exhibition in the same year. It then joined the collection of monuments that grace the summit of Calton Hill.

During the Second World War, many of Edinburgh's metal memorials were taken away to be melted down into ammunition, and for a while this hard-won monument was in danger of playing a less dramatic role in another campaign. However, due to its long history and a local public outcry, it was left in state on the hill, an unusual and ambiguous piece of British history.

Statue of Allan Ramsay
PRINCES STREET GARDENS

It has been suggested that it is degrading for one of Edinburgh's most eminent citizens to be immortalised in a statue wearing his nightcap, but in Allan Ramsay's time (1686–1758), such items were considered fashionable, and it seems unlikely that the poet would have minded – he was renowned for his good humour.

It is, perhaps, an appropriate reminder of his origins as a wig maker, a profession he abandoned to become a bookseller in 1718. From this grew his passion and talent for literature, in particular poetry. He began to publish collections of poetry, including the *Tea Table Miscellany* which brought together many Scottish songs and ballads, and later was an inspiration for Robert Burns, amongst others.

Ramsay's own works began to appear sporadically around 1721, but it was not until 1725's *The Gentle Shepherd* that he began to receive real critical acclaim. This pastoral work became one of the most popular Scots works of its time. Shortly afterwards, Ramsay established the first library in Britain.

This statue, carved from Carrara marble by Sir John Steell, was erected in 1865. It stands in a prime position at the crossroads of Princes Street and The Mound, reflecting Ramsay's contribution to the Scots' literary world.

Statue of Field Marshal Haig

CASTLE ESPLANADE, CASTLEHILL

There are a number of objects of interest that stand on the Castle Esplanade, a curious collection of reminders of Edinburgh's past. The most fascinating, and macabre, is the drinking fountain in the north-east corner. Art nouveau in style, this is made up of images of witches and serpents and marks the place where local women accused of witchcraft, met a horrific end. Hundreds of women were burned at the stake here throughout the fifteenth, sixteenth and seventeenth centuries.

Not far away from here stands this beautifully cast, bronze equestrian statue of Field Marshal Haig. Haig, an Edinburgher by birth, was commander of the British troops during the First World War. When this statue was unveiled in 1923 in the aftermath of the allied victory, Haig was something of a national hero. His radical front-line strategies, however, have since been looked at with hindsight, and controversy still surrounds his methods of fighting.

CASTLES &
STATELY HOMES

The homes of monarchs and aristocrats that lie scattered around Edinburgh reflect the lives and times of these figures. Many of these places have played a role in some of Scotland's most famous events – in particular, Edinburgh Castle itself.

The Palace of Holyroodhouse
CANONGATE

The processional stretch of the Royal Mile leads eventually to the gates of the magnificent Palace of Holyroodhouse, home of kings past and present, and alive with the ghosts of Edinburgh's history.

The massive wrought-iron gates open on to a suitably regal forecourt from which rises the impressive stone palace. It was built under the orders of James IV in 1498, although little of the original building is left today. Fifty years after its construction, the palace suffered serious damage by the Earl of Hertford's troops and a century later Cromwell's army left their own mark on it. By the time the monarchy was restored, there was little left of the grand palace that Holyrood had once been.

In the 1670s, Charles II ordered the palace to be restored, and Sir William Bruce redesigned and reconstructed large parts of the building. In the event, Charles II never even visited Holyrood to appreciate the marvellous craftsmanship, but we have him to thank for the continued existence of this royal home.

Carving
PALACE OF HOLYROODHOUSE, CANONGATE

This carved relief of the royal arms is found above the main entrance to Holyrood. A visit to the palace is like taking a journey through the capital's turbulent history. The rich surroundings enhance the atmosphere of ancient and dramatic events, where Scotland's kings and queens have lived and died.

James V's tower is the oldest surviving part of the palace and Mary, Queen of Scots' own apartments were on the second floor. Here she held court with some of Edinburgh's most distinguished figures, including John Knox (whom she later accused of treason). Here also, the queen undertook her unwise union with Bothwell after the murder of her husband Lord Darnley. The queen's secretary Rizzio was murdered in the palace in one of the most infamous incidents in Scottish royal history, and a plaque marks the exact spot where this took place. On a lighter note, in another part of the palace is the long Picture Gallery, which contains no less than 111 portraits of Scottish kings and queens by the Dutch painter Jacob de Wit, most of which, however, are based more on legend than fact.

Lauriston Castle
NEAR CRAMOND

The present house was built around the original sixteenth-century tower, and the building spreads out in a curiously ordered manner, at the same time managing to appear quite unplanned and spontaneous. The first castle burned down in 1544 and much of the additional part of the house is Jacobean in influence, designed by William Burn. This is a fairy-tale castle: small but magical, its four storeys enhanced by conical corner turrets and beautiful stonework. Lauriston stands in its own perfectly landscaped gardens that stretch to the shores of the Firth of Forth.

One of the most famous proprietors of Lauriston Castle in the eighteenth century was John Law, a local financier and gambler, who moved to France where he rose quickly to become a major authority in finance. While here he concocted a scheme to boost France's economic development, which involved circulating paper money rather than gold. Always a gambler, Law knew this was a risk, and in the event it did not pay off – the financial market crashed in 1720 and Law died a poor man.

Lauriston's last owner was an Edinburgh cabinet-maker, who bequeathed his home and marvellous collections of furniture and antiques to the city on his death in 1926. This now forms a beautiful exhibition within the castle, making its interior as charming and fascinating as its exterior.

Stevenson House
HADDINGTON

Very few documented, historical records of Stevenson House survive today, and as a result its continual history is difficult to trace. There is no doubt, however, that this is an ancient site. It is known that a house of some description has stood here for hundreds of years, and the first charter in which it is mentioned dates from 1235. This old house and its successors have been in continual habitation since the thirteenth century, at which time the house and its lands were owned by the Cistercian nunnery based nearby at Haddington.

The present house largely dates from the sixteenth-century Restoration period, although in the late seventeenth and early eighteenth centuries additions were made along the south range of Stevenson House. As well as being a beautiful and historic home, Stevenson House is also unique in that it is the only domestic courtyard house in Scotland that is still occupied.

Tantallon Castle
NEAR DIRLETON

Surrounded on three sides by the sea crashing on the rocks below, and on the fourth by a moat, it is not difficult to gauge Tantallon's strategic importance in medieval times. The Castle has seen more military action than any other fortification around Edinburgh, except perhaps Edinburgh Castle.

Built at the end of the fourteenth century, it was the home of one of Scotland's most notorious clans – the Douglas family, the Earls of Angus – for many years. One of the greatest sieges laid on Tantallon Castle was led by the young James V. The Sixth Earl of Angus held a great deal of power and sway in the early 1500s and while the king was in his minority, the earl used his influence to keep him a virtual prisoner in the city. On achieving his majority James V charged Angus with treason and launched an assault on the Douglas family stronghold. It is a testimony to the strength of Tantallon's construction that, although James was the ultimate victor in the battle, it was as a result of lengthy negotiation rather than the strength of his attack. Douglas escaped abroad, and James V took ownership of the castle.

This magnificent fortification was eventually destroyed by Cromwell in 1651 after a 12-day siege and was never repaired, its remnants now standing as an eerie reminder of Scotland's violent history.

Dirleton Castle
DIRLETON

The extensive ruins of the Castle are the dominant feature of the village of Dirleton. The original castle was built in the thirteenth century by the de Vaux family and parts of this still remain, most notably the Lord's Hall, a room that despite its decayed state, still reflects some of its former majesty. The Castle was later extended and modified by the Halyburton family, who added the Great Hall. Later owners also included the infamous Ruthven family, members of which were involved in the murder of Mary, Queen of Scots' favourite Rizzio.

Dirleton Castle's best-known resident was the tragic Dorothea, wife of the Earl of Gowrie. Gowrie was a rebellious man, and after his part in a conspiracy to attack Stirling Castle was discovered, James VI confiscated all his family lands and possessions, including the Castle, had the unfortunate earl executed and left his even more unfortunate widow and 15 children destitute. Dorothea survived until the castle and lands were restored to her a few years later, but the story does not have a happy ending. It seems her sons had inherited their father's rebellious nature and after the involvement of two of them in the 'Gowrie Conspiracy' – a mysterious affair whose aim seemed to be the king's assassination – Dorothea was once again left destitute.

Blackness Castle
NEAR SOUTH QUEENSFERRY

When the Act of Union was passed in 1707, Blackness Castle was one of only four castles in Scotland permitted to maintain their fortifications – an indication of its strategic and historical importance.

Surrounded on three sides by the Forth, and jutting out on a rocky promontory, Blackness is one of the most dramatic and mysterious sights around Edinburgh. The castle's original date is unknown, and the tower that remains today almost certainly dates from the fifteenth century, but the rest of the castle may be even earlier. The tower is likely to have been an additional fortification built when the castle was a major fortress. It has witnessed some great events, including a siege by Cromwell, but by the seventeenth century was being used as a state prison, and its fortunes declined from this time until in the nineteenth century, it eventually became no more than a storage for gunpowder. Today it is a relic, but one of the darkest and most dramatic relics Edinburgh has to offer.

Craigmillar Castle
NEAR DUDDINGSTON

In the sixteenth century Craigmillar Castle was situated beyond the boundaries of Edinburgh, although today its site just south-east of Duddingston village makes it very much a part of the city. It became a favourite spot for Mary, Queen of Scots during her reign, and many tales associated with the castle are related to the unfortunate queen. Mary's father, James V, made this his home for a short while in 1517, and after large-scale damage was inflicted by the English Earl of Hertford, the castle was rebuilt to provide Mary with a place of refuge. She fled here after the brutal murder of her secretary Rizzio in 1566, and local legend states that it was here at Craigmillar that the plot to murder Lord Darnley was hatched the following year.

Although its fame dates back to the sixteenth century Craigmillar is much older than this. Some of its surviving parts were constructed during the fourteenth century, including the tower house. By the middle of the seventeenth century, the whole west wing had been renovated and turned into an unusual stately home, but a hundred years on, the place was evacuated and has been uninhabited ever since. The sprawling ruins are some of the most fantastic in Edinburgh.

Dalmeny House
NEAR SOUTH QUEENSFERRY

The site of Dalmeny House has been the seat of the Earls of Roseberry for three centuries. The current house dates from 1815, and is the handiwork of William Wilkins – a magnificent example of neo-Gothic architecture, absorbed into an impressive, but imposing, pile – around which stretch landscaped gardens and parkland.

The interior of Dalmeny House is in keeping with its style: from the fine hammerbeam hall to the furniture and furnishing, everything complements everything else in a Gothic feast in the Scottish style. Dalmeny's biggest attraction is its fine collection of paintings, and the portraits include works by Reynolds, Gainsborough and Edinburgh's own Raeburn. The most unusual feature is the Napoleon Room, an exhibition given over to items and pieces of memorabilia that once belonged to the great French General. These were collected by the fifth Earl of Roseberry, who extravagantly indulged his fascination of the nineteenth-century hero.

Edinburgh Castle
CASTLEHILL

Edinburgh Castle has been destroyed and rebuilt a number of times since its construction as a hunting lodge by Malcolm III in the eleventh century. Little now remains from this period, the oldest surviving part of the castle being St Margaret's Chapel, dating from the twelfth century.

The first major structural changes to the castle were made in 1313, when the Scots finally recaptured the castle from the English. In order to prevent their old enemy from ever being able to use it as a defence, the king ordered that it be dismantled. It was rebuilt half a century later under the orders of David II. From this time it developed into the city's major asset, playing the role of royal palace as well as central focus of military defence. It saw its last true military action during Bonnie Prince Charlie's brief residence in 1745. After this, its role as a fortification declined.

Penicuik House
PENICUIK

The town of Penicuik, situated at the foot of the rolling Pentland Hills, is just within the southern limit of Edinburgh's boundaries, and the ruins of Penicuik House are the main feature of the town.

The house was built to designs by Sir James Clerk in 1778, whose father had played a large part in the creation of the grounds – the House's most splendid feature. These are liberally scattered with thousands of trees and a plethora of buildings such as pavilions, bridges and watchtowers, an eighteenth-century trait. When Sir John died in 1755, his son continued his work, completing the collection of monuments with a Chinese gate and an obelisk. These creations make for a fascinating journey through the grounds, providing an insight into contemporary architectural trends.

The house itself is typical Scots Palladian, and the grandeur of its style can still be appreciated, despite the fact it was all but destroyed by a fire at the turn of the nineteenth century. The House was never properly rebuilt, and the nearby stables were converted into the family home – an unusual and picturesque residence adjacent to the ruins.

Hopetoun House
NEAR SOUTH QUEENSFERRY

Two architects were mainly responsible for the magnificence of Hopetoun House: Sir William Bruce and William Adam. Bruce designed the earlier part of the house at the turn of the eighteenth century, and the excellent interior carvings and ceiling paintings are all part of his complete vision. In 1721, Adam extended Hopetoun, enhancing its grandeur with the addition of a palatial façade and the rooms now known as the State Apartments. Another significant feature of the house is the unusual rooftop platform, from which the views of the Firth and the surrounding countryside are unsurpassed. The works of each of these architects complement each other in a harmonious, perfectly unified whole and together they have created arguably the most impressive stately home on the shores of the Firth.

Since it was built, Hopetoun has been the seat of the Earls of Hopetoun, and part of the house is still occupied by them. Fortunately, the public have a free rein around the rest of the house, and can wander amongst the exquisite interiors – mainly attributable to Adam – which are a suitable reflection of eighteenth-century high society.

Linlithgow Palace
LINLITHGOW

On the edge of the beautiful Linlithgow Loch lie the evocative ruins of Linlithgow Palace, where history echoes through the cavernous rooms and around the ancient walls. A long line of Scottish monarchs has an association with Linlithgow: David I first built a manor house here in the twelfth century, although the present palace dates from the time of James I. One of the most tragic tales associated with the palace tells how Queen Margaret stood at the top of the north-west tower watching for her husband James IV to return from the Battle of Flodden in 1513. The legend also tells how James was told his fate by a ghostly apparition in the nearby St Michael's Church. Margaret, of course, waited in vain.

James V and Mary, Queen of Scots were both born at Linlithgow; Charles I stayed here in 1633 and Bonnie Prince Charlie passed through a century later, shortly followed by the Duke of Cumberland and his troops who, in their eager pursuit of the Jacobite rebels, left the fires burning, reducing the palace to the massive, awe-inspiring ruins it is today.

HISTORIC EDINBURGH

Throughout the city and its suburbs lie numerous museums and other buildings that tell the tale of Edinburgh's rich history. All serve as a reminder of some of the city's greatest events and as a testimony to its most colourful characters.

Gladstone's Land
LAWNMARKET

In 1617, one Thomas Gledstane bought a humble property on the site of the house that now bears his name. As his fortunes grew, this small house was extended and modified until it became a fine example of a seventeenth-century merchant's home. Rising to a height of six storeys, the Gledstane family did not occupy the whole building, confining themselves to the third floor and increasing their wealth by renting out the rest of their home.

All six storeys have now been carefully restored to represent the style of Gledstane's era and the museum gives a good idea of how the prosperous middle classes would once have lived in Edinburgh. Keeping to the theme of the merchant classes, there are a number of exhibits showing the kind of goods that would have been traded in the seventeenth century, including magnificent collections of pottery and porcelain, and the style of the interior is accurate rather than overwhelmingly opulent. Particularly fine are the typical, arcaded ground floor and the hypnotic painted ceilings.

Holyrood Abbey
CANONGATE

Legend tells how King David I was hunting in the woodland that once covered this whole area, when he was attacked by a stag. A silver cloud appeared in the sky, from which descended a holy cross. At the sight of this the stag fled, and in acknowledgement of this miracle, King David founded the Monastery of the Holy Rood. The year was 1128, and it is from this time that Edinburgh's tumultuous religious history grew.

It was not long before the humble monastery had grown into an abbey, and the lives of an illustrious trail of Scottish monarchs became entwined with this place. James II, III and IV were all married in the Abbey; the most famous wedding of all to take place here being that of Mary, Queen of Scots, to the ill-fated Darnley. James V and Charles I were both crowned here, and James III's grave is amongst those numbered here.

The tide of the Reformation was indiscriminate, however, and not even its royal history could save the Abbey from destruction. Subsequent restoration work culminated in the new roof in 1758. Ten years later this gave way, and was never repaired, and eventually the Abbey crumbled into the evocative ruins we see today.

Edinburgh Castle
CASTLEHILL

The first castle was built here by Malcolm III, who intended to use it primarily as a hunting lodge, but there had undoubtedly been some kind of fortification here for centuries. Eventually, Malcolm's lodge grew into the principal home for the Scottish monarchy, and despite regular attacks by the English – sometimes successful, sometimes less so – the Scots managed to win back their greatest asset. The most famous story tells how in 1314, Thomas Randolph, Earl of Moray, scaled the sheer rock face with a group of just 13 men to recapture the castle from the English during the Wars of Independence.

One of the castle's most intriguing unsolved mysteries stems from the discovery in 1830 of a small coffin, containing the remains of a baby wrapped in a silk shroud embroidered with the letter 'J'. This was discovered behind the panelling of the room in which it is known that Mary, Queen of Scots gave birth to James VI. Was this the body of the real heir to the Scottish throne? Like so many other royal mysteries, this will probably never be solved.

The Honours of Scotland
EDINBURGH CASTLE

One of the greatest attractions at the castle is the Crown Room, where Scotland's Crown Jewels are now kept. The crown itself was made for James V, but the gold circlet that has been incorporated into it was actually worn by Robert the Bruce. The oldest piece is the sceptre, adorned with miniature figures of St James and St Andrew, the Virgin Mary and the Christ Child. The third piece, the sword, was created in Italy by Domenico da Sutri and given to James IV by Pope Julius II.

The jewels were first removed from the castle after they had been used in the coronation of Charles II. Enraged by the Restoration, Oliver Cromwell tried to steal them and have them destroyed, but they were smuggled out and hidden just in time. When the danger had passed, they were returned to the castle, where they remained until the Act of Union in 1707, after which they were put away. After a few years, it was generally accepted that Scotland's Crown Jewels were lost forever, but in 1818, following a search instigated by Sir Walter Scott, they were rediscovered, locked in a chest in a small room in the castle. Since then they have been on display for all to admire.

Roman Fort
CRAMOND

Cramond's strategic importance is obvious from its location at the mouth of the River Almond and the Firth of Forth, and the village name means 'fort on the river'. It had been known for many years that Cramond was an ancient site, dating back far beyond its eighteenth-century heyday, and relics from Roman times have been periodically discovered here. It was only in 1954, however, that the foundations of this Roman fort were uncovered.

This area was once the northernmost line of the Roman frontier, and the fort would have been constructed as a protection for the harbour down below, which was vital for survival to the Romans whose supply ships would have docked here. It was built in AD 142 by order of Emperor Antonius Pius, although the evidence suggests that it was abandoned shortly afterwards. Emperor Septimus Severus rebuilt the fort early in the third century as a headquarters from which he planned his attack on the north-east of Scotland. Low walls now outline the various buildings which include barracks, workshops, the line of the ramparts, the headquarters and the 'via principalis'.

Old Royal High School
REGENT ROAD

Of all the buildings in Edinburgh inspired by classical Greek architecture, the Old Royal High School is indisputably the finest. The brainchild of Thomas Hamilton, its design was based on the Temple of Theseus in Athens, and it is a fantastic, sprawling collection of pavilions and colonnades. Its setting could not be more impressive either, its lofty position commanding views of Arthur's Seat.

The idea for a new school belonged to the City Fathers, who intended it to be the city's finest educational establishment. Work began on the school in 1825 and was finally completed in 1829. In the course of its history it has educated many of Edinburgh's most famous sons, among them Robert Adam and Alexander Graham Bell.

The building ceased being a school in the 1960s and since then has been used for a number of temporary purposes, including the Crown Office Headquarters and the Prosecution service in Scotland.

Gateway
GRASSMARKET

The Grassmarket is, as its name suggests, an ancient market place, where farmers would sell their hay and seeds. But over the centuries, it grew into one of Edinburgh's most notorious areas, and has been the scene of numerous crimes, rebellions and murders.

It was one of the main sites for public executions, and a cross in the market place remembers the many Covenanters who were martyred here. The last recorded public execution took place in the Grassmarket at the end of the eighteenth century, by which time hundreds of unhappy Edinburghers had lost their lives.

The most famous tale associated with the Grassmarket is that of the notorious body snatchers Burke and Hare. This, the seamiest area of Old Edinburgh, was their haunt. This infamous pair would walk the Grassmarket area looking for victims, who they would ply with alcohol and then strangle, selling the bodies for a tidy sum to Robert Knox, a respectable medical professor at the University, who then used the bodies to teach his students the principles of dissection. Whether or not he had his suspicions as to the dubious origins of this steady supply of cadavers is not known. Burke and Hare were finally caught, and Burke was hanged on the evidence of his unscrupulous partner in crime.

Robert Louis Stevenson's House
HERIOT ROW

The Stevenson family lived in Heriot Row in Edinburgh's New Town from 1857, when the young Robert was just seven years old. Stevenson later followed in the family tradition by studying engineering at the University, but felt no calling for this vocation and switched instead to law. At the same time he began to spend more and more time mixing with the 'low life' of the Old Town. It was from this that he gained much inspiration for his later novels. By the time he was called to the Bar in 1875, Stevenson had decided that his future lay in writing.

He left his comfortable middle-class home in Heriot Row in 1879 determined to see the world, and hopefully find a place more suitable for his weak constitution than the damp Scottish climate. He went first to France, where he met his future wife, Fanny Osbourne, and then on to Switzerland. He returned to Scotland – to the Highlands – for a while, but eventually left for good, visiting America and finally making his home in Samoa, where he died in 1894.

Despite his travels, Stevenson never forgot his early influences, and his love for Scotland and the great impression both the country and its people had on him are reflected in his writing.

The Heart of Midlothian
HIGH STREET

Outlined in cobbled stones just outside the High Kirk of St Giles, is the Heart of Midlothian, marking the site where the Old Tolbooth used to stand: the town prison and place of execution. This building was known as the 'Heart of Midlothian', and was a dark and dreary building, as such a place would be. It was here that many a notorious figure took their final bow.

Throughout the centuries, the Old Tolbooth, which was built in 1466 and extended in the next century, has served many civic purposes. Its original use was as a chapter house for St Giles, then in a perhaps more distinguished role, it played host for some years to parliamentary meetings and served as a somewhat lowly law court. It was only later that it adopted its new title as city prison.

The building has long since disappeared, but the heart-shaped memorial in the road serves as a reminder of the different ages in Edinburgh's past, some more illustrious than others. It is a tradition in the city, incidentally, to spit on the Heart of Midlothian, a ritual that is supposed to bring good luck.

Waterloo Bridge
CALTON

Waterloo Bridge, to the east of Princes Street near the foot of Calton Hill, is a cleverly designed and magnificent feat of engineering. It is actually a series of triumphal arches that rise 15 metres (50 ft) above what is now a busy road below. The bridge was planned, however, to disguise that it was a bridge at all, and it is only across the one arch pictured here that one notices its height.

Work began on the bridge in 1815, and its major success lies in the fact that, as intended, those using it can enjoy the magnificent panorama towards the Port of Leith to the north, and south to the city centre, then obviously quite a different spectacle to the hub of modern life it is today.

All along the bridge, with only one gap over this arch, the high façades of the buildings are ornamented with pilasters and porticoes, lending a regal air to the structure. It is a fitting testament to early nineteenth-century imagination and architecture.

John Knox's House
HIGH STREET

Halfway down the Royal Mile is the building known as John Knox's House. It is an unusual, three-storeyed residence, with an outside stairway and a sundial. Today it houses a museum with displays portraying Knox's life and works. There is actually very little that suggests this was ever the home of the infamous Scots Protestant reformer, but it is generally thought that he stayed here during the 1560s, possibly while he was minister of St Giles, a short walk away.

Knox was born *c.* 1514, and was training for the priesthood before he converted to Protestantism. When the Catholic Mary of Guise became queen, Knox travelled to Switzerland where he came under the influence of John Calvin. He published a number of works expounding his theories, which were radical enough to cause even the Protestant Elizabeth I to ban him from England. He returned to Scotland in 1559, after the death of Mary of Guise and became a leading figure in the Scottish Reformed Church. A number of audiences with Mary, Queen of Scots, led to accusations of treason, but these were not upheld and Knox continued to preach his views until his death (reputedly in this house) in 1572.

Canongate Tolbooth (The People's Story)
CANONGATE

This remarkably well-preserved building dates from the sixteenth century. Its unassuming and orderly aspect, complete with clock and tower, however, reveals little of the building's history. This was once the administrative heart of the Canongate, back in the days when this part of the city was a separate burgh. Here in centuries past, the town council met and made all the decisions most affecting Edinburgh's citizens. Here the law courts held session and here also, in the eighteenth century, those unfortunate enough to be found guilty were imprisoned. Unlike its earlier counterpart further up the Royal Mile, near St Giles, this was one of the better prisons: cleaner, and less dark, dingy and disease-ridden and, it appears, was reserved for a higher order of prisoner. Historian Hugo Arnot wrote in 1777: 'Debtors of a better sort are commonly taken to this prison, which is well aired, has some decent rooms, and is kept tolerably clean.'

Today, this marvellous building houses the 'People's Story', a museum recounting the lives of the ordinary citizens of Edinburgh over the past two centuries.

Inchcolm Abbey
THE FIRTH OF FORTH

The tranquil island of Inchcolm lies about 4.8 km (3 miles) out in the Firth of Forth, and is now uninhabited. It was once the site of a thriving and industrious abbey, however, and its romantic remains are a marvellous spectacle on this otherwise deserted island.

An Augustinian priory was established here by Alexander I in 1123. His ship had been wrecked in the Forth nearby, and the king was helped by the hermit who lived on Inchcolm. Alexander founded the priory in recognition and gratitude for this help. A century later it was elevated to the status of abbey. Even out here, though, the religious settlement could not escape the effects of the Reformation, when it was largely destroyed by the English. It was restored in later times, and some parts of the original building remain. These include a small church and a chapter house. The other site of interest on Inchcolm is a cave in the north of the island, which some claim to have been the hermit's abode, although this is largely speculation.

Lady Stair's House
(The Writer's Museum)
LAWNMARKET

Lady Stair was a great society figure in the eighteenth century, and a great character too, by all accounts. She was married to Viscount Primrose, but she was left a widow while still a young woman, and she embarked upon her second marriage to the Earl of Stair, a colonel of the Royal Scots Greys and a society gentleman overfond of the bottle. Lady Stair was an admirable match for him though, reputedly taking pleasure from shocking people with bad language and a violent temper. The lintel over the door to the house is therefore somewhat ironic in its inscription which preaches 'Fear The Lord & Depart From Evil'.

The house was built in 1622, but little of its original seventeenth-century character remains due to extensive restorations in the late nineteenth century. Today, the building houses the Writer's Museum, a small and intriguing exhibition of the lives and works of Scotland's greatest literary heroes: Robert Burns, Robert Louis Stevenson and Sir Walter Scott.

Deacon Brodie's Tavern
LAWNMARKET

Deacon Brodie's Tavern is just one of the many reminders around the city, particularly the Old Town, of Edinburgh's most notorious villain. It is not uncommon for criminals to become celebrated figures after their lifetimes, and Deacon Brodie's cause was much enhanced by Stevenson's novel *Dr Jekyll and Mr Hyde*, which drew its inspiration from this tale of mystery and intrigue.

William Brodie was, to all appearances, an upstanding member of the community. He held a post as city councillor and was generally highly thought of in respectable circles. Brodie had a darker side, however, and was given to gambling, drinking and womanising. When his trade as a cabinet-maker began to limit his ability to partake in these activities, Brodie turned to crime. He would make impressions of the house keys of the members of the higher society that he visited in his official capacity, and have replica keys made. In the dead of night, he would then return to the houses and make off with anything of value.

This double life finally caught up with him after a failed robbery at the Excise Office, and he was captured while attempting to flee to America. The final irony of the tale is that when he was hanged in 1788, it was on gallows made by his own company.

Gillespie Plaque
ROYAL MILE

Edinburgh is not only a city of kings and queens, although their stories naturally tend to dominate the city's history. One of the greatest features of Edinburgh is the great diversity of its inhabitants: many noble names are amongst the role of distinguished Edinburghers, but there is also a plethora of lesser known, but none the less interesting, characters whose lives give a broader perspective of Edinburgh's history.

This plaque commemorates James Gillespie of Spylaw, an eighteenth-century merchant native of the city. James and his brother John were both bachelors, and thrifty ones at that. They built themselves an empire in the form of a snuff factory and a retail outlet, which amassed them a modest fortune. When he died, James Gillespie bequeathed this fortune to the city, with instructions that it should be used to build a hospital for old people which, true to his orders, went up in 1802, and a school for poor boys. This, too, was built according to his orders. The old gentleman would probably turn in his grave at the sight of this school today, which is a semi-private establishment.

Huntly House Museum
CANONGATE

There are a number of buildings along the Royal Mile that have been turned into museums of various kinds. Huntly House now houses a collection of exhibits on Edinburgh's local history, which mainly consist of details about local industries, including pottery and clockmaking. The museum's main object of interest, however, is the original National Covenant dating from 1638, which some say was signed in blood, although tests have failed to prove conclusively whether or not this is true.

The building itself has a fascinating history. It is one of the oldest surviving structures along this stretch, dating back to the sixteenth century, when it was a respectable town house. Like so many others, it was virtually destroyed at the hands of the English in 1544, but was carefully restored later in the century. The Incorporation of Hammermen acquired the house in 1647 and turned it into a series of flats, and it remained thus until the nineteenth century when it finally fell into decay. In the early twentieth century the City of Edinburgh took on the job of rebuilding it and in 1927 it opened its doors again, as a museum. It has been carefully maintained since then.

AROUND EDINBURGH

In the countryside that stretches out for miles around Edinburgh lie many picturesque villages and small towns. Each of these places has its own historic tales to tell, of the industry and practices that made up these once-thriving communities.

Cottages
SWANSTON

Nestled at the foot of the Pentland Hills is one of Robert Louis Stevenson's favourite villages – Swanston. The writer spent many summers here at Swanston Cottage, built by his father Thomas, admiring the tranquillity of the village and the views of the nearby city afforded by its situation.

The whitewashed cottages are spread out around the village green, although their thatched roofs are an unusual sight in Scotland. Dating from the seventeenth century, these were once used by the workers of the 'ferm toun', farms that were run by a group of people rather than just one proprietor.

Swanston once had an abundance of clear spring water, and it was from here that, after a lengthy series of legal problems, Edinburgh was finally allowed to supplement its water supply. Although Swanston is lacking in certain amenities – there is neither church nor shop – it retains its traditional charm and beauty.

Main Street
INVERESK

At one time, the parish of Inveresk extended right to the mouth of the River Esk, as the village's name implies. Today, the name applies just to the village itself, but Inveresk is not a place that sprang up around Edinburgh during the seventeenth and eighteenth centuries. It is remarkably ancient, dating back to Roman times, when a fort and settlement grew up in this area, and many relics of these times have been uncovered in and around Inveresk.

Today, however, there is little that associates the village with those far-off, ancient days, for the architecture is undeniably and proudly Georgian in style. Rows of mansion houses rise regally from behind the trees and high walls, dominating the road leading to the manor house. There is little mix here of the larger houses and the typical Scots cottages, for the mansion house owners eventually pushed out the cottagers, and their dwellings ceased to exist. Today, this makes for an unusually rich, luxurious and, dare we say it, upper-class aspect. This culminates in the carefully tended Inveresk Lodge Gardens, set in the grounds of what is now a National Trust House, one of Inveresk's finest features.

The Water of Leith
DEAN VILLAGE

Lying in a valley to the north of Edinburgh's New Town on the banks of the Water of Leith, Dean Village is one of the most attractive spots the area has to offer.

From the twelfth century until late Victorian times, the village was a thriving milling community, with 11 mills powered by the river and two granaries. The Incorporation of Baxters (or bakers) once owned five of the mills here, and their mark – two crossed bakers' shovels carrying loaves – can be seen on some of the houses that still stand by the waters. Sadly, few of the mill buildings still survive, and today the village is a tranquil and undisturbed spot, a far cry from the hub of industry it was for over 700 years.

It is, none the less, a fascinating place, with leafy walks along the Water of Leith, past St Bernard's Well (see page 116) and up to the magnificent Dean Bridge. Built by Thomas Telford in 1832, this is one of the area's most famous and splendid attractions, with its four arches carrying the road across the water, and its views down into the valley below.

Tron & Dovecote
STENTON

The tranquil atmosphere that pervades the small village of Stenton hides a grim and grisly past. For centuries this quiet, unassuming place played host to the rituals – not uncommon at the time, but certainly barbaric – of witch burning. Here many women, believed to have associations with the Devil, were burnt alive, to the rather macabre pleasure of hundreds of onlookers. Stenton was certainly not the only site of such persecution, but it was one of the last places to surrender these practices and its reputation, whether by natural fascination or commercial contrivance, has remained.

The Tron, which stands on the village green, is a more pleasant relic of Stenton's history. This was used for weighing the wool at the local wool fairs that would take place on and around the village greens, of which Stenton has two. Other features of interest in the village include the Rood Well, an old site of pilgrimage lying at the entrance to the village, and the early nineteenth-century kirk, which incorporates the tower of the original sixteenth-century kirk.

Preston Mill
EAST LINTON

Dean Village was once a concentrated area of one of Lothian's major industries – grain milling – and relics of this can be found all around the outskirts of Edinburgh. At East Linton is one of the best-preserved examples of a grain mill, and here the visitor can witness the ancient methods of milling in one of the oldest working watermills in the country. It was used commercially up until the 1950s, the last of the many mills that were once scattered along the banks of the Tyne. Today, the National Trust for Scotland has recreated the mill as it would have been in its heyday.

Standing beside the River Tyne, this is a romantically picturesque place. The red-pantiled, two-storey sandstone mill dates mainly from the eighteenth century, although parts of it may date from earlier centuries. There are drying kilns, old-fashioned wooden machinery and the essential working waterwheel. The mill even comes complete with its own genuine millpond which, in typical story-book fashion, lies in the shade of apple trees and is home to hosts of ducks.

Seafront
PORTOBELLO

Edinburgh's seafront town takes its name from the first house that was constructed here. Its owner had fought with Admiral Vernon against the Spanish at Peurto Bello in 1739, and on his return to Scotland he settled in this area and built his home here, calling it Portobello. As the town grew, it took its name from the small thatched cottage.

The fine, sandy beach lies three miles east of the city centre, and is popular with both locals and tourists. Like many British seaside towns, Portobello had its heyday in the nineteenth century, and the grand houses that line the streets are typically Georgian and Victorian. After the First World War, the town suffered the fate of many such places, with days of past leisure and wealth. Its pier was destroyed and its popularity waned. Sir Harry Lauder, renowned in music-hall circles, was born here in 1870 when the town was a thriving resort, and this remains one of Portobello's main claims to fame.

Gifford Kirk
GIFFORD

The seventeenth-century village of Gifford lies a short drive away from Edinburgh, and is one of the many pleasant spots on the outskirts of the city. Like most of these places, Gifford has its historical associations. The Reverend John Witherspoon, one of the signatories to the American Declaration of Independence, was born here. On a more romantic note though, Gifford was also home to a known wizard, Sir Hugo Gifford, in the thirteenth century. Sir Hugo's legacy to his home village was a marvellous underground hall, 'Goblin Ha'. The story of Sir Hugo and Goblin Ha caught the imagination of Sir Walter Scott, who incorporated it into his *Marmion*.

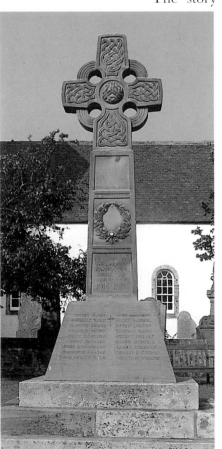

Besides the picturesque, whitewashed cottages and church, the village boasts one of the finest estate houses in the area, Yester House. The house was built in 1745, and at the time many of the old village cottages were destroyed and reassembled to lend a more dignified air to Yester House's situation; today the rows of cottages run neatly along the road leading to the large house. The whole village exudes the same air of quiet dignity and careful preservation that characterises so much of Edinburgh's environs.

Village Green & Kirk
DIRLETON

The dominant feature of Dirleton is undoubtedly the evocative remains of the great thirteenth-century castle (see page 149) that lie on a hill overlooking the village. But the village itself is also worth visiting; it is a typically picturesque place that seems to be largely untouched by time.

The stone cottages are set out along the road, rather than huddled around the two village greens, and most date from the eighteenth and nineteenth centuries. The origins of the village stretch further back than this, though, and it is possible that a village existed here in medieval times, its straight layout one of the features that points to this.

The stone-roofed church, situated on the side of one of the village greens, dates from the seventeenth century. Here on the green a coven of witches were burnt at the stake. It is said that these may even have been the famed witches of North Berwick, although this claim is unsubstantiated.

The Colonies
STOCKBRIDGE

The rise and development of Stockbridge is largely due to Sir Henry Raeburn, one of Scotland's most famous painters. Born here in 1756, when the suburb was no more than a small estate by the Water of Leith, Raeburn's origins were humble. Before he was 30, his fame had spread nation-wide and this, along with his marriage to a wealthy widow, allowed him to buy an estate in his birthplace, which he gradually extended, and later built houses on.

The Colonies, pictured here, were – and still are – some of the most popular residences in the area. They were constructed in 1861 as a trial, which turned out to be successful, and housing schemes along similar lines were subsequently built all over the city. The Colonies were a series of two-storey terraces, each storey comprising its own independent cottage with entrances and gardens on either side.

Today, many of the thatched cottages that characterised the area around Raeburn's time have disappeared, and nineteenth-century tenements are an overriding feature of the modern village. Despite this, Stockbridge is a delightful place to spend time and enjoy the pleasant situation, the street-side cafés and bars, and the antique shops and markets for which the area is now renowned.

Cramond Inn
CRAMOND

The ancient village of Cramond, situated at the mouth of the River Almond to the north-west of Edinburgh, is a major attraction for those seeking to escape from city life. This is not surprising, for Cramond is a veritable haven of tranquillity, enhanced not only by its pleasant situation but also by a fascinating collection of relics, including the remains of a Roman fortification, an old bridge dating from medieval times and a picturesque church with a fifteenth-century tower.

Rows of whitewashed houses lead down a steep hill to the small harbour at the foot of the village. Incongruously nestled amongst the houses, this inn still serves the same purpose as it has since the seventeenth century – to provide good ale and food for those passing through, iron workers and tourists alike. Well preserved and deceptively large, the inn offers a hospitable welcome to those enjoying Cramond's many attractions. Despite Cramond's popularity with visitors, it retains an atmosphere of solitude, and at times can be found perfectly empty, with only the sound of the water below and the wind in the surrounding countryside for company.

Hawes Inn
SOUTH QUEENSFERRY

This historic little town is situated on the shores of the Firth of Forth between the impressive landmarks of the two Forth Bridges. Since ancient times, this has been the crossing point for trips across the Forth, a tradition begun by St Margaret in the eleventh century, who would take the ferry from here to her Palace in Dunfermline. For centuries, the ferries made this trip, until the construction of the bridges provided a quicker and easier access route across the Forth. The town still plays host to an annual ferry fair, however.

South Queensferry retains much of its ancient charm, particularly in the old buildings that line the narrow High Street, including an old Tolbooth. The pub pictured here has its own literary and historic associations. Dating from the late seventeenth century, this was once a coaching inn, and was featured in Scott's *The Antiquary*. As if being mentioned in a novel by Edinburgh's favourite son wasn't enough, the inn was further immortalised by another of Scotland's great literary heroes, Robert Louis Stevenson. The inn provided the setting for the capture of David Balfour, hero of the novel *Kidnapped*, by his uncle – the start of his adventures.

Village Cross
CULROSS

Walking through the small town of Culross is an unusual experience – a genuine step back in time – for the place has been restored to recall its sixteenth- and seventeenth-century heydays so carefully that it is difficult to imagine that the twentieth century rushes frenetically along just a few minutes away.

At one time, Culross was a large port, carrying on a prosperous trade in a variety of goods, including fish and iron. The Industrial Revolution took its toll here though, and eventually the trade dwindled and the harbour silted up. Culross became, like many other ports, a shadow of its former thriving self. In 1932, the National Trust for Scotland moved in and worked its magic with the town, recreating this beautiful Royal Burgh. It would have been a pity to allow the place to crumble into oblivion, for its origins are truly ancient – it is the site of a religious settlement founded by St Serf as early as the fifth century, with an abbey built over this in the early thirteenth century. The parish church that now stands in Culross does not date from much later than this – *c.* 1300. The original central tower has stood firm through the ravages of time, although the rest of the building was reconstructed in the 1630s.

Forth Road Bridge
SOUTH QUEENSFERRY

The town of South Queensferry is dominated by the two bridges spanning the Firth of Forth at this point, a captivating and dramatic spectacle.

The Forth Road Bridge is one of the longest suspension bridges in the world – indeed at the time of its completion in 1964, it was actually the largest, spanning 1¼ miles to Fife. The towers at either end of the bridge rise to a majestic 156 metres (512 ft) above the water, and the whole bridge used nearly 40,000 tons of metal in its construction, an amazing feat of engineering.

The beauty of this structure can be well appreciated from the shores of the Forth, particularly at night, when the entire bridge is illuminated. But it is the views afforded from the bridge, which allows pedestrian access, that truly complete the spectacle.

The one pity regarding the Road Bridge is that it brought an end to the ferry service that had run since St Margaret's time either across the Firth of Forth from this landing in Queensferry to Fife, or to the island of Inchcolm in the middle. But progress cannot be halted, and commercial ferry services still allow those with the time to experience the pleasure of this ancient crossing.

Forth Rail Bridge
SOUTH QUEENSFERRY

Described as the greatest bridge in Britain, the Forth Rail Bridge is a magnificent feat of nineteenth-century engineering. Carrying a double railway line 1½ miles across the Firth of Forth, this mighty structure reaches 110 metres (360 ft) above the water at its highest point.

The bridge took seven years to build, from 1883 to 1890, and, as often is the case with such mighty works of human endeavour, cost nearly 60 men their lives. It was created by Sir John Fowler and Benjamin Baker and was intended to complete the hitherto inadequate rail network between the south-eastern parts of Scotland with the north. The collapse of the Tay Bridge in 1879 caused the Forth engineers to design their bridge with extreme caution, and the Forth Rail Bridge was created to withstand the worst of conditions, combining solidity with grace.

Together with its neighbour the Forth Road Bridge, this provides one of the most impressive sights in the outskirts of Edinburgh. Both bridges have been carefully maintained so that they may each continue to serve their purpose and represent the pinnacle of engineering achievement of their respective eras.

Edinburgh Past and Present

This map shows how Edinburgh looked in the seventeenth century. Some features are still instantly recognisable: the Castle, of course, and the spire of the High Kirk of St Giles in the centre, along the roadway that is now called the Royal Mile. From the castle the city walls stretch out to the south, then run northwards along the foot of the Salisbury Crags and what is now known as Holyrood Park. The walls played an essential part in the defence of Edinburgh at this time. It was a century of great turmoil for Scotland's capital, and the marauding English armies focused a great deal of attention on the city. Oliver Cromwell was one of the leading figures in the assaults in and around Edinburgh.

The northern boundary of the city at this time was the marshy Nor' Loch, and the city's entire population lived a cramped and malodorous life within the confines of the city walls and the Old Town Ridge. By the early eighteenth century, the situation had become intolerable, and plans were formed to extend the boundaries of the city to the north. The Nor' Loch was drained, and became the Princes Street Gardens, delineated by Princes Street itself on the north side. The fields depicted here made way for James Craig's development, the New Town – a grand vision of sweeping avenues and magnificent Georgian residences that changed the face and shape of Edinburgh for ever. In succeeding years, the development extended to the north and west into what became known as the Second New Town, embracing suburbs such as Dean Village and Stockbridge that were once miles distant from the city centre.

The Old Town

14, 15, 20, 28, 40, 46, 54, 55, 58, 61, 62, 63, 66, 68, 71, 72, 79, 87, 88, 89, 92, 98, 100, 102, 126, 128, 129, 130, 131, 132, 139, 141, 154, 160, 161, 162, 163, 166, 168, 171, 172, 174, 175, 176, 177

The New Town

21, 22, 23, 29, 30, 31, 32, 33, 34, 35, 36, 37, 41, 42, 43, 46, 47, 48, 52, 53, 67, 69, 70, 73, 74, 75, 76, 77, 78, 83, 86, 90, 91, 93, 94, 95, 96, 97, 99, 101, 106, 107, 127, 133, 134, 135, 136, 137, 138, 140, 165, 167, 170

Surrounding Area

16, 17, 18, 19, 24, 25, 38, 39, 49, 50, 51, 56, 57, 60, 80, 81, 82, 103, 108, 109, 110, 111, 112, 113, 114, 115, 116, 117, 118, 119, 120, 121, 122, 123, 144, 145, 146, 147, 148, 149, 150, 151, 152, 153, 155, 156, 157, 164, 173, 180, 181, 182, 183, 184, 185, 186, 187, 188, 189, 190, 191, 192, 193, 194, 195

The regions of Scotland are currently in the process of changing. Those defined in this book are according to local Tourist Information offices.

Index

Act of Union, 10, 68, 150, 163
Adam family, 61, 97
Adam, John, 72, 156
Adam, Robert, 73, 77, 79, 101, 165
Adam, William, 156
Age of Enlightenment, 10
Alexander I, 173
Ann Street, 103
Antonius Pius, Emperor, 164
Apostles, 46
Apprentice Pillar, 56
aqueducts, 123
Argyll aisle, 62
Arnot, Hugo, 172
Art Nouveau, 141
Arthur's Seat, 16, 40, 94, 108, 110, 120, 165
Assembly Rooms, 88
Athena, 126
Athens, 130, 136, 165
bagpipes, 20, 41, 63
Baker, Benjamin, 195
ballet, 31, 42
Balmoral Hotel, 22, 69, 83, 99
Baronial architecture, 96
Bass Rock, 19
Battle of Bannockburn, 25
Battle of Dunbar, 25, 121
Battle of Flodden, 9, 129, 157
Battle of Prestonpans, 114
Battle of Trafalgar, 128
Bell, Alexander Graham, 165
Bing, Rudolf, 31
Blackford Hill, 70
Blackness Castle, 150
Bonnie Prince Charlie, see Stuart, Charles Edward
Bothwell, 25, 145
Boyd, George, 93
Braid Burns, 82
Braid Hills, 82
British Army, 33, 127
Brodie, William, 28, 175
Bronze Age, 14
Bruce, Sir William, 144, 156
Burke and Hare, 28, 166
Burn, William, 146
Burne-Jones, Sir Edward Coley, 50
Burns Monument, 130, 136
Burns, Robert, 62, 136, 140, 174
Caledonian Hotel, 69, 83
Calton Hill, 15, 40, 70, 110, 126, 128, 130, 136, 139, 170
Calvin, John, 171
Calvinism, 9
Cambridge Street, 34
Camera Obscura, 71
cannon, 139

Cannonball House, 92
Canongate Kirk, 55
Canongate Tolbooth, 172
Canongate, 55, 89, 98, 144, 145, 161, 171, 172, 177
Castle Esplanade, 20, 32, 92, 141
Castle Rock, 8, 14, 54
Castlehill, 14, 66, 71, 92, 98, 102, 141, 154
Catholicism, 55
Cavaliers, 25
Chambers, Sir William, 76, 97
Chantrey, 138
Charles I, 9, 46, 61, 62, 157, 160
Charles II, 25, 100, 144, 163
Charlotte Square, 52, 77, 86, 91, 101, 138
China, 113
Choragic Monument of Lysicrates, 130, 136
Christ's Church at the Tron, 53, 94
Cistercian nunnery, 147
City Chambers, 72
City Fathers, 165
City Observatory, 70
City of Edinburgh, 82, 139, 177
Clark, George, 109
classical architecture, 126
Clerk, Sir James and Sir John, 155
Clock Tower, 22, 83
Clow, William and Alexander, 63
Colonies, the, 189
comedy, 20, 31
Commonwealth Games, 81
Corinthian architecture, 58, 97, 136
Costorphine Church, 60
Costorphine Hill, 39
Costorphine, 60
Covenanters, 11, 19, 61, 62, 166
Craig, James, 11, 61, 70, 76, 77, 86, 90, 97, 138
Craigleith, 24
Craigmillar Castle, 152
Cramond, 118, 146, 164, 190
Cromwell, Oliver, 10, 25, 122, 144, 148, 150, 163
Crown Jewels, 163
Crown Office Headquarters, 165
Crystal Palace, 67
Culross, 193
Da Sutri, Domenico, 163
Dalmeny House, 153
Dalmeny Kirk, 49
Dalmeny, 49
Darnley, Lord, 145, 152
David I, 54, 115, 120, 157, 161
David II, 154

De Vaux family, 149
De Wit, Jacob, 145
Deacon Brodie's Tavern, 175
Dean Bridge, 182
Dean Village, 116, 182, 184
Declaration of Independence, 187
Dirleton Castle, 149, 188
Dirleton, 148, 149, 188
'Doors Open Day', 41
Doric architecture, 116
Douglas family, 148
Doyle, Sir Arthur Conan, 134
Dr Jekyll and Mr Hyde, 28, 175
Drummond, George, 86
Duddingston Loch, 114
Duddingston, 114, 152
Dunbar Castle, 25
Dunbar, 25
Dundas, Henry, 91
Dundas, Sir Laurence, 52, 76
Dunfermline, 192
Dunsapie Loch, 108
East Linton, 184
Edinburgh Airport, 38
Edinburgh Astronomical Society, 70
Edinburgh Castle, 14, 20, 25, 29, 32, 33, 40, 47, 54, 66, 87, 99, 148, 154, 162, 163
Edinburgh Episcopalian Church, 46
Edinburgh Festival Fringe, 30, 34
Edinburgh International Conference Centre, 74
Edinburgh International Festival, 10, 20, 30, 31, 32, 36, 42
Edinburgh University, 35, 79, 112, 117, 130, 167
Edinburgh Zoo, 39
Edward I, 25
Edward II, 25
Edward the Confessor, 120
Elizabeth I, 9, 171
Episcopacy, 9, 53, 61, 62
Esk Valley, 56
Eyebroughty, 24
Falkirk, 123
Federation of Master Builders, 134
'ferm toun', 180
Festival Theatre, 35
Fidra Island, 24
Fife, 109, 110, 118, 194
First World War, 36, 39, 141, 186
Firth of Forth, 15, 19, 40, 82, 109, 110, 116, 120, 128, 146, 150, 156, 164, 173, 192, 194, 195
fishing, 110, 121
Floral Clock, 107

Forrest, George, 113
Forrester, Sir Adam, 60
Forth and Clyde Canal, 123
Forth Estuary, 118
Forth Rail Bridge, 192, 195
Forth Road Bridge, 192, 194
Fowke, Francis, 67
Fowler, Sir John, 195
Frazer, Major Andrew, 52
Free Church of Scotland, 52
Gainsborough, 153
Geddes, Patrick, 71, 102
'Geordie Boyd's Mud Brig', 93
George IV Bridge, 88
George IV, 138
George Square, see Charlotte Square
George Street, 52, 77, 86, 91, 101, 138
George VI, 115
Georgian architecture, 11, 76, 86, 91, 96, 97, 181, 186
Georgian House, the, 101
ghosts, 11, 28, 72, 144
Gifford, 187
Gifford, Sir Hugo, 187
Gillespie, James, 176
Gladstone's Land, 160
Glasgow, 123
'Glasshouse Experience', 113
Gledstane, Thomas, 160
Glyndebourne Opera, 31
'Goblin Ha', 187
'Goose-Pie House', 102
'Gowrie Conspiracy', 149
Gowrie, Earl of, 149
Graham, James Gillespie, 90
Grassmarket, 11, 28, 34, 92, 166
Gray, John, 132
Great Disruption, 52
Great Michael, 109
'Green Men', 50
Greenhouse Place, 42
Greyfriars Bobby, 60, 132
Greyfriars Kirkyard, 9, 61, 132
Guardian Royal Exchange, 91
Guest, Crispin, 21
Haddington, 50, 147
Haig, Field Marshall, 141
Halyburton family, 149
Hamilton, Thomas, 165
hammerbeam roof, 53, 68
Hanover Street, 138
Hawes Inn, 192
Heart of Midlothian, 168
Henry VIII, 9
Hepburn, Sir John, 33
Heriot Row, 167

Hertford, Earl of, 144, 152
High Kirk of St Giles, 9, 47, 53, 62, 63, 68, 129, 168, 171, 172
High Street, 43, 62, 63, 68, 72, 92, 98, 129, 168
Highland cattle, 38
Highlands, 16, 18, 167
Holmes, Sherlock, 134
Holyrood Abbey, 8, 55, 87, 115, 120, 161
Holyrood Park, 15, 16, 57, 80, 81, 108, 114, 115, 120
'Honest Toun', 121
'Honours of Scotland', 163
Hopetoun House, 156
Hopetoun, Earls of, 156
Hungary, 120
Huntly House Museum, 177
Hygieia, 116
Inchcolm Abbey, 173
Inchcolm Island, 173, 194
Incorporation of Baxters, 182
Incorporation of Hammermen, 177
Industrial Revolution, 10, 193
Ingliston, 38
International Holography Exhibition, 71
Inveresk Lodge Gardens, 181
Inveresk, 121, 181
Inverleith, 112, 113
Jacobean, 146
Jacobites, 19, 157
James I, 19, 157
James II, 55, 160
James III, 160
James IV, 109, 144, 157, 160, 163
James V, 145, 148, 152, 157, 160, 163
James VI (James I of England), 9, 79, 114, 162
James, VII, 63
John the Baptist, 46
Kemp, George Meikle, 135
Kidnapped, 192
King Harold, 120
King Herod, 43
Knights of the Order of the Thistle, 55, 63
Knox, John, 9, 145, 171
Knox, Robert, 166
Lady Stair's House, 174
Laing, Gerald Ogilvie, 134
Lamb, 24
Lanarkshire, 123
Lauder, Sir Harry, 186
Lauriston Castle, 146
Law Courts, 68

Law, John, 146
Lawnmarket, 93, 98, 100, 174
Leith Walk, 112
Leith, 57, 70, 118, 122, 170
lighthouses, 19, 24
Linlithgow, 157
Little, Clement, 79
London, 10, 42, 89, 134
Lord Lyon King of Arms, 129
Lorimer, Sir Robert, 63
Lothian Road, 36, 48, 58
Lothian, 11, 16, 184
Louis XIII, 33
Malcolm III, 54, 120, 154, 162
Marchmont, 96
Marlin's Wynd, 53
Marmion, 187
Marquis of Montrose, 129
Martyr's Monument, 61
Mary King's Close, 72
Mary of Guise, 171
Mary, Queen of Scots, 9, 25, 122, 129, 145, 149, 152, 157, 160, 162, 171
Meadowbank Stadium, 80, 81
Meadows International Exhibition, 139
Meadows, the, 96, 117
Medieval, 46, 60, 62, 87, 110, 129, 190
Melville Monument, 91
Mercat Cross, 129
Merlion, Walter, 53
Military Tattoo, 20, 32
Mill's Mount Battery, 40, 92
mill-pond, 184
milling communities, 116, 118, 123, 182, 184
Monastery of the Holy Rood, 161
Moray Place, 90
Moray, Earl of, 90
Morrison Street, 74
Mound, the, 93, 102, 106, 138, 140
Murray, Patrick, 43
Murrayfield Stadium, 80
Museum of Childhood, 43
musicals, 20, 31
Musselburgh, 121
Mylne's Court, 100
Mylne, James, 103
Mylne, Robert, 100
Napoleon Bonaparte, 153
Napoleonic Wars, 126
Nasmyth, Alexander, 58
National Covenant, 9, 61, 177
National Gallery of Scotland, 78, 106
National Monument, 126, 130

National Portrait Gallery, 136
National Trust for Scotland, 181, 184, 193
Nelson Monument, 15, 40, 128
Nelson, Admiral Horatio, 128
Neo-classical architecture, 73
New Town, 10, 15, 22, 41, 47, 52, 61, 70, 86, 87, 90, 91, 93, 94, 96, 97, 101, 112, 135, 138, 167, 182
Newhaven, 109, 118
Nicolson Street, 35
Nor' Loch, 93, 94, 106
North Berwick, 24, 188
North Bridge, 22, 53, 94, 97
North British Hotel, see Balmoral Hotel
Old Observatory, 70
Old Royal High School, 165
Old Tolbooth, 98, 168, 192
Old Town Information Centre, 53
Old Town Renewal Trust, 41
Old Town, 10, 15, 20, 28, 41, 62, 66, 68, 72, 73, 83, 86, 87, 88, 93, 94, 96, 97, 98, 99, 100, 102, 106, 138, 167
One o'Clock Gun, 40, 128
opera, 20, 30, 35, 42
Osbourne, Fanny, 167
Outlook Tower, 41, 92
Palace of Holyroodhouse, 89, 98, 100, 138, 144, 145
Palmerston Place, 46, 47
Paolozzi, Sir Edouardo, 134
Paris Exhibition, 133
Parliament House, 68
Parliament Square, 68
Parthenon, 126
Penicuik, 155
Pentland Hills, 18, 116, 155, 180
'People's Story', the, 172
Picardy Place, 134
Picardy Regiment, 33
Pinkie House, 121
Pitt the Younger, 91
Plague, the, 72
Playfair, William, 70, 78, 79, 126, 130
Playhouse Theatre, 42
'Pontius Pilate's Bodyguard', see Royal Scots Regiment
pop concerts, 42
Pope Julius II, 163
Portobello, 186
Pre-Raphaelites, 50, 62
Presbyterianism, 9, 47, 51
Preston Mill, 184
Primrose, Viscount, 174
Prince Albert, 115, 120

Princes Street Gardens, 29, 69, 83, 94, 99, 102, 106, 107, 117, 127, 133, 135, 140
Princes Street, 21, 22, 40, 48, 69, 73, 78, 83, 86, 93, 99, 106, 112, 127, 135, 138, 140, 170
Prosecution Service, 165
Protestantism, 55, 171
Public Record Office, 77
Queen Margaret, 157
Queen Street, 86
Raeburn, Sir Henry, 78, 153, 189
Ramsay Garden, 102
Ramsay, Allan, 61, 102, 107, 127, 140
Ramsden, Harry, 109
Randolph, Thomas, 121, 162
Raphael, 78
Reformation, 47, 62, 161, 173
Regents Road, 136
Register House, 73
Reid, Robert, 68, 77
Rembrandt, 78
Restoration, 10, 147, 163
Reynolds, 153
Rhind, Bernie, 127
River Almond, 118, 164, 190
River Esk, 121, 181
River Tyne, 184
Rizzio, 145, 149, 152
Robert the Bruce, 121, 163
Roman fort, 164, 190
Romanesque architecture, 49
Rood Well, 183
Roseberry, Earls of, 153
Ross Fountain, 29, 133
Ross Open Air Theatre, 29
Ross, Daniel, 133
Rosslyn Chapel, 56
Roundheads, 25
Royal Bank of Scotland, 52, 76
Royal Botanic Garden, 112, 113
Royal Charter, 79
Royal College of Physicians, 112
Royal Engineers, 52, 67
Royal Exchange, 72
Royal Highland Show, 38
Royal Mile, 8, 41, 47, 53, 55, 66, 87, 88, 89, 92, 94, 98, 129, 132, 136, 144, 160, 170, 172, 175, 176
Royal Museum of Scotland, 67
Royal Observatory, 70
Royal Proclamation, 129
Royal Scots Greys, 33, 127, 174
Royal Scottish Academy, 106, 138
Ruthven family, 149
Salisbury Crags, 15, 94, 128

Scotch Whisky Heritage Centre, 66
Scott Monument, 99, 135
Scott, Sir George Gilbert, 47
Scott, Sir Walter, 110, 163, 174, 187, 192
Scottish Agricultural Museum, 38
Scottish National Orchestra, 36
Scottish Parliament, 68, 126
Scottish Reformed Church, 171
Second New Town, 90
Second World War, 10, 139
Septimus Severus, Emperor, 164
Sheeps Heid Inn, 114
shipbuilding, 109, 122
Short, Maria Theresa, 71
Signet Library, 68
Simpson, Dr James, 127
Slum Clearances, 100
Smith, James, 55
South Loch, 117
South Queensferry, 150, 153, 156, 192, 194, 195
sports, 80
Spylaw, 176
St Andrew and St George's Church, 52, 77
St Andrew's Square, 52, 76, 77, 86, 91, 101, 138
St Andrew, 54, 163
St Anthony's Chapel, 57, 120
St Baldred, 19
St Bernard's Well, 116, 182
St Bernard of Clairvaux, 116
St Clair, William, 56
St Columba, 54
St Cuthbert's Kirk, 48, 58
St George's Church, 77
St Giles Cathedral, see High Kirk of St Giles
St James's Court, 34
St John's Kirk, 48, 133
St Margaret's Loch, 108, 115, 120
St Margaret's Chapel, 54, 154
St Margaret, 54, 58, 120, 192, 194
St Mary's Church (Haddington), 50
St Mary's Episcopalian Cathedral, 46, 47
St Michael's Church (Linlithgow), 157
St Ninian, 54
St Serf, 193
stained glass, 53, 54, 55
Stair, Earl of, 174
Stair, Lady, 174
Stark, William, 68
Steell, Sir John, 135, 140
Stenton, 183
Stevenson House, 147

Stevenson, Robert Louis, 15, 18, 24, 167, 174, 175, 180, 192
Stevenson, Thomas, 180
Stewart, Dugald, 130, 136
Stirling Castle, 149
Stockbridge, 103, 189
Stone Age, 14
Stuart, Charles Edward, 89, 92, 114, 115, 154, 157
Supreme Court of Scotland, 68
Swanston, 18, 180
Tantallon Castle, 148
Tay Bridge, 195
Tea Table Miscellany, 140
Telford, Thomas, 182
Temple of Theseus, 165
tenements, 96
The Antiquary, 192
The Gentle Shepherd, 140
theatre, 31
Thistle Chapel, 63
Tolbooth St John's, 92
Town College, 79
Traverse Theatre, 34
Treasure Island, 24
Tron Kirk, see Christ's Church at the Tron
Union Canal, 123
Usher Hall, 36
Usher, Andrew, 36
Van Dycke, 78
Vernon, Admiral, 186
Victoria Street, 88
Victorian Edinburgh Exhibition, 71
Victorian, 113, 114, 182, 186
volcanoes, 14, 15, 19
Walker, Barbara and Mary, 47
Wallace, William, 54
Warrender, Sir George, 96
Wars of Independence, 162
Water of Leith, 116, 182, 189
Waterloo Bridge, 170
Waverley Market, 21
Waverley Station, 21, 22, 69, 94
West Bow, 88
West Register House, 77
whisky, 66
White Horse Close, 89
Wilkins, William, 153
witches, 28, 141, 183, 188
Witherspoon, Reverend John, 187
Writers' Museum, the, 174
Yellowcraig, 24
Yester House, 187

THE
GLORIOUS
DEAD

With special thanks to
Ian Dunkley

Also by the Author

FICTION
Writing Therapy

NON-FICTION
Discover Countries: The UK
Discover Countries: India
Fatherhood: The Essential Guide
Creative Writing: The Essential Guide
Homer's Iliad: A Study Guide

THE GLORIOUS DEAD

TIM ATKINSON

Unbound

This edition first published in 2018

Unbound
6th Floor Mutual House,
70 Conduit Street,
London W1S 2GF

www.unbound.com

Text Design by Ellipsis, Glasgow

A CIP record for this book is available from the British Library

ISBN 978-1-78352-589-8 (trade hbk)
ISBN 978-1-78352-591-1 (ebook)
ISBN 978-1-78352-590-4 (limited edition)

Printed in Great Britain by CPI Group (UK)

*To the memory of the men who served
their King and Country first with a rifle,
then with a shovel.*

In Memoriam

James Alexander Burns, Sergeant Major,
14th/20th King's Hussars

Philip S. Chattaway, Second Lieutenant,
Cheshire Regiment

John William (Jack) Dove, Private (Gunner),
Sherwood Foresters

James Gardam, Private,
Duke of Wellington's (West Riding)

John Harding, Private,
Royal Marines Light Infantry PO9349

John Thomas Haw, Gunner,
Machine Gun Corps (Heavy Branch)

Frank Larkinson, Private,
8th Battalion Lincolnshire

William Frederick Mallett, Rifleman,
King's Royal Rifle Corps

Arthur F. J. Newman, Private,
12th Battalion, Royal Sussex Regiment 39th Division

James Henry Paul, Private,
6th Battalion Australian Imperial Force

C. Seagroatt, Private,
Royal Fusiliers

Only the dead know the end of war.

– Plato

In peace, sons bury their fathers.
In war, fathers bury their sons.

– Herodotus

War Diary or Intelligence Summary: Army form C. 2118
1918

DIVISION MAIN DRESSING STATION—Remy Siding
Map Sheet 28; Grid reference: L.22 d.6.3

December 25th – Church Parade at which the following messages were read to the Battalion:

CHRISTMAS MESSAGE FROM
THEIR MAJESTIES THE KING AND QUEEN

Another Christmas has come round and we are no longer fighting. God has blessed your efforts. The Queen and I offer you our heartfelt good wishes for a happy Christmas and many brighter years to come. To the disabled, sick, and wounded, we send a special greeting, praying that with returning health you may be comforted and cheered by the vision of those good days of peace for which you have sacrificed so much.

GEORGE, R.I.

MESSAGE TO HIS MAJESTY THE KING FROM
FIELD MARSHAL SIR DOUGLAS HAIG

Your Majesty's gracious message has given universal pleasure to all ranks of the Armies in France. They join with me in sending most respectful thanks, and beg to be allowed to send to their King and Queen the earnest hope that the years to come may bring your Majesties all happiness. The never failing confidence and encouragement which we have received from you, Sir, throughout the fluctuating fortunes of four and a half years of war have been ever a source of strength to us, and the gracious message which your Majesty has sent to the disabled, sick, and wounded will bring them comfort and reward.

Signed, D. Haig, F.M.

CHRISTMAS MESSAGE FROM FIELD MARSHAL SIR DOUGLAS HAIG TO ALLIED TROOPS

This Christmas Day sees our united efforts crowned with a glorious victory. I desire to wish all ranks of the Armies under my command a very happy Christmas and a brighter and happier New Year. The self-sacrifice, endurance, and devotion to duty of our troops have gained the admiration of the whole world, and at this time, when everything is being done to accelerate demobilisation, I feel sure that the same splendid qualities, which have carried us through these past years of war, will help strengthen us in reconstructing our Empire. My thoughts are with you all on this memorable Christmas Day, and I wish you God Speed.

Signed, D. Haig, F.M.

1

'I'm going to have to take his head off, sir!'

Jack plants a shovel in the soil. The flag by the open grave flaps in the breeze like an injured bird. A match flares and Jack cups his hand around the flame to light the Woodbine hanging from his lips. He shuts his eyes, inhaling deeply, turning his face to feel the warmth of the sun on his skin. 'I'm sorry, lad.' He looks into the hole and shakes his head. 'I'm never going to get you out o' there in one piece.'

Towards the top of the slope an officer in hand-tailored uniform is briefing the rest of Jack's platoon. 'Look for the signs,' the man nods, pointing to a rathole with his swagger stick. 'And take your time.' A few of the soldiers look up. One picks dirt out of his fingernails, another watches as a group of starlings stab the ground with open beaks. A noisy squabble suddenly breaks out over grubs and worms, and then the birds are gone.

The bare strip of land below the crest of the hill west of Zonnebeke has been searched now two, three, four times, but that doesn't mean the team don't expect to find more bodies. Only now, they'll be harder to spot. 'Take care too.' The sergeant – Townend – is narrowing his eyes as he looks at the men. 'Remember to watch where you're treading. There's still

3

live shells lying around in these fields. Maybe pockets of gas, too.'

Each of the Army search teams is organised in the same way – a platoon commanded by a junior officer but with an NCO to supervise the dirty work. A survey officer from the Army Directorate of Graves Registration and Enquiries divides the featureless landscape into map squares, marker tapes are laid across the mud, then the men split up into their sections and line up. A whistle blows. The line moves. Heads are bowed, shoulders hunched. The pace is slow, the scrutiny meticulous.

'Body!' someone calls out, holding up a hand and stopping. The whistle blows again and the search line shuffles to a halt. Townend strides across to take a look. Another white marker flag is planted.

'Location, Sergeant?' Lieutenant Ingham, safely back aboard the little duckboard raft, waits – blue pencil poised above the 1:20,000 trench map.

'Er . . .' Townend squints at the compass he is holding, pushing back his cap and scratching his head with a muddy finger.

'Belgium, sir,' a voice shouts out.

The whistle blows. The laughter stops. The line moves on. And Jack Patterson appears with a shovel and a sack to start the digging.

'So, sir, as I were saying.'

'Saying, Patterson?'

'Yes, sir. About 'is head.'

'Couldn't quite catch what you were asking me back then.' Ingham – his boots now muddy – crouches by the hole Jack has been digging, staring at a skull that seems to be growing like a swollen fungus out of the sodden ground. 'What with the men—'

'Aye, sir,' Jack smiles. 'Likes his little jokes does Ocker.'

'Ocker?'

'Private Gilchrist, sir.'

'Ah, yes, yes. Gilchrist. Yes, of course.' Ingham nods grimly. 'It's in the blood, y'know.'

'The blood, sir?'

'*Australian* ...' Ingham taps his nose. 'Gilchrist, that is. "Ocker", as you men call him.'

Jack squints into the low sun. Above his head the January sky is clear. From time to time small green-brown clouds of smoke drift from ammunition dumps the ordnance teams are detonating.

'Well, sir. As I was saying—'

'Yes, yes. Carry on.'

'Well, sir ... if you'd just take a look, sir, you'd be able to see for yourself.' Jack nods towards the open grave, but Ingham isn't coming any closer.

'That's the top of his head, sir, that is.'

'Really? Yes, yes, I can see—'

'Which means—'

'Which means?'

'Well you see, sir, that means he's stuck fast, sir.' Jack stands up, rubbing the small of his back, taking a long, last drag on his cigarette. 'I'll never get him out o' here in one piece. Reckon I'm going to have to take his head off before I can even think about doing any proper digging.'

'Yes, yes ...' Ingham shuts his eyes tight but the image still flashes vividly across his retina. 'I see.'

'Perhaps if I could have a bit o' help, sir? Ocker – Gilchrist, sir – he's right handy with a shovel.'

'Mm, mm.'

'Aye, sir. And Ocker don't mind rummaging around in a dead fella's pockets, neither, getting his hands all mucky feeling round for the cold meat ticket along with any other little bits and pieces.'

'Cold meat ticket?'

'Sorry, sir. Identity bracelet.'

'Yes, man, I know what it is.'

'Sir?'

'I'm just not sure, well . . . Let's show a little more respect shall we, Patterson?'

'Aye, sir. Very good, sir.'

Ingham stands up, a little too quickly. 'I'll see if Sergeant Townend can spare someone,' he rocks on his heels. 'Private Fuller might be—'

Jack clears his throat and coughs, loudly.

'Look – do you want some help extracting this corpse or don't you, Patterson?'

'Yes, sir. Sorry, sir.'

'Very well then,' Ingham swallows hard. 'Continue with the exhumation for the time being.' He clasps a gloved hand over his mouth. 'And I'll see if any of the search . . . team . . . can be . . . spared to help you.'

'Very good, sir.' Jack salutes casually. 'Thank you, sir.'

Ingham nods quickly. In a splash of muddy boots he is gone, hurrying back to the top of the field, not bothering this time to avoid the puddles.

Little has changed here since the Armistice. Twisted clumps of rusted, tangled wire lie scattered where the last artillery bombardment tossed them. The ground is as wet as it was two years ago at Third Ypres. Why isn't Ingham sinking? Jack is wondering. Why aren't the enemy machine-guns cutting him down to size? Where is the Hun* artillery?

The men at the top of the slope are in no-man's-land, struggling to maintain a straight line as they walk through mud, across shell-holes and over the top of old trenches, prodding the ground with sticks every step of the way. Now and then one of them will stop and, crouching down, start probing the thick, green slime with a long, thin blade improvised from an old machine-gun cleaning rod. The sharpened point slices through the mud like a rapier and is sensitive to the slightest touch of what might be a body – but might equally be an unexploded shell.

'Sergeant Townend?'

'Yes, sir?'

'Can you spare a couple of your men? Patterson needs assistance with the latest body that he is exhuming.'

'The search team's gone and got another for him here, sir,' Townend sighs, nodding to the latest marker flag he's planted. 'Sir?'

'Sergeant Townend?'

'We really can't spare any more men for digging, sir.'

'Yes, yes, I know we're short of manpower, Sergeant. I've put in a request.'

'There's six – six – in Patterson's section,' Townend shrugs. 'And one of them is worse than useless. And as for Gilchrist . . .'

'We have to do what we can with the tools that we've got, Sergeant. It's not ideal, I know . . .'

'We're going to run out of tarpaulins soon, sir, an' all.'

'Well then, in that case we'll sew the bodies into sandbags,'

---

* See Glossary, page 380.

Ingham snaps. 'Christ knows there's not much left of these poor blighters any more.'

'No, sir.'

'And in the meantime, Patterson has a body—'

'I'll have to call "B" section's search off, sir. There won't be enough of 'em left to cover their map square.'

'Then let "B" section concentrate on what's already been found,' Ingham says, 'helping Patterson with the exhumation. The other men can carry on with their searches.'

'Very good, sir.' Townend blows the whistle and all the men stop walking. The flares of half-a-dozen half-smoked fags are followed by quick, desperate puffs of smoke. '"B" Section – Gilchrist, MacIntyre?'

'Yessir.'

'Get down that hill and give Patterson an 'and, will you?'

'Which one, Sarge?'

'You what?'

'Which hand?'

'Ha-bloody-ha,' Townend shakes his head. 'And as for you' – he turns on Fuller – 'I don't find anything here to laugh about, do you?'

'N-n-no, sir!'

'No! So you can just piss off down to that hole Patterson's digging an' all . . . before I dig you one of your own right here.'

'Ye-es, sir!'

'And Skerritt?' Skerritt nods quickly, like a dog. 'You might as well go with 'em. You'll be bugger all use here on your own. And as for the rest o' you' – he turns back to the men in the other sections – 'show's over. Back to work.'

The whistle blows. The line moves on.

*

'So what have we got here then, Jacko?' Ocker says, pulling on a large pair of thick rubber gloves and striding down the hill. 'Boy or girl?'

'You what?' Jack pushes his cap back, scratching his forehead with a muddy finger.

'Jeez! Not flamin' twins, is it?'

'Why don't you take a look for yourself, Ocker lad.' Jack steps to one side, leaning on his shovel. 'Be my guest.' The men gather round the hole. Someone whistles through his teeth.

'Here you go, mate.' Ocker is crouching by the corpse, taking the cigarette stub from his lips.

'Don't you—'

'Yer bloody daft—'

'Oh come on, mate,' Ocker looks up, still holding his fag end to the corpse's teeth. 'He was bloody gasping! Looks like he hasn't had a smoke in years!'

'Aye, and it looks like young Fuller here is about to donate him a bit o' second-hand breakfast to go with the baccy you've just given him,' says Jack.

'Oh Jeez, you're right – he's gonna perk.'

'Then get him away from my trench – quick!'

MacIntyre is suddenly dragging Fuller by the collar. 'Well done, Jacko,' he shouts over his shoulder. The sound of Fuller's retching is growing louder. 'Lovely turn of phrase, as usual.'

'Sorry, Mac.'

'Don't mention it, son.'

Jack steps back into the hole, picking up his shovel. 'Aye, well. I've enough on getting this landowner out of here in one piece without clearing up the contents of that lad's stomach an' all. There'll be six foot o' shovelling just to get down to this fella's boots, I reckon. If he's wearing any.'

'Then let's hope that he is,' says Ocker, climbing back into the shallow trench.

'For your sake, maybe.'

'For all our sakes, Jacko. A nice pair of boots and a maker's name'll make everything we have to do a lot easier. Let's face it, there's not a lot else here to go on.'

But Jack is crouching down beside the body, idly rubbing his thumb against one of the remaining brass shoulder titles. 'Not so fast, Ocker. We might not need to dig so deep to find out t'fella's shoe size after all – look!' A glint of metal flashes briefly in the sun. 'What d'you make o' this then, lad? I reckon you can just about make out t'regiment here, if you look close enough.'

'It's down to my quick work that you can make out anything at all, Jacko.' Mac joins them, squatting on his haunches, watching as Ocker slowly wipes away another layer of sticky filth accumulated on the tattered epaulettes. 'If I hadn't given young Fuller the order of the boot just now, you'd not have seen anything for his bellyful of bacon and eggs.'

Ocker nips out his cigarette and leans forward, polishing the brass letters on the tattered fragment of army uniform with a gloved finger. 'What do you reckon, mate. Is that an "F" or a "B"?'

'Can't tell. We ought to get Skerritt over to take a dekko.'

'Eyes like a eagle, that fella!'

'Eyes is about all Fritz left intact on him an' all, poor sod. Hey, clean a bit more o' that crap off it, will you?'

Ocker blows the last of the remaining dirt from the metal letter. 'It's an "F", mate – look! A flamin' "F" . . . for certain.'

'Bloody hell!'

'Yup, and there's an "R" and an "F" and then . . . nothing. But there would've been something . . . there, look – the last letter's broken off, you can see where it's snapped.'

'Flying Corps?'

'Reckon so, mate. That's why he's flamin' well standing to attention. Must've fallen out of the sky and sunk straight into the mud like a Mills bomb.'

'Rubbish, son – he's a Fusilier, surely?' Mac squints to take a closer look. 'That's all there is – "R" and "F". Why do ye have to go imagining a "C" that's snapped off?'

'What does an Aussie know about the British Army anyway?'

'Leave off, fellas – look, there's no trace of a hackle!'

'No? He's right, Mac. There's no hackle here.'

'Rifle Brigade, then?'

'It's an "F", Mac, not a flamin' "R". I've already told you.'

A deep thud shakes the earth. A cloud of brown smoke, much nearer now, drifts across the battlefield. Instinct kicks in and the men all duck briefly for cover, before standing up and carrying on as if nothing's happened. Fuller, however, is lying flat in the grave with his fingers in his ears.

'You must be desperate, mate,' says Ocker. 'That's all I can say.'

'You what?' The boy looks up, wiping his mouth on his sleeve.

'You and this fella.' He nods in the direction of the grinning skull, just inches away from Fuller's moist face. 'I just hope you'll both be very happy together.'

'Aye,' says Jack. 'And we'll all be invited to t'wedding. But let's just get him out of this shithole shall us, before you two decide to start arranging anything?'

'Oh . . . Jesus . . . fuckin' . . . Christ!' Fuller is scrambling to get out of the hole as quickly as he got in.

'I reckon the wedding's off,' Jack laughs.

'Hey, Fuller?' The boy turns. 'Make yourself useful. Go and fetch us some sandbags, will you?'

'OK, skip!'

'And bring us a bucket while you're at it?'

'A bucket?' Fuller shouts over his shoulder. 'What the fuck d'you want a bucket for?'

'So you can build some flamin' sand castles,' Ocker calls out. 'What the bloody hell do you think I want it for?'

2

The old ex-RAMC ambulance bounces along across the weed-strewn cobbles of the Menin Road and into the Grote Markt. 'That's right,' Ocker shouts as Blake, the platoon driver, eases off on the accelerator. 'Give 'em one last ride to remember.'

The wagon stops and the engine judders to a standstill in the empty market square. Four years of constant shelling have left Ypres little more than a bombed-out ruin, but just three months after the Armistice the roads have all been cleared and piles of stone line the streets, covered in a thin layer of snow.

'Right.' Sergeant Townend jumps down from the cab, and runs his stick along the canvas sides of the truck. 'Everybody out!'

'They can't hear you, Sarge,' a muffled voice replies.

'You what?'

'They're all flamin' dead!'

Lined up inside the ambulance, sewn into sacks tied with luggage labels, the results of the morning's exhumations drip and settle on the wooden stretcher shelves.

'Come on,' Jack says, unbolting the tailgate of the old green Albion lorry that has been following the motor ambulance back from Zonnebeke. 'I've had enough of this.'

'Me too,' says another soldier, jumping down and wiping his brow with a tartan handkerchief.

'What's the plan then, Jacko?' asks Ocker as he watches Sergeant Townend turning on his heels and striding off across the cobbles.

'The plan?' Jack narrows his eyes and frowns as he stares after the NCO. 'That depends on where's Townend's going. Anyone know?'

Skerritt grunts and raises his hand.

'Anyone who can talk!'

'Said he was going to see that the coolies have dug the graves,' Ocker says. 'Before we all march over there and tuck these coves in.'

'The what?' says Fuller. 'Coolies?'

'Y'know – little Chinese fellas,' Ocker puts a finger to the corner of his eyes and pulls the skin tight.

'Well he'll be lucky,' Jack says, 'after what happened yesterday.'

'Wha— why?' Fuller shrugs. 'What happened yesterday?'

'Later, sunshine.' Ocker slaps a hand on Fuller's shoulder. 'When you're older.'

'I'm bloody nineteen I am!'

'Yeah, yeah – and I'm the King o' the flamin' Belgians.'

'Come on,' says Mac, folding up his handkerchief. 'Put us all out of our misery. What did happen yesterday, Jack?'

'A Chinaman were murdered,' Jack says. 'That's all.'

'Murdered?'

'Aye, lad, killed.'

'The fate you took so much trouble to avoid, son,' Mac mutters.

'But?'

'Aye. An' now they're all confined to barracks at De Clijte until they catch the bugger that did it.'

'Then what, Jacko? What'll they do to him?'

'Shoot 'im, I reckon.'

'Shoot him?'

'Someone really ought to tell the coolies that the flamin' war is over,' Ocker laughs. 'Don't you think?'

'Poor wee beggars.' MacIntyre stuffs the tartan handkerchief back into his tunic pocket. 'Have yer no seen the conditions they're working under?'

'Poor flamin' fools, more like,' says Ocker.

'Never mind all that now, lads,' Jack interrupts. 'We're wasting precious time here. Townend's going to be at least half an hour before he finds out what's actually happened. He'll be expecting t'Chinks to have dug t'graves ready for this lot.'

'So he's got a bit of a surprise coming.'

'Aye. Now, what about Ingham? Anyone know where he's off to?'

'Well he won't be digging no graves!' says Fuller.

'Not officially, anyway.'

'Nah, he's gone to fetch the sky pilot,' Ocker tells them. 'If he can find one, that is. So, anyway, I reckon, as that's Ingham and Townend taken care of . . .'

'What?'

'I reckon we've time for a beer, if we're quick about it. What d'you think, Jacko?'

'Why not,' Jack says. 'The local?'

The men all cheer. 'The local!'

The 'local' – such as it is – is little more than a wooden hut above the cellar of Monsieur Steenvan's old café on the

15

bombed-out corner of Station Straat and Malou Laan in Ypres. Not much to look at. Not that the men mind.

'The crafty old bugger certainly seems to have a knack for making money,' Ocker says. 'Skittles off to Poperinghe within minutes of the Jerries taking over back in 1914 . . .'

'Someone had to make sure the British Army's thirst was quenched,' Mac interrupts.

'. . . and then as soon as the fighting's over he's back in Ypres like a shot staking the family's claim on its old *estaminet*.'

'Not that there was much left of it by then,' says Jack.

'There is now, though, ain't there?' Fuller says. 'Thanks to us!'

'Less of the "us", sunshine.'

'I 'elped him build it an' all,' Fuller protests. 'You wasn't the only ones scrounging bits of wood and old corrugated iron for him.'

'Keep yer voice down, will yer,' Jack hisses.

The subterranean world of cellars and crypts close to the railway station in Ypres is proving fertile soil for the new buildings that are rising from the city ruins. Entreaties from the British to leave the area untouched go ignored. Only round the ancient Cloth Hall and the cathedral is no building work allowed. A stencilled sign swings on a wire that surrounds the cordon sanitaire. A solitary guard nods as the men hurry past.

THIS IS HOLY GROUND
NO STONE OF THIS FABRIC MAY BE TAKEN AWAY
IT IS A HERITAGE FOR ALL CIVILISED PEOPLES

'Only the British Army could make a bloke stand guard over a pile of rubble,' Ocker says to the sentry. 'Worried the locals are going to pounce on you and rebuild the place while your back's turned are you, mate?'

'Actually, you know, that's exactly what they are worried about,' says Blake.

'What's that, mate?'

'And he hasn't even had a drink yet, either!'

'Yeah, but don't argue with him. He's armed and dangerous, ain't you, Blakey? Armed with that Bible that goes everywhere with 'im.'

But Blake is ignoring them. '*I can think of no more beautiful monument to the dead . . .*' He stops for a moment, closing his eyes as he tries to remember the rest of the speech he has read in the papers.

'What? No more beautiful monument than this old pile of stone?'

'*A more sacred place for the British race does not exist in the world.*'

'Blimey,' Fuller laughs. 'Who the hell said that?'

'Winston Churchill, actually.'

'Oh, yeah?' the boy says. 'Has he ever seen the place?'

'Aye, lad,' Jack says. 'Commanded one o' the Jock battallions at Plug Street Wood. Isn't that right, Mac?'

'It is so.'

'Well, either way, it's just a heap of bleedin' rubble now,' says Fuller.

'Oh, fair dinkum, mate, it's a very nice pile of rubble!'

'Cleared a lot of it myself,' says Jack. 'And under fire, an' all.'

'No doubt when this *wee chicken-hertit callan*' – Mac turns, poking Fuller in the chest with his finger – 'was still tied ti'is mammy's apron strings.'

'Me mam was ill,' the boy snaps.

'Aye, laddie, we know. She tied the apron strings tae tight.'

The men hurry down Boter Straat, turning left towards the Rijkswachtkazerne. A cart piled high with furniture squeaks down a narrow alley followed by an old dog with a limp. Heading into Station Straat, the men arrive at the door of the 'local'. A painted sign above the door reads 'British Tavern', but Jack isn't ordering drinks in English.

'*Zes pintjes*, er . . . *asjeblief?*' He removes his cap and walks up to the bar. Two locals in heavy coats look up briefly from a game of cards. Another customer smiles, but not at them. A young girl laughs before the woman serving turns and begins drawing down a jug of beer. 'Hey, lass.' Jack ruffles the girl's dark hair. 'What's does little Françoise find so funny?'

'You!' the girl replies with a cheeky smile. Along the bar her elder sister Katia stands decanting a foaming mug of cloudy auburn liquid from a pewter jug. A line of chipped earthenware tankards stands waiting in a row along the wooden counter. Katia knows Jack's order, however he chooses to say it.

The bar of what was once a modest family hotel is little more than a low trestle table set before a row of wooden barrels. The larger casks tilt forward slightly on the cracked stone floor. Wine flasks with brass taps squat on the shelf above, together with a few old, unlabelled bottles. 'Why do you try to speak Flemish?' the little girl asks. Jack takes the first of the mugs the barmaid has filled and closes his eyes, taking a long, slow drink.

'Why not?' He licks the moustache of foam from his lips.

'It is *grappig*, that's all.'

'Funny? What, me saying it in t'first place?' Jack says. 'Or the way I say it?'

18

'Both,' Françoise replies, wrinkling her nose.

'Well,' Jack shakes his head and pouts. 'That's a fine way to encourage a chap who's trying his best to learn the local lingo.'

'Don't be sad!' the girl looks up him at him.

'How could I be sad,' Jack smiles, picking Françoise up and spinning her round, 'with thee here to make me laugh. Friends?' Jack puts the girl down and offers her his hand. '*Vrienden?*'

'*Vrienden!*' the girl smiles.

'Now, Françoise' – he passes her the tray – 'be a good girl an' take these over to the men, will yer? I just want to have a quick word with your big sister.' The girl curls her fingers round the edges of the tray, without once taking her eyes off the beer. 'Steady now!' Jack calls. 'Be careful, lass. Them lads is thirsty!'

'You should not ask her to do that, Jacques.' The older girl is standing watching, smiling, idly circling a tea towel on the bar. 'She is too young.'

'She's not!' Jack says. 'I were doing more than carrying trays when I were her age, I reckon.'

The woman smiles and shakes her head. 'I think I can imagine!'

'Anyway, how else is a fella going to get a moment to himself with—'

'*Bier alsjeblieft!*' The young woman breaks off to serve another customer. Their brief conversation moves too fast for Jack to follow, but it is obvious that the man is something of a regular. She is getting him a glass Jack notices – a clean one, too.

'Hey, Katia, *geef me een kus!*' The man is dangling a crumpled banknote in the air like bait. As Katia reaches for the cash the man snatches it away, grabbing her wrist with his free hand.

'*Nee!*' the woman is struggling. '*NEE!*'

He pulls her towards him and puckers his lips before looking around. But nobody else is laughing.

'Cheers!' Jack leans across and clinks his mug – hard – into the man's round, stemmed glass, spilling some of the beer.

'Cheers, yer fat Belgian bastard.'

'Cheers?' the man looks puzzled for a moment. 'Cheers? *Vaar kom je vandaan?*'

'*Hij komt uit Engeland.*' Katia is smoothing down her apron and replacing a pin in her hair.

'Ah, English!' the fat stranger shouts. 'You are English. Tommy?'

'No – Jack.'

'Ha, ha – *erg grappig.* Very funny.'

'*Françoise, ga in de rug en haal papa. Vertel hem de heer de Wulf hier.*'

The girl trots off behind the counter to fetch her father while Katia resumes the slow, circular movement of the towel she is rubbing on the surface of the bar. Her hair, hurriedly pinned back after the brief exchange across the bar, still escapes in a few loose strands. Her cheeks are flushed with embarrassment and anger.

'Hey, Jacko, you joinin' us, mate?'

'Ah, he's too busy with the *langue d'amour!*'

'I'll be along in a minute, lads.'

'We haven't got all day, you know.'

'Yeah, come on, Jacko,' Ocker says, bringing back the empty tray. 'We've time for another if you're quick about it.'

'Blimey, that can't have touched t'sides,' Jack picks up one of the empty tankards.

'Thirsty work, grave digging,' says Ocker. 'You should know that, Jacko.'

'Love?'

Katia picks up the pewter jug. The barrels only travel a short distance by road from the brewery in nearby Poperinghe, but the beer is always lively. Monsieur Steenvan's eldest daughter, as her father taught her, is taking great care filling each of the mugs in turn. But time and the men's thirst are pressing.

'Happen I'll take these over,' Jack tells her, putting the half-filled mugs on a tray. 'Bring us the jug across later. We'll top 'em up for ourselves.'

'Hey, *je negeert me* – you are ignoring me.' The fat man with the beer glass is turning to address the half-empty room. 'They are ignoring me – Tommy and his girlfriend. Look at them.' He laughs, making another grab for Katia's hand, knocking the jug she is holding in the process. 'Hey! Give that to me. I need a top-up, too.'

'Look, mate, there's a flamin' queue here,' Ocker says, elbowing past the man to help Jack with the tray. 'And you' – he shoves the man away – 'you're at the back, you fat ugly bastard.'

Jack catches the stranger's arm as he shapes to throw a punch, but he can't prevent him sticking out a boot and sending Ocker, together with the beers, crashing to the floor. 'Now that weren't very friendly, was it?' Jack pulls the man back, sharply.

'Let go of my arm,' he winces. But Jack's grip tightens and he twists the man's wrist, forcing the stranger to turn sharply in an attempt to unwind from the pain.

'Leave this to me, Ocker lad.' Jack shoves an arm up the man's back, but Ocker is already scrambling to his feet and aiming a full-blooded punch at the fat man's gut. As he doubles over, Ocker's knee cracks hard into the man's jaw through a cushion of soft flesh. Jack releases the grip on his wrist and the man goes sprawling across the wet floor.

'No, please – stop!' cries Katia, holding her hands to her face.

'Come on, lads.' Blake is standing up and flapping his arms. 'Enough! No need for violence.'

But Ocker hasn't finished. 'You want your mates to know you've been in a proper fight, don't you, cobber?' He kneels beside him, lifting the man by the scruff of the neck and slapping his cheeks.

'Smashed a perfectly good jug there too, Ocker. As well as spilling our beer.'

'Reckon we ought to rub his fat face in that, Jacko. What do you think? After all' – he lifts the man by the scruff of the neck again – 'obviously missed the main event, didn't you, mate?'

'Too bloody fat to fight,' says Jack. 'Wouldn't fit that gut in t'trenches.'

'Come on now, lads, you've had your fun,' Mac interrupts. 'And I want my beer.'

Katia has turned away and is already filling up another jug.

'That's enough now, Ocker. Come on – the beer's ready.' Jack takes the fresh jug Katia has just filled and moves towards the table.

'Enough? Mate, I've only just started!'

'Later, Ocker. Leave it. You'll have the redcaps on us if you aren't careful.'

The fat man struggles to his feet, slipping on the wet floor but suddenly smiling as he drapes a heavy arm around Ocker's shoulders. The few remaining customers in the tiny bar have fled, leaving their cards on the table. 'We are all friends here, heh?' the fat man is slurring. 'Heh! Heh?'

'Jeez, this guy's a nutter,' Ocker shakes his head. 'You

should've let me finish him off just now when I had the chance.'

Jack starts picking up the broken pottery shards, placing them back on the sticky tray. 'Sorry, love. Tell your pa we'll make it up to him. But he won't miss that jug. Not when he sees what else he's got coming to him.' Katia calls to someone in the back room of the *estaminet*. 'Scrounged a few elephants the other day. Some decent lengths o' timber, too.'

'Elephants?' She looks puzzled.

'Aye, lass. Old sheets of iron just like them ones.' He points to the ceiling. 'I'm sure your pa will find a use for 'em. As well as all the other stuff.'

'I can find a use for them,' the fat man shouts, wiping his face on a handkerchief. 'I can pay for them,' he reaches in his jacket pocket for a wad of notes. 'With this!'

'They're not for sale,' Jack says.

'Ha, Steenvan pays you in . . . beer, no?'

'No!'

'Ah!' He turns and winks at Katia. 'Maybe *la belle Katia* is what you are after, eh?'

'I've told you,' Jack says, 'they're not for sale. 'Not to you, anyhow.'

'But, Jacques,' Katia slowly shakes her head, 'you don't understand. Monsieur de Wulf is—'

'Hey! *Wat is er gaande?*' Her father appears at the curtained door between the small kitchen and the bar. His dark eyes flit round the room before noticing the broken pottery shards on the bar.

'Katia!' he shouts. '*Wat gebeurt er?*'

'*Het was een ongeluk, papa,*' the girl spreads her hands and shrugs. 'An accident . . .'

3

'I thought we weren't meant to be calling this place Cooler Cemetery no more?' shouts Ocker as the men hurry up the road to the Minneplein a short time later. The sun feels surprisingly warm on their cheeks as they stride along the cobbles. Or is it the beer?

Sergeant Townend is waiting, looking flustered, at the cemetery gates. 'You what?'

'Prison cemetery. I thought we was banned from using that name now?'

'We are,' says Townend as the men arrive.

'Might as well be though,' Ocker says. 'Mightn't it?'

'Might as well be what?'

'Might as well be a flamin' prison.' He nods at the rows of wooden crosses. 'After all, these poor sods aren't about to make a bid for freedom anytime soon, are they?'

'Not,' the chaplain interrupts, 'until the Glorious Day of Resurrection, anyway.'

'Sorry, Padre!' Ocker smiles to himself. 'Didn't see you over there, what with your head buried in your book. Learning your words, are you?' The other men laugh. 'Though if you don't mind my saying so' – he grins at Jack – 'I'd have thought

24

you'd have your script off pat by now – you know, the number of times you've had to spout this mumbo-jumbo.'

'Shut it, Gilchrist,' says Townend, 'and get digging.'

'Right you are, Sarge,' he says. 'But why is the sky pilot here in the first place? Aren't we just tucking these coves back in?'

'It's a committal service, isn't it, you joker.'

'Dunno, Sarge,' Ocker shrugs. 'Is it?'

'I'm afraid it is.' The padre closes his book and points to the row of stretchers by the wire fence. Slowly drying in the winter sun are the bones of over a dozen men of the Duke of Cornwall's Light Infantry, alongside the bodies that Jack and his men have recently been exhuming. 'I'm afraid none of these poor souls will have received God's blessing,' the padre goes on, 'given—'

'Given that they was buried alive in the crypt of the cathedral,' Townend mutters.

'I don't know, Sarge,' Ocker smiles. 'I'd have thought that the cathedral would've been the best place for 'em, actually.'

'Well, I'm afraid it wasn't,' says the padre sharply.

'No, of course not,' Ocker shakes his head. 'Otherwise the Big Fella up there might've sorted His Almighty Flamin' act out and seen to it to save these poor blighters – along with that fancy house of His.'

'So they was trapped, then?' Fuller whispers, looking at the sacks.

'Aye, laddie,' Mac nods. 'And they've been stuck beneath the cathedral since 1915, when a Fritz shell brought it crashing down above their heads.'

'The poor blighters!' Fuller shakes his head. The chaplain is opening his mouth but letting out a sigh, rather than adding to the discussion. Townend clears his throat.

'Right, now we've got that little bit o' history cleared up,' the sergeant says, swallowing hard, 'do you think we can get started?'

'What's the hurry, Sarge?' asks Ocker. 'These fellas in some kind of rush for eternity are they?'

'Very funny, Gilchrist,' Townend smiles, twisting his face with what in anyone else would be pleasure. 'Although you'll be laughing on the other side of your ugly Antipodean mug when you find out what the hurry is.'

'I'll bet.'

'Truth is,' Townend goes on, 'there's a bit more work for you lot than you might have been expecting.'

'C'est la vie,' says one of the men.

'C'est la guerre,' says another.

'Say what you bleedin' well like,' says Townend. 'But the graves ain't been dug yet.'

'You what?'

'No! So you'll be needing these.' He starts handing out the pickaxes and spades.

'As if we haven't dug enough holes in this flamin' country,' says Ocker.

'Just stop moaning and get digging!' Townend snarls. 'Look sharp and you might even get to dig yourself a fuckin' tunnel to Australia.'

'I'd stand a better chance of getting back home if I did,' says Ocker. 'And it'd probably be a darn sight quicker, too.'

'Quicker than waiting for Ingham to get around to sorting out your demob, son, and that's a fact,' adds Mac, picking up a shovel.

'Too right, mate. Anyway, Sarge' – Ocker winks at Jack and puts on his most innocent expression – 'I thought it was the coolies who were meant to be digging the graves?'

'They was,' says Townend. 'That's the change of plan.'

'Yeah, the coolies got a Blighty one, didn't they, Sarge?'

'You what?'

'And meanwhile we get their fatigues,' says Fuller. 'In addition to our own. Well, I ain't here to dig no graves.'

'Look, Fuller,' Townend takes a step in the boy's direction. 'Cut the fuckin' crap before I put my boot up your FUCKIN' clacker.' Fuller trips and falls over a freshly filled grave mound as he backs away. Laughter.

'Don't waste your breath on him, Sarge,' says Ocker. 'He'll not end up digging any more than a worm's tucker anyway.'

'I bloody well will!' Fuller pauses for a moment. 'A worm's . . . what?'

'Never mind, son. Oh, and another thing, Sarge.'

'What is it this time, Gilchrist?'

'Don't go and waste a decent banjo on this fella, either.'

'You what?'

'No – give him the entrenching tool. Or better still a flamin' toothpick,' Ocker laughs. 'In fact, why don't you send him back out fossicking in them fields again, the flamin' fairy. He'd be a lot more use to us out there than he will be here.'

'Just 'cos I didn't spend four years hiding in a fucking funk hole in case a Jerry took a fancy to me hat.' Fuller bares his teeth.

'Cut it out, lads. We've got work to do, in case you hadn't noticed.' Jack unrolls the cemetery plan, anchoring the corners on the ground with stones. 'And a sight more work than we'd intended.'

Ypres Prison Cemetery, south of the Leie Kanaal and opposite La Plaine d'Amour, already contains well over a thousand graves. The remains of the old field ambulance depot and the casualty clearing station are still visible by the road. The pockmarked walls of the town's old prison still rise over the field, battered but reasonably intact. *Couldn't knock that over, could yer, eh, Fritz?* The land is slowly being cleared to make room for men buried at several smaller graveyards – Broadley's Cemetery and The Esplanade – nearby, as well as casualties like these from the town of Ypres itself.

'Right, that's our plot over by the road.' Jack points to a vacant area in the farthest corner of the graveyard. 'Plot V, row AA. One Five Three Company seem to have commandeered the rest of t'blinkin' cemetery, don't they, Sarge?'

Townend nods absently, then turns to light a cigarette. 'Mm.' He shakes the match out. 'Right, then. Fuller?'

'Yes, Sarge?'

'Go and fetch the corner flags from the truck, will you?'

'Yes, Sarge.'

'And don't forget the football, neither!' The men laugh. 'Playing the stiffs this afternoon, are we, Sarge?'

'It'd be the only chance you lot'd have of winning anything.'

'Sergeant Townend!' The chaplain thinks he's heard enough. 'A word if I may, please. With the men.' Townend frowns, then nods. Ocker rolls his eyes. 'Let's just remember where we are, shall we?' He pauses, looking at each of the men in turn, before he goes on. 'And why we're all here.'

A sudden chorus of coughs is accompanied by a shuffling of feet on the gravel path. Townend idly rolls a ball of phlegm around his mouth; Ocker absent-mindedly brings a cigarette to his lips.

'There's a time and a place, you know, soldier,' the chaplain says, stuffing the fag into Ocker's tunic pocket.

'Sorry, your honour.'

'And our duty here this afternoon' – he turns to the rest of the men – 'is to give these fine, brave soldiers a decent Christian burial.'

The brief, uncomfortable silence is broken by the sound of Fuller's boots crunching on the gravel path on his way back from the truck, carrying the flags.

'Pardon me, your reverence, but . . .' Ocker rolls the extinguished stub of his cigarette between his finger and his thumb, before putting it back to his lips.

'What is it, son?'

'Well, I was just thinking . . .'

'Go on.'

'I was just wondering . . . how do we know that these coves was actually Christian? I mean, some of the fellas we dig up hardly even look human, the state they're in.'

'Quite!' The chaplain looks down, briefly. 'No – that's a very good question.'

'Is is, sir?'

'But you know, I don't think they'll mind too much, Private Gilchrist.'

'Yeah, I suppose you're right, Padre,' shrugs Ocker. 'I'm not sure they care much either way in their condition.'

'What I mean, Private Gilchrist, is that they'll not mind being mistaken for good Christian gentlemen.' The chaplain closes his eyes. 'In fact, come the Dreadful Day of Judgment, I rather suspect that they'll consider it to be something of an advantage.'

'You think so, sir?' says Ocker, staring at the muddy bundles laid on stretchers at their feet. 'I reckon these poor fellas have already met the Dreadful Day of Judgment, if you ask me.'

'Pardon me, sir,' Townend interrupts, his hand half-raised as if he's unsure whether he should be seeking permission. 'But the dreadful judgment that awaits us'll be jankers if we don't get a shift on digging these graves. So, if you don't mind . . .'

'Of course.' The chaplain waves a hand.

'Right then, you lot . . .'

'You talking to us, Sarge?' Ocker nods towards the row of stretchers. 'Or to them?'

'Just get this fuckin' trench dug,' Townend says. 'And get these fellas laid down side by side.'

'As opposed to upside down or standing on their heads, eh, Sarge?'

'Oh very funny. Very amusing.'

'We're doing it, sir,' Jack salutes.

Once the ground is marked, the spadework starts. Solid, brown-green shovelfuls of soil are stacked like bricks as the trench grows deeper. One of the men starts humming to the regular rhythm of the digging. Within minutes, the men are whistling. Then singing.

Digging, digging, digging, always flamin' digging.
Digging all the morning, and digging all the night.

Digging, digging, digging, always flamin' digging.
Roll on till my time is up and I shall dig no more.

War Diary or Intelligence Summary:
Army form C. 2118
1919

DIVISION MAIN DRESSING STATION—Remy Siding
Map Sheet 28; Grid reference: L.22 d.6.3

March 8th – Salvage and clearance operations continued with
C and D Coys both receiving drafts from other regiments.
Cpt. MORRIS, Lt. DEWHURST, Lt. BRADLEY and 23
Other Ranks left for demobilisation.

March 10th – Drill and P.T., with kit inspection by R.S.M.
YARDLEY. Battalion selected to send one officer and 20
other ranks for duties in connection with Paris Peace
Conference.

March 11th – Inspection by C.O. and selection of other ranks
eligible for Army of Occupation. 2/Lt C.S. MURRAY M.C.,
D.S.O. selected to lead.

March 12th – 2/Lt. INGHAM and 23378 Sgt. TOWNEND
organise training for burial party. Remainder – P.T. and
route march.

March 13th – Drill. Paris Party special programme of training.

March 14th – Lt. Col. C.E. ATKINSON awarded CROIX DE
GUERRE avec Etoile en Argent; Capt. S. KINSELLA
awarded Belgian Decoration Militaire.

March 15th – Arms saluting and Platoon Drill.

March 16th – Church parade held in YMCA Hut No. 2.

March 17th – 2/Lts. JENKINS, DOUGLAS and 16 Other Ranks
left Battalion for demobilisation.

March 19th – Lt. Col. GOODLAND, Army Directorate of
Graves Registration and Enquiries and Imperial War Graves
Commission, dined at HQ Mess as guest of the C.O.

4

'Busy in here tonight.' Ocker is standing in the food queue, mess-tin at the ready, back at Remy Farm HQ. The railway sidings where supplies of men and horses used to be unloaded daily are much quieter now. Goods trains no longer carry guns and shells; the wagons, when they come, are filled with spades and pickaxes and wheelbarrows.

'Busy? You should have seen it back in Seventeen, laddie!' Mac laughs. 'Why, this place is no more than a tenth of the size it used to be.'

'Which is why we all get plenty o' space in our billets,' Jack chips in.

'Yeah – we could 'ave a hut each if we wanted to, Jack, couldn't we?' Fuller says as the queue shuffles forward. 'Why don't they give us a hut each all to ourselves, eh?'

Mac turns and stares at Fuller. 'Perhaps they think we need to keep an eye on certain members of this platoon, eh? Maybe they're worried that some of us . . .' he pauses. 'Well, let's just say that now you're here, son—'

'At long last.'

'—now you're here we'd hate it if anything happened to ye.'

'Yeah, it'd be an awful shame if you're demob came up before you'd 'ad a chance to get to know the place.'

'It'd be a criminally negligent act if yon mammy's boy went home even a day before the rest of us.'

'Look, 's not my fault they took so long getting round to me call up, is it?'

'Perhaps not, son, perhaps not. But then—'

'Yeah?'

'What stopped you from enlisting, eh?'

'This ain't fair. Tell him, Jacko. He's always getting at me, is Jock.'

'Mac.'

'Always on at me for not being here sooner, not getting sent out quicker. But I'm here now, ain't I?'

'Now there's no more fighting to be done.'

'At least I got a gun. At least I'd do some fighting if there was any to do. Why does no one ever have a go at Blakey. He's a fuckin' conchie!'

'Aye, and a conchie with the DCM an' all.'

'The DC what?'

'Distinguished Conduct Medal, sonny. He might not have carried a Lee Enfield, but he carried plenty of wounded men back from no-man's-land on a stretcher.'

Skerritt suddenly grunts, jabbing a finger at his chest.

'Brought you back too, did he, Skerritt? Well, we'll not hold that against him, shall we?' Ocker slaps him on the back. 'Seeing as he brought the pretty 'uns as well.'

'Aye, and brought most of 'em back here to Pop an' all,' Jack says. 'On his little ambulance.'

'No wonder he knows them roads like the back of his hand.'

'And drives the wagons so well.'

The mess queue shuffles slowly forward. No one speaks for a moment. Fuller is unsure whether to let the matter drop or try to change the subject.

'So who turned up here first then, Mac?'

'The French, of course, son. Back in Fifteen.'

'Chose a decent spot for it, didn't they?'

'Aye, of course – out of range of the guns—'

'Most of the time!'

'Right next to the railway, too.'

'And no more than half a mile from Pop!'

A short distance south-west of Poperinghe on the road to Steenvoorde, close to the hamlet of Lijssenthoek, the hospital and now battalion HQ has seen many changes. As the war ebbed and flowed, and the site dipped in and out of range of enemy guns, the base has variously been a dressing station, a field hospital, or a field ambulance HQ. But throughout the war its strategic location endured, and the camp is now a small town in its own right, with hard paving, electric lighting, its own water supply and a vegetable garden.

'Watch out.' Jack nudges Ocker as the others join the queue at the canteen. Skerritt stares at the quartermaster, busy ladling out steaming hot, thick brown stew into a line of proffered mess-tins. The CO strides over, inspecting rations and talking to one or two of the men as they wait in line for the food. At the far end of the hut a brazier spits with flame as someone adds more wood. 'Summat's up.'

'What makes you think that?'

'The CO's being friendly, that's what.'

Major Rennard is moving slowly along the line. The major's eyes, nose, and mouth – his entire expression – seems to be puckering in the centre of his face. Thin lips twist into a smile beneath a clipped moustache like a flattened toothbrush.

'Jeez! That smile must hurt,' Ocker starts humming, then singing, gradually getting louder as the major gets closer.

It took a long time to get it hairy.
Took a long time to grow.
It took a long time to get it hairy,
For the toothbrush hairs to show.
Goodbye, Charlie Chaplin,
Farewell, tufts of hair,
It took a long long time to get it hairy,
Now my top lip's quite bare!

'Expecting company, are we, sir?' Major Rennard is at the back of the queue now. At the far end of the long Nissen hut – which tonight is doubling as temporary Officers' Mess – the light of oil lamps casts a busy shadow. Orderlies are laying out a long wooden table with the regimental silverware. A candle in a bottle is placed in the middle of the red-and-white-checked tablecloth that the quartermaster must have scrounged from somewhere.

'Yes, Private, as a matter of fact we are. A trainload of re-inforcements is arriving in the morning. Labour Company men, pioneers and so on. Men to help you chaps with the digging.'

'Pardon me, sir – but you're not getting out the silverware for them, are you?'

'No, of course not. As a matter of fact Colonel Goodland will be arriving shortly and joining us in the Officers' Mess,' Rennard replies. 'Well, he won't be joining us in the Mess since the rather unfortunate conflagration there . . . But the colonel will be dining tonight as an honoured guest of the Battalion.'

'Colonel Goodland?'

'That's right, Private – Colonel Goodland.'

'In civvies, is he?'

'What d'you mean "in civvies", Private?'

'Well,' Ocker says, 'there was this bloke sniffing round the cemetery we was working at this afternoon, sir, after Lieutenant Ingham had gone off for a bit with Fuller.'

'Gone off . . . for a bit?'

'Yeah, he does that all the time, sir.'

Jack coughs theatrically. The noise and bustle of the Nissen hut seems to cease for a moment.

'Anyway, sir, just thought that might've been the colonel, sir – you know, arrived early, like?'

'That weren't Colonel Goodland, yer daft bugger,' Jack says.

'Who was it then?'

Major Rennard makes a move, but only as far as to fetch Ingham, reminding him loudly of his duty to ensure the comfort of the men under his command. 'You go and talk to them, Ingham,' Rennard tells him. 'Damned if I can understand a word they're saying. Something about Colonel Goodland at the concentration cemetery your platoon was working at earlier today. And some nonsense about you going off with Private Fuller?'

'Leave this to me, sir.'

'So who was it then?' Mac joins the others in the queue. 'Who was yon fella hanging about the cemetery earlier?'

'Whoever it was, Private MacIntyre, I can assure you it most certainly would not have been Colonel Goodland.' Ingham suddenly appears at Mac's shoulder. 'For a start, the colonel will be in uniform, naturally.'

'So what's the colonel after then, sir?' says Ocker. 'Planning another stunt for us, are they?'

'I beg your pardon?'

'Well they know how much we miss the old days – being fired at and bombed and blown to bits and all that kind o' thing.'

'What is he "after", Gilchrist? What is he "after"? I can assure you that the colonel isn't "after" anything. He is paying us a courtesy visit to discuss the increasing overlap of our joint roles. Ultimately, it will be up to chaps like the colonel and the Imperial War Graves Commission to look after the cemeteries that we are creating.'

'*We*, sir?'

'He is also coming,' Ingham goes on, ignoring the interruption, 'to ask the CO if we have any recommendations to make as to suitable candidates for further service when the Army leaves and the Commission takes men on as part of its permanent staff.'

'I need a recommendation, sir.'

'Why's that, Gilchrist?'

'Need you to recommend me for my flamin' demob, sir. Reckon you could ask the colonel to hurry it along for me, do you, sir?'

'Watch your language, Private Gilchrist.'

'Why? Demob a dirty word, is it, sir? We certainly don't hear it often enough, not around here.'

'I'm sure that your demobilisation will be dealt with through the usual channels.' Ingham turns to leave.

'Yes, sir, but I just thought as you and the colonel was having tucker together . . .'

'That won't be an appropriate subject for our discussion on this occasion, Gilchrist.'

'It's all right for you lot,' Ocker calls as Ingham starts to walk away. 'Couple of hours on a bloody cattle boat across the usual *Channel* and you're back home again in Blighty with your hands inside some sheila's stockings.'

'Private Gilchrist!'

'It'll take me flamin' weeks to get back down under!'

'Colonel Goodland is a representative of the Imperial War Graves Commission!' Ingham turns on his heels, and is suddenly marching back to where the men are standing in line. Struggling to keep his voice down he has now given up the effort and pretence of smiling. 'He is coming to discuss the smooth handover of responsibility for the military cemeteries AND NOT YOUR BLOODY DEMOB!'

'Oh yeah, mate? Sure he's not coming here to discuss your little secret dealings with the locals, too?'

'MATE? *MATE*? HOW DARE YOU!'

'OK, I'm through with this.' Ocker turns to leave. 'I wasn't bloody hungry anyway.'

'PRIVATE GILCHRIST!' Ingham's face is turning crimson and his voice is rising to a pinched squeak of unconcealed anger. 'How – bloody – DARE – you? Townend? SERGEANT TOWNEND!'

'Sir?'

'Put that man on a charge, will you? Right away.'

'Really, sir?'

'Yes, really, Sergeant Townend.'

'On what grounds, sir?'

'Insubordination, Sergeant. Gross – bloody – insubordination. I've had just about enough . . .'

Townend leans in close to the officer's ear. 'Do you really think that's a good idea, sir?' he whispers. 'What with the colonel due at any moment?'

'Discipline, Sergeant Townend, is to be maintained at all costs. This is still the Army, after all. I'm sure the colonel . . .'

'Yes, sir, but . . .'

'And although there might no longer be a war on we must . . .'

'Pardon me, sir, but we can't really afford to lose any more men, can we? We're hopelessly below strength as it is, sir. The coolies have either killed themselves or gone on strike, and if we lose another man we're in trouble, sir. Even if he only gets twenty-four hours, sir. That's a day lost.'

'Well, yes, I suppose . . .'

'And there's hardly enough of us out here to do the job as it is, sir. And then the visitors from England is arriving all the time. And the state of some of the cemeteries, you've said it yourself, sir, well . . .'

'I see your point, Sergeant.'

'And, sir, Gilchrist, sir – whatever his faults, he ain't no slacker, sir. In fact, he's a bloody hard worker. Second only to Patterson, I reckon, in the soil-shifting department. And he don't mind getting his hands dirty either, grubbing about in all them dirty, smelly bodies rummaging for the cold meat tickets. They reckon it's 'cos he's got no sense of smell, sir. Did you know he hasn't got no sense of smell?'

'You've made your point, Sergeant.'

'Yes, sir.'

'Very well then. I may overlook the matter on this occasion. But, Sergeant?'

'Yes, sir?'

'Remind the men in this platoon that in future they are to address an officer only when either yourself or another NCO is present.'

'Another NCO, sir?' Townend scratches his head as Ingham walks away. 'We haven't got another NCO!'

Colonel Goodland, a Canadian working for the Imperial War Graves Commission, is based at Longuenesse just outside St Omer, over the border in France. The eighteenth-century château, together with the remains of the military hospital, has served as HQ for the Graves Directorate and its civilian opposite number, the War Graves Commission, since the unit absorbed the Red Cross drawing office and moved from the forests of Hesdin in early 1919.

'So what is it that your men want?' the colonel asks over supper later that same evening. 'Apart from more money.'

'And women,' Ingham adds with a grin. Major Rennard glares, his red face glistening in the candlelight.

'I'm afraid the Commission can't do anything about that, Captain. It's not like the army with its *maisons tolérées*.'

'It's second lieutenant actually, Colonel.'

Goodland nods. 'I should've known.'

'Well no, sir, of course, sir. I wasn't suggesting . . .' Ingham stammers, looking round the table.

Captain Harris comes to Ingham's rescue. 'It's merely another of the comforts of home that helps keep the men happy,' he says.

The colonel smiles. 'You have a good team here, Major Rennard,' he gestures to Harris. 'I know the Graves Registration Unit that you're working with has been impressed.'

'That is credit, I suppose, to the work of Lieutenant Ingham and his clowns with spades and mattocks,' Rennard reluctantly concedes. 'Not proper soldiering, of course, all that digging. They're sending some Labour Corps chaps over shortly and I was hoping . . .'

'Hoping, Major Rennard?'

'Well, I was wondering, perhaps, whether this lot . . .' He waves a hand towards Ingham. 'Whether they might be rebadged. You know, absorbed into the Labour Company.'

'Leave the regiment, sir?' gasps Ingham.

'War's over, Ingham. No point in pretending to be soldiers

any more. And your men, well . . . they're good at what they do, of course, but—'

'My men are the best,' says Ingham proudly. 'Work like niggers, they do, sir, with ne'er a shirker among 'em.'

'Yes, quite.'

'Private Patterson is one of the best diggers in Flanders, sir, and there's a capital chap we've been sent from the Australian Expeditionary Force who is second to none in terms of, er, well . . . getting his hands dirty.'

'Getting his hands dirty?'

'He, er . . . he's the best man we've got for finding traces of a chap's identity.'

'I see.'

'And there are others, too. Young Fuller. Skerritt – quiet chap, rather badly injured at Arras – and MacIntyre – MacIntyre was at Mons, sir!'

'That's good to know.' Goodland nods and turns back to the CO. 'I'll be frank with you, Major Rennard. We're going to need some of your men when it comes to the Army packing up and going home and the Commission taking over responsibility for the war cemeteries. That's why I'm here.'

'Can't you get the men from Blighty? Plenty of men at home without a job, so I hear.'

'Yes, but there simply isn't the appetite for it back home. The Army Directorate of Graves Registration and Enquiries has barely five hundred men to call on at present. Even if they all stayed on after demob we wouldn't have enough. There are still over one hundred thousand isolated graves to find and men to rebury. It's an enormous task.'

'Couldn't we employ some local labour?' Captain Harris suggests.

'Not practical,' says Goodland. 'They've tried in France but the French can't even find men for their own reconstruction work. I'm sure the same would apply here in Belgium.'

'Quite,' says Ingham. 'And civilian labour from England?'

'They're doing what they can, but there's a lot of opposition from farmers who are still short of agricultural men. Then there are building yards, factories, the railways. The Army has begun re-enlisting men but it's a slow process. And meanwhile—'

'Meanwhile visitors are arriving in ever larger numbers keen to pay their respects at the graves of their loved ones.'

'Spot on, Ingham,' he says, turning to the CO. 'Fine brandy, by the way.'

'Thank you, sir,' says Rennard. 'Courtesy of Ingham here, actually. He's our mess orderly.'

'Really?'

'An 1899 Hermitage Réaux.'

'My word.' Goodland raises his eyebrows. 'And where did you manage to get hold of a bottle of that?'

'Lieutenant Ingham has his sources.' Rennard taps the side of his nose.

'Well, I'd better not ask too many questions I suppose.' Goodland takes another sip. The men sit in silence for a while. The candles in the officers' mess flicker in the growing darkness. The camp is quiet now. Sentries have been posted and the remaining men stood down for the night. And as soon as they're off duty most of the men can be found heading straight for the town like a group of energetic children freed from school. The quartermaster and Colonel Goodland's driver are playing cards under an oil lamp in a tent. An owl hoots in the darkness.

'You know, Colonel.' Ingham swirls the clear brown liquid round the bowl of his brandy glass as cigars are passed round. 'I sometimes wonder . . .'

'You do?'

'I sometimes wonder if it wouldn't be a whole lot easier to ship all the bodies that we're finding back to Blighty. It's what so many of the relatives want, after all.'

Goodland trims the end of his cigar, then leans towards the candle in the middle of the table, puffing the tobacco into life. 'I'm sure I don't need to remind you of the Adjutant-General's decree from April 1915, do I, Ingham?'

'Of course not.' Rennard looks defiantly across the table, but Ingham refuses to catch his eye.

'A wartime expedient, no doubt. Initiated on practical, no doubt, as well as hygiene grounds.'

'But one still very much in force,' Rennard glares.

'Of course, sir,' Ingham smiles.

'That's the way it is, Ingham. That's the way it is to be.'

'So the Commission believes that all men, irrespective of rank, are to be buried in the common cemeteries regardless of . . . family wishes?'

'That's right, Lieutenant,' Goodland says. 'The view of the Army Graves Directorate and the Imperial War Graves Commission is as one on the matter. Every man who laid down his life for King and Country is to be treated equally.'

'But we're not, though – are we, sir?' Ingham is puffing through billowing clouds of tobacco smoke. 'We're not equal with the men. Therefore how could we possibly be treated equally?'

'Equal in sacrifice, Lieutenant, equal in sacrifice. That's the abiding message of the Commission. That's what we stand for. These boys all made the same sacrifice; death is no different whether you're an officer or a soldier in the ranks.'

'Yes, of course, but—'

'That's the way they're going to do things. And that's the way most of the men we bury would have wanted it.'

'But what about the families? What about the widows, orphans . . . grieving parents? What about what they want? There are families, Colonel Goodland – Canadian families, I need hardly remind you – who by dint of geography will in all probability never have a grave to visit or a stone at which to lay some flowers. Your countrymen and women, Colonel Goodland!'

'So what is it you're suggesting, Ingham?' Major Rennard turns back, having had half an ear on the conversation while discussing the state of the horses with the veterinary MO. 'That we go round digging men up and shipping them back home if someone in the family can afford to pay? Do you want to leave great gaps in the graveyards where those with money and influence have been able to secure the exhumation of a body?'

'If it means laying a man to rest in the bosom of his family . . .'

'These men ARE his family, Ingham, dammit!' The CO splutters as he relights his cigar.

'In war' – Goodland leans across the table – 'a man's family is his regiment, his battalion, company, platoon. You ask these fellows and most of them would have said the same – if I die, I want to be buried with my men on the line I gave my life to defend. Don't send me home; this is my home.'

'Some corner of a foreign field, eh?' adds Ingham. 'That's rather a romantic notion if you ask me.'

'Romantic or not, Ingham, those are our orders.' The CO wipes his mouth on his napkin.

'I am aware,' Goodland adds, 'that certain . . . approaches have been made. Some families back home, people of wealth and influence . . .' He stops and looks at Ingham for a moment. The Mess falls silent. Ingham swills the remaining brandy round his glass.

'Of course . . .' Ingham starts, but then thinks better of replying.

'Of course?'

'Of course those orders weren't always strictly adhered to, sir, were they?'

'If you're referring to Lieutenant Gladstone of the Royal Welch Fusiliers, Ingham—'

'One of many.' Ingham stares into his glass.

'One of a few, a very small number to have been—'

'Captain John Liddell V.C.,' Ingham interrupts. 'Lieutenant Alan Leggett, Lieutenant Vernon James Austin . . .'

'As I said, a *small* number of men, early in the war, to have been returned home at the request of relatives.'

'Exactly, sir – home, to the land that bore them. And to the bosom of their families.'

An orderly stokes the brazier, sending fresh gouts of smoke into the hut. A late train hisses in the railway sidings.

'There really isn't any more to say on the matter,' Goodland says at last. 'This isn't some socialist plot to nationalise the dead, you know.'

'No, sir. Nor would it appear a gracious concession to the solemn entreaties of King Priam, either.'

Goodland frowns. The CO clears his throat then suddenly rises to his feet. 'Gentlemen.' He lifts his glass. Chairs scrape as officers stand as one to raise their glasses in response. 'The King!'

5

Beside the old Ypres–Roulers railway, south of St Julien, the shattered relic of a copse called Wild Wood contains the remains of seventeen men killed in battle and buried hurriedly among the blackened stumps of trees. Over a year and a half later, little has changed. The splintered wood is still the only feature on an otherwise empty, bombed-out landscape. The Poelcapelle road fades to earth like a scar.

'Some men of the Tenth Battalion Gordon Highlanders are buried' – Ingham pauses before jabbing his forefinger at a square on the map that indicates their ultimate destination. 'Here!'

The men lean over the bonnet of the truck. The Albion is parked on the cobbles in the middle of the old Grote Markt. Behind them are the surviving walls of the old Cloth Hall and the rubble of St Martin's Cathedral. Pillars and doorways are shored with timber buttresses; wooden scaffolding surrounds the remnants of the bell tower; grass grows from the tops of walls.

'So it's just a simple exhumation job this morning, eh, sir?' Ocker says. 'Dig 'em up and bring 'em home.'

'That's right.' Ingham nods before correcting himself.

'Actually, no – not "home", Private Gilchrist. None of these men are going home.'

'No, sir.' Ocker picks dirt from underneath his fingernails. 'A bit like us.'

'According to our information' – Ingham smooths the map again – 'the men were killed during the initial phase of the advance to Pilkem Ridge and were buried here—'

'—on July 31st 1917,' Mac interrupts. 'Aye, I know.' The rest of the men slowly turn their heads.

'Correct, Private MacIntyre.' Ingham fakes a smile. 'Of course, I should have realised.'

'Realised what?' Fuller whispers. 'Realised what?'

Ocker shakes his head and holds a finger to his lips.

'Anyway,' Ingham carries on. 'These men – these *brave* men – are to be transferred to White House Cemetery at St Jean. Graves have already been prepared for them in the concentration area – Plot Three. It's a little higher than the battlefield burials, so it should be better drained.'

'Which row, sir?'

'Which row? Now let me see, Row . . . Row . . . Row H. Yes.'

'And are they "known", sir?'

'I believe so, yes. Their details were recorded at the time by the battlefield burial party . . .' Ingham looks across the bonnet of the truck. Mac is carefully filling his pipe. 'And the graves have survived reasonably unscathed. Sergeant Townend and I located them while on reconnaissance the other day.'

'Very good, sir.'

The men dismiss and begin gathering their equipment: sacks and shovels, petrol cans filled with cresol, seventeen canvas sheets, some ropes and stretchers, several pairs of rubber gloves. This is the kind of work they like: simple, clean, straightforward. Map references; digging, then reburying. Not the searching, not the wandering, not the constant prodding with probes improvised from old machine-gun cleaning rods, not the constant emptying of muddy pockets, rubbing filthy teeth to inspect for fillings and extractions.

'Sergeant Townend?'

'Yessir!'

'You will supervise the exhumation. I will meet you at White House Cemetery at 1430 hours with the chaplain.'

'Very good, sir.'

The men climb aboard the truck. Jack and Ocker load their bicycles on board, standing them between the wooden shelves that line each side of the wagon. There won't be room on the return trip for all the living and the dead.

'So, what was it like, Mac?' asks Fuller as the truck bounces off along the cobbles. 'Was it . . . did you? I mean . . .'

'I know what you darn well mean, laddie,' Mac growls. 'And well, I'll tell ye shall I? Shall I? D'you really want to know?'

Fuller suddenly doesn't seem so sure. But it is too late now.

'For once,' Mac shuts his eyes, 'on the morning of July the thirty-first, you might just have said things were going quite well. The bombardment had been good—'

'That makes a change,' chips in Ocker.

'The weather was dry too, that first morning—'

'Aye, but that was soon to change,' says Jack.

'Who's telling this story?' Mac glares.

'Sorry, Mac.'

'Aye, well. As I was saying, things started pretty well. We'd set off from Cambridge Road towards the Blue Line – we were just north of the railway – it was a misty old morning as I remember, and that did us no harm. These fellas . . .' He jerks a thumb in Jack's direction. 'The Yorkies – well, they were on our left flank and on our right . . . oh, my, on our right – the

48

Ninth Black Watch, the Argyll and Sutherland Highlanders, the King's Own Scottish Borderers, Scottish Rifles – the flower of Scotland.'

'The "Yorkies"?' Fuller shrugs.

'West Yorks Regiment,' Jack says.

'So you was there as well?' He turns to Jack.

'Not personally,' says Jack. 'Second Battalion. Regulars, like Uncle Mac here.'

'Good soldiers,' Mac says. 'In front of our own lines, too. At Birr Cross Roads, between Railway Wood and Zouave Wood. Not that we could tell where they were. Or where we were, for that matter.

'Why not, Mac?'

'Och, man,' Mac shakes his head. 'The guns blasted just about every last feature from the landscape. The maps might as well have been some fantasy world for all their likeness to reality. Dakar Farm – not even a ruin; Verlorenhoek – no more a village than a brick-stained puddle in the mud. Our guns had rubbed out the lot and blown the tops off the trees and torn the branches from the trunks and split whatever was left down the middle.'

'Blimey!'

'Aye, son. And there were times I wished that "He" had done just that.'

The rumble of the Austin motor rises from beneath their feet, filling the silence between each new reminiscence.

'So you was all attacking? This was the big 'un?'

'Heck, no,' Jack laughs. 'This was just the . . . *hors d'oeuvre* as they'd say round here.'

'The or – what?'

'Starters, lad. This was just the prelude, the first act, the warm-up. This wasn't "it". This wasn't top of t'bill. This was what you did first, in order to be in with a chance to go for the big 'un later on,' Jack says. 'If you was lucky,' he adds, quietly. 'Or unlucky.'

'The trials, mate,' says Ocker, looking up. 'To see if they'd make the first eleven.'

'We were all supposed to leapfrog from one objective to another,' Mac continues. 'First, the blue line – that was Fritz's front-line trenches – then, the black line . . .'

'The Albrecht-Stellung.'

'Aye, and then on beyond their third line of defences to the green line.'

'It was a grand plan,' Jack says.

'Oh, it was that all right,' Mac nods. 'Daddy Plum at his very best. Do you remember those great big relief maps he'd had made of the ridge?'

'No, Mac, that wasn't this time,' Jack says. 'That was later.'

'Was it?'

'Aye, much later. That was after old Gough had been sacked.'

'Sacked, was he?'

'Probably when the butcher's bill got too big,' Ocker adds. 'Even for him.'

'Aye, well . . .' Mac's voice trails off. Gears grind as the truck slows behind a farm cart, then accelerates again to overtake. Tyres swish through puddles and the truck steers sharply round surviving shell-holes.

'So it didn't go too well then?' Fuller asks.

'It was hailed as a great success,' Mac says. 'If you call jumping off at ten minutes to four in the morning in the dark with the dawn barely visible into a hail of machine-gun bullets a success.'

'Hadn't the artillery barrage destroyed them all?'

'Oh aye, laddie – of course it had! And there was dancing to the bagpipes as we skipped across.'

'To be fair, Mac, they'd done a pretty good job that time.'

'Well, I suppose . . .'

'But you can hardly blow up everything . . .'

The truck's exhaust backfires suddenly and the men lurch forwards then recoil back, bumping into one another. Skerritt, having tumbled from the bench, is frantically wrestling Jack's heavy bike back upright.

'Language please, Private Skerritt! There are ladies present.'

'Where?' Fuller looks round quickly.

'Right here,' says Ocker, grabbing Fuller's head and planting a loud smacking kiss on his left ear.

'You bloody barmy sod . . . you nearly deafened me.'

'Come on, lad.' Jack lifts the big black bicycle and helps Skerritt back to his feet. 'You're fine, lad. No harm done.'

'Hey, that was right on bloody cue, that bang,' laughs Ocker. 'Pity your guns couldn't get their timing right a little later, in September, when you had us lot taking Polygon Wood.'

The truck rumbles on along the Menin Road. Seen through half-closed eyes, the open tailgate of the wagon looks strangely like a stage: loose canvas curtains at the sides, a hooped pro-scenium arch framing a cinematic reel of black-and-white film running backwards. Ypres retreats into the distance; sunlight flares briefly on a tangled remnant of the pre-war tramlines by the roadside; black stumps of trees rear out of nowhere like the remnants of some shattered regiment before slowly retreating back into the distance; a flash of white dazzles as the bleached bones of a dead horse catch the sun. And like road-side markers, the skeletal remains of gun limbers, water carts, supply wagons and camouflage screening pass before the eye has time to notice.

For a long time no one says a word. The only sound above the engine noise is Skerritt, still moaning quietly in the corner with his hand over what remains of his mouth. Soon afterwards, the truck pulls off the road and the engine shudders to a standstill.

'Right, you lot!' Sergeant Townend calls out from the front. 'We're here. Journey's end. Come on – shake a leg.'

'Want to sit this one out?' Jack puts his hand on Mac's shoulder. 'We can manage, you know.' The others are already jumping down from the truck and unloading the tools.

Mac turns and looks at Jack in silence for a moment. 'Not on your life, son,' he says quietly. 'Not on your life.'

The tallest things remaining in Wild Wood are the rough crosses marking out the men's graves. The ground is wet and marked with puddles but the graves are relatively unscathed. Even the great tidal wave of the German spring offensive in the year following this forgotten, futile forward movement seems to have had little impact on this tiny corner of a foreign field.

'Right, let's get on with it then,' Mac says, taking a shovel and striding purposefully towards the farthest grave. 'Spread out that tarpaulin here,' he calls to Fuller. 'The rest of ye – get digging.'

The graves aren't deep. None of these hasty battlefield burials ever are. Unless men were laid to rest in an old trench or a recent shell-hole, battlefield graves are as shallow as decency – and enemy gunfire – will allow.

But the men dig carefully, each shovelful of earth releasing the now familiar wet scent of cordite and decay. The first of the bodies lifts easily, the remains of a waterproof groundsheet holding the bones together. Skerritt has been silently sprinkling cresol over each of the canvas shrouds and uncoiling the ropes. As each of the remaining bodies is exhumed, the remains are carefully laid out for inspection.

'You know' – Jack straightens up, wiping a filthy hand across his brow – 'I sometimes reckon these lads'd be better off staying put.'

'What? And do us out of a job?' Ocker looks up from the black remains of the ID bracelet he's examining.

'There's too many of these tiny battlefield cemeteries,' Townend says. 'And your friends' – he turns to Jack – 'they want their country back.'

Scattered randomly across the Salient, cemeteries like these prove no more than temporary resting places. Some effort at concentration and consolidation is essential. Belgian farmers need to put the soil to use. The returning population needs feeding. Fields have to be cleared, roads restored, and the bodies tidied away to cleanse the stench of war that rises out of the poisoned fields with the water. The living matter more now than the dead.

'Anyway,' Mac says, 'the lads deserve better than this.'

Shortly before midday the last corpse is lifted. Townend records the particulars in the large, leather-bound ledger, examines the identity disc and satisfies himself that this wet, black mix of soil and what was once a man is who it is supposed to be. Or was.

Standing staring at the slimy, blackened carcasses, one by one the men remove their caps. Ocker crosses himself casually, peels the rubber gloves from his hands, then quickly lights a cigarette. The noise of the match striking the side of his box is the loudest sound for miles around.

'You were asking what it was like?' Mac turns to Fuller. The boy can feel hot tears pricking at the corners of his eyes.

'Well, son . . . now you know.'

6

At the British Tavern near the railway station in Ypres, Jack and the others are busy singing, drinking, laughing, forgetting. The unexpected personal links to Wild Wood have made them more aware than usual of what they're doing – as well as who it is they might be lifting and reburying. Such an awareness, as always, takes several hours – and a great many more pints – to erase.

> *If the sergeant drinks your rum, never mind.*
> *If he kicks you up the bum, never mind.*
> *He's entitled to a tot, but not the bleeding lot.*
> *If the sergeant drinks your rum, never mind.*

Applause marks the end of each verse as the few locals sitting huddled at the tiny round tables nursing their *petit blancs* or swirling chipped tumblers of rosé eagerly anticipate the end of each song. But most of the time the men sing on, adding new verses and getting louder all the time.

> *When this lousy war is over, no more soldiering*
> *   for me,*
> *When I get my civvy clothes on, oh how happy I*
> *   shall be.*

No more church parades on Sunday, no more begging
  for a pass.
You can tell the sergeant-major to stick his passes up
  his arse.

The more they drink, the more inventive they become. The more explicit too. But as the evening wears on and the strong Belgian beer begins to take effect, the men's repertoire dwindles to the few familiar, oft-repeated marching songs, songs that echo to the tread of boots, songs that send a sharp reminder of the blisters burning holes in the soles of your feet and songs that can still make you feel the cold trickle of rain dripping down your neck.

> *It's a long way . . .* tramp!
> *to Tipperary . . .* tramp!
> *It's a long way . . .* tramp!
> *to go . . .* tramp! tramp!
> *It's a long way . . .* tramp!
> *to Tipperary . . .* tramp!
> *to the sweetest girl I know . . .* tramp! tramp!
>   tramp!
> *Good-bye . . .* tramp! *Piccadilly . . .* tramp!
>   tramp!
> *Fare-well, Leicester Square . . .* tramp! tramp!
> *It's a long, long way to Tipperary,*
> *But my heart . . .* tramp!
> *Lies there . . .* tramp! tramp!

'You know,' Jack shouts above the din, 'I never really liked that bloody song. Where the bloody hell is Tipperary anyway?'
'It's in Ireland, Jacko, you peasant.'

55

'So nowhere near t'bloody fighting then?'

'Aye well.' Mac leans across the table. 'That's where we all thought it was going to be.'

'Thought it was where what were going to be?'

'The fighting, laddie.'

'Oh, aye?'

'I was garrisoned there myself for a time. If there was going to be trouble, it was going to be Ireland. That's what they'd all told us.'

'Yeah,' Fuller slurs, 'and Ireland kept its fackin' . . . English g-g-garrisons too, didn't it? Full o' regulars like Mac here, while the likes of us . . .' He burps, and wipes his wet lips across his tunic sleeve. 'The likes of us gets posted to the battle-field whether we likes it or not.'

'Aye, lad. Turning ploughshares into Lee Enfields, eh?'

'Ha! Ploughshares to Lee Enfields. Ha. I like it, Jack. I like that . . . what is a ploughshare anyhow? Ingham was going on about ploughshares the other days. Shw— shwer, - swords! Yeah, that's it! Swords into . . .'

'Bloody hell!'

'The Irish fought too, y'know, laddie. Enlisted, many of them, unlike some here that I could mention.' Mac raises his eyebrows.

'What's that supposed to mean?' Fuller tries to sit a little taller in his seat.

'Ah, ye know well enough.'

'Personally' – Jack glances at Mac and tries to change the subject – 'personally I preferred "Goodbye-ee", me. Aye, that were my favourite.'

'But it ain't though, Jacko. Is it?'

'Isn't what, lad?'

'It ain't *goodbye-ee*. Not for us, anyway. We're still stuck 'ere, ain't we?'

Fuller has by now draped a heavy, sweaty arm across Jack's shoulders in an effort to stay on his seat. He is shouting above the noise of the bar directly into Jack's left ear. 'You'd think the coolies could have done this, Jacko, wouldn't you? You'd think the Chinks could've dug these graves and buried these fackin' corpses. Not us.'

Jack smiles, wipes his ear and sucks hard on his cigarette.

'I mean, that's what they was brought here for – to dig; to fetch and carry; bury. But not us. We're soldiers, Jack, you and me. We're fighting men we is, fighting men, ain't we – fighting for the King and fighting for our country?'

'Oh my God, come on, lad, let's get you home.'

'No no no, Jack. No. I'm fine. Honest. Hon—'

'Ocker. OCKER!'

'What is it, mate?'

'Come over here, will yer? Help me get Fuller back to camp. He's gone. Look at 'im.'

Ocker slides his hands underneath Fuller's arms and lifts him back to his feet. The two men then take an arm each and wrap it round their necks and slowly drag the lifeless body out through the door of the bar.

'Don't mind us,' Jack calls to Katia. She looks at the mess on the floor, then glowers at Jack. 'Sorry, love.'

Outside, the night is dark and the air is damp.

'Give over, man – we can't put him on his bike.'

Ocker is leaning the boy against a wall and trying to lift one of his legs over the crossbar. 'Then how the heck are we supposed to get him back?'

'I don't know,' says Jack. 'We'll have to walk it, I suppose.'

'It's bloody miles, Jacko. It'll take hours. And by the time we get back here your ol' lady will have shut up shop.'

'My ol' – what?'

'Come on, Jacko. We all know you'll soon have your feet tucked under Monsieur Steenvan's family table. And your todger—'

'Thanks, Ocker, I think we get the picture. What I meant was that I'm sure she'll—'

'I'm sure she will for you, mate. Anything for *Monsieur Jacques!*'

The strains of another song drift out from the bar on the still evening air:

In our little wet home in the trench
That the rainstorms continually drench
There's a dead cow nearby with its hooves in the sky
And it gives off a terrible stench.

'Ah, Christ Jesus! We're missing a good 'un this evening thanks to this bleedin' bum brusher,' grumbles Ocker.

'Aye, well,' says Jack. 'It's not as if we haven't heard 'em all before.'

'Invented some of 'em.' The two men laugh. Meanwhile, on the cobbled pavement, Fuller stirs.

'Come on, yer bastard, on yer feet. I'm not carrying you home.' Fuller turns away again and is sick. 'Happen we'll just leave him for a bit to sober up,' says Jack.

Ocker crouches down and slapping Fuller gently on the cheek, starts crooning in his ear:

Bon soir old thing!
Cheer-i-o chin chin

Na-poo, toodle-oo
Good-bye-ee.

'Come on, Ocker lad, let's have another.'

'You're on,' says Ocker. 'Hey listen, Jacko,' he says as the two men push their way back into the bar, 'they're singing your song!'

> *Oh landlord you've a daughter fair, parlez-vous?*
> *Oh landlord you've a daughter fair, parlez-vous?*
> *Oh landlord you've a daughter fair,*
> *With lily white tits and golden hair,*
> *Hinkey, dinkey, parlez-vous . . .*

Jack pushes his way back to the counter. 'Sorry, lass,' he says to Katia as the men start on verse three.

> *Nein, nein mein Herr she's much too young,*
>   *parlez-vous?*
> *Nein, nein mein Herr she's much too young,*
>   *parlez-vous?*
> *Mais non, mon père, I'm not too young,*
> *I've just been fucked by the butcher's son.*
> *Hinkey, dinkey parlez-vous.*

'I don't mind,' the woman smiles, refilling the men's mugs. 'It is only . . . fun, yes? It is a bit of fun. The men like to have their bit of fun.'

'Nay, lass, I didn't mean t'singing,' Jack says, nodding his head in the direction of a fresh pile of sawdust in the middle of the floor. 'I meant that young 'un being unable to hold his beer.'

'*Ah, oui*. That is not fun, Jacques, you are right. That is not so much a bit of fun.'

'Good for business, though. Well, not that exactly but . . . well, you know what I mean.'

Jack can tell she isn't angry. Not with him, anyway. And the men are good for business, even if some of them like Fuller still can't hold this foreign beer. But what the hell, Jack thinks. He makes sure the bar is always busy. The British Tavern does a brisk trade from Number One Auxiliary Labour Company. And there is always a welcome here for the men, and an especially warm one for him.

'Will I see you?' he asks her. 'Later on?'

'I don't know, Jacques,' she says. 'My father—'

'The ol' bastard.'

'Jacques!'

'Sorry, love.'

'He is just . . . protective of me,' says Katia. 'He wants what is best for his daughters. That is all. You would understand, Jacques. You would understand if you too had a daughter.'

Jack stops and stares at her for a moment. 'Who's to say I haven't?'

She smiles, then looks down at the jug she's holding. 'You are too young I think to have daughter, Jacques.'

'You reckon?' he winks. 'Might've started young for all you know.'

'You will be telling me you are old enough to be my father next.'

'Nay, lass. Although yer little sister . . . reckon I could easily have been her father.'

'You are teasing me, Jacques. Stop.'

'How old is she anyhow?'

'Françoise is just a girl. She is only . . . *treize ans.*'

'*Dix, onze, douze* . . . Thirteen!'

'*Oui*, she is thirteen. And so to be her father you would have to be at, er . . . *un moment.*'

'Well, let's drop it, then, eh, love? Anyway, I'm no cradle snatcher. It's you I'm after.'

'After?'

'You know what I mean, lass. So – later?'

'Maybe,' she smiles. Jack watches closely as she turns to serve another customer. The flickering light of candles dances in the dark brown of her eyes, fringed with the few stray strands that have escaped the heaped, pinned loaf of auburn hair she has hurriedly piled on her head. Her mouth is open slightly, lips parted as if on the verge of speaking, but the only words he wants to hear remain unspoken. Her pale white cheeks are flushed with the heat of the bar and the heavy work she has been doing.

'I'm not taking no for an answer,' he tells her when she finally turns to face him. 'I saw t'way you were looking at that chap you was serving just now.'

'You are jealous, Jacques.' She looks back at the customer a little farther up the bar. 'That man – he really *is* old enough I think to be *mon père*,' she laughs.

'Bit like that fat bloke who was trying to kiss you the other week. Where is he tonight, anyhow?'

'Who?'

'Ol' fatso.'

'You mean Monsieur de Wulf?'

'If you say so.'

'The man you . . . how is it said?'

'The man we taught a lesson, aye. In manners.'

'You should not have done that, Jacques.'

61

'He had hold of you. He was hurting you. And he spilt our beer.'

'He is an important man,' she looks down at her feet. 'And a . . . *de valeur* – he is a valued customer.'

'Well, he'd better not try anything like that again, that's all I'm saying.'

'Ah, *mon chevalier!*' She clasps her hands together, fluttering her eyelashes.

'Hardly in shining armour though, eh, love?' Jack looks down at his mud-stained tunic.

'I don't mind.' The smile returns.

'Anyway, you never did tell me where he is this evening.'

'Monsieur de Wulf? He is meeting your captain, I think. He is speaking to him about some of the land clearance. I think that is what he said he was doing.'

'Aye,' Jack grumbles. 'Wanting to get us to do some work for him for nowt, I'll bet.'

'Nowt?'

'For nothing. Something for nothing. Isn't that what de Wulf does best? Getting everyone else to do t'grafting for him while he sits on his fat arse and counts the money!'

'Not joining us tonight then, Jacko?'

'View better over there, is it, mate?'

'Smell is, certainly!'

Jack turns. 'Just coming, lads,' he calls over, before quickly turning back to Katia. 'Hey, lass,' he beckons her closer. 'I've got something for you. Message for ol' fatso next time you see him. And for your father, an' all.' He leans across the bar, takes her head in his hands and pulls her towards him, kissing her lips, hard.

'Whoooooooaaaaaaa!' A huge roar goes up from the men.

62

Katia pulls away, looks down at the floor and smooths her hands down her apron, blushing furiously.

'Blimey, Skerritt, mate, you'd be picking your jaw off the floor by now,' Ocker says, 'if you had one. Ain't you ever seen a sheila getting kissed before?'

'Put the wee lassie down will you, yer great oaf?' Mac shakes his head as Jack takes his seat with the men.

'But I wouldn't put her down for long if I was you, mate,' Ocker chips in.

'Oh, I don't intend to,' Jacks says quietly. 'I don't intend to.' He takes a long drink from his mug and then realises, with a sudden shock, that the taste of her lips and the gentle, lavender fragrance of her skin, the soft touch of her smooth cheek and the warm sensation of her firm hand on his arm, have vanished.

'Damn!'

War Diary or Intelligence Summary: Army form C. 2118
1919

DIVISION MAIN DRESSING STATION—Remy Siding
Map Sheet 28; Grid reference: L.22 d.6.3

May 4th – Ceremonial drill; programme of educational classes under supervision of Capt. J.K. HARRIS resumed today with book-keeping and commercial subjects added to arithmetic, reading and writing and Empire history.

May 8th – Draft of 1 officer and 6 Other Ranks proceeded to Town Hall, Poperinghe, as firing squad for execution of 44735 Wang Jung Zhi, 107th Chinese Labour Company.

May 11th – Capt. S.F. KEIGHTLEY M.C., 2/Lt. N. GRAINGER and 40 O.R.s left Battalion for duty with No. 6 Prisoner of War Company ETAPLES.

May 12th – C.O. inspected billets. Exhumations east of the Ypres-Roulers railway completed.

May 14th – Draft of 3 Officers and 47 Other Ranks (for Rhine) proceeded to Calais to join 10th Suffolk Regiment, 61st Division.

May 16th – Salvage work undertaken in Wood N.36.a., M.35b and adjacent battery positions. Captain E.R. WINNICK gave a lecture in the Salvation Army hut entitled 'An Approach to Peace'.

May 18th – Further salvage work carried out, same location as on 15th inst. Parades held under Coy Commanders.

May 21st – Capt. ARMSTRONG, Lt. WILLIAMS, 2/Lt. LEWIS and 26 O.R.s left Battalion for demobilisation.

May 23rd – Battalion reorganised into two Companies (Nos 1 & 2), No. 1 being composed of men for the Post Bellum Army or Army of Occupation, No. 2 consisting of all others except those under the control of Transport Officer and Quartermaster and those attached to Graves Registration Unit.

May 26th – Battalion Auxiliary Labour Coy (G.R.U.) to proceed north to ref: map BELGIUM 2.L. 1/100,000 in accordance with Army Orders 137 (below).

ARMY ORDER No. 137

The 1st Aux. Labour Coy will relieve the 19th G.R.U. exhumation unit in the Ypres salient, sub-section Y on the 28th inst.

Sick parade on 28th inst. will be brought forward and take place at 0615 to allow for any members of clearance party to attend if necessary.

Breakfast will be served at 0630.

Coy to form up in one column before Battalion Orderly Room (Hut 7) at 0700 hours.

Stores and equipment will be loaded onto vehicles at 0705 hours on 28th inst. Coy transport unit consisting of 1 Mobile Field Ambulance, 1 Motorised Stores Wagon and 1 troop transport vehicle.

Dress will be fighting order. Leather jerkins will be worn. Shovels to be slung over right shoulder. Each man to carry canteen in canteen cover properly fastened to haversack.

7

Almost imperceptibly, by early May, spring has arrived – the first since the end of the war. Birds begin to sing; the few remaining trees and shrubs and bushes shimmer in a pale green halo of new growth. And as winter and war give way, the Flanders mud becomes a little drier – at least on the surface.

'Still hitting water though,' Jack says when the men assemble that morning to receive their orders. 'Only got to dig a few feet and it's sodden.'

'All that rain's got to go somewhere, Jacko!'

'Aye, well, I'd just as soon it didn't have to go in my boots.'

With longer days and warmer weather the earth appears to breathe again once more. Grass begins to grow in fields and tiny wild flowers – calendula, oxlip, violet – begin to dot the barren landscape like a galaxy of stars.

'Right, men,' Ingham briefs the platoon. 'We're covering several adjacent squares north of Ypres from now on – map sheets twenty-nine and thirty.'

'Is it searches, sir?' Jack asks.

'Searches mainly, yes, but some cemetery concentrations too.' Ingham checks the typed orders. 'And so to reduce time wasted in travel we'll be taking the tents and the mobile kitchen and staying in the field for a few days. The weather is set fair this week, so I'm told.'

Jack sighs, much louder than he had intended.

'Apologies, Private Patterson, if that interferes with your nascent romantic enterprises.'

'No, sir, it's just that . . .' Jack stops short and looks down at his boots.

'It's just that it does,' Ocker says. 'Interfere with his love life, that is.'

'Mind you,' adds Mac, 'all that cycling to and from Ypres each evening is giving the laddie devilishly strong thighs, isn't that so, Jack?'

'Hmmm, really, really?' Ingham is nodding.

'Give o'er,' Jack says, swatting Mac's hand away from his leg like a fly.

'Aye, sir. D'ye reckon we can get him a transfer to the cycling corps? Only takes him half an hour you know!'

'Hmmm . . .'

'Give over, Mac, it's not the cycle ride that's given Jacko legs like a bloody buffalo, is it, *Jacques-the-lad*, eh?'

'Don't know what you're on about, yer daft bugger . . .'

'Private Patterson?'

'It's not a problem, sir,' Jack lies, aware that Ingham has started giving him an old-fashioned look.

'Jolly good,' Ingham says at last, clapping his hands. 'That's settled then. Patterson will tear himself away from the bosom of his best-beloved—'

'It's not her bosom that's the main attraction, sir!'

'Shut it, Ocker!'

'—and we will be away until . . .' Ingham consults their orders, 'until next Friday. Now, Sergeant – fall the men in and we'll get the equipment issued.'

Shortly afterwards they are on the road – not north-east, as anyone taking any notice might have been expecting, but almost due east along the gentle incline down to Vlamertinghe. 'Pardon me for asking, sir,' says Jack, 'but why are we going this way? I mean, if we're trying to save time and everything we could've just gone straight to Poelcapelle across country via Langemark rather than via Ypres. Not that I'm complaining or owt.'

'I bow to your superior local knowledge, Patterson,' Ingham says, passing the map he has been holding to Jack. 'And I'd hate to squander such a valuable resource. When we alight in Ypres you will move to the cab with the driver and myself and navigate.'

'Very good, sir.'

Ocker stifles a laugh. Townend mutters at the prospect of sitting in the back.

'Nevertheless,' Ingham goes on, 'since you ask, there does happen to be a good reason for going this way and for stopping off in Ypres.'

By now the truck is turning past the railway station and along the narrow Vooruitgangstraat towards the Rijkswachtkazerne. Ingham orders Blake to slow down, briefly, tantalisingly close to the corner of Station Straat. Jack can almost see the sign for the British Tavern swinging at the end of the street, but Ingham is looking for something – or someone – else.

'Pull in here please, Blake,' he says as the truck turns into the Grote Markt. 'Sergeant Townend?'

'Yessir?'

'Get the men down and let them stretch their legs for a minute, will you?' He stops and looks at Jack. 'But make sure no one leaves the market square! I'll be back in a couple of minutes.'

'Yes, sir.'

'Bad luck, Jacko,' one of the others mutters.

Ingham marches off across the cobbles, the studded heels of his boots sparking on the stone like a pocketful of loose change.

'Right, lads, you heard the officer. Stick close to the truck. And no funny business!'

'Surely we've time for a quick one, if we hurry?' Ocker asks.

'Not a chance,' says Townend. 'And anyway' – he looks at his watch – 'your minute's up. Now get yer arses back on board.'

'Say please!' says Ocker.

'Get up there into the back of that van before I kick your arse from here into the fuckin' engine.' Reluctantly, the men begin to make a move. 'Not you, Patterson,' Townend smirks. Jack's shoulders slump heavily and he jumps back down from the tailgate. 'You're up front with the map – remember?'

'Hey, Jacko! Don't let it go to your head, mate. Don't go all *lah-di-dah* on us.'

'He'll have a stripe by the time we get there,' Fuller jokes.

'Aye, and a medal too!'

'Give over.'

Jack walks round to the front of the truck, takes a step up onto the running board, then hauls himself into the cab. Townend is busy fiddling with the bolts on the tailgate, so, sitting on the hard wooden bench and staring absent-mindedly through the mud-splattered half-windscreen, only Jack notices the brief exchange occurring in the shadows underneath the scaffolding that shrouds the campanile. Monsieur de Wulf – greasy, corpulent, smiling like a shark – and Lieutenant Ingham are deep in conversation. Their heads briefly draw near to one other as if they are about to kiss. But de Wulf's lips aren't puckering: his mouth is moving; he is whispering in

Ingham's ear. Then, almost unnoticed, a small brown parcel changes hands and de Wulf disappears quickly through a gap in the ruins.

By now, Townend is standing at the front of the truck, waiting to crank the starter. Ingham climbs abroad and freezes momentarily as he catches Jack's eye, before settling himself alongside the driver and giving Townend the signal to start the engine. As the truck shudders into life the driver releases the huge brake-handle, two-handed like a railway signalman switching points, before grinding into gear, turning towards the market square and heading out past the cathedral and along Elverdingestraat. Not a word is spoken.

On the outskirts of the town by the Leie Kanaal, the truck passes the remains of a British Mark IV tank. At that moment Jack is looking down, studying the map, trying to decide which road is best to take. Blake knows better than to ask any awkward questions, but the men in the back of the truck can see it clearly as they pass and it retreats into the distance.

'Well, would you look at that,' laughs Ocker. 'Bloody tank corps late to the party as ever.'

'Broken down, too,' adds Mac. 'As usual.'

'That wasn't there the other day, was it?'

'Never seen it before in my life.'

'Christ knows where they've found that.'

'Or how the hell they've dragged it here,' adds Mac.

'Or why?'

'Stripping 'em for parts, ain't they?' Fuller smirks, pleased with himself for once for knowing something that the others don't. 'And then selling off the metal. And them two big howitzers they brought here all the way from Houthulst Forest.'

'Oh aye, son. And who told you that?'

'Lieutenant Ingham did,' says Fuller, forgetting he's been sworn to secrecy.

'And you want to know who moved 'em, do you?' The men stare at one another. 'Well,' Fuller smirks, 'you're looking at him.' The men all turn and look at Fuller for a moment, open-mouthed. Then suddenly, together, they are laughing uproariously. Mac is forced to get the hanky out of his tunic pocket once again and dab his eyes.

'It's true!' Fuller says indignantly. 'Me and Ingham towed 'em here from Zonnebeke behind that fat bloke and his tractor.'

'What did you say, son?'

'What the flamin' hell is that man up to?' Ocker shakes his head.

'Swords into ploughshares, that's what he kept saying. Said it was in the Bible, he did. Said that made it right, y'know. Proper.'

'Sounds proper dodgy to me,' says Ocker. 'Otherwise he'd have surely asked one of us to do it.'

'Fat chance!' says Fuller. 'He wanted me particular. Said I was the perfect man for the job.'

'I'll bet he did.' Townend shakes his head.

The truck rattles along and they sit for a while in silence. No one thinks about what they've just heard or what they've witnessed.

If you want to find the lance-jack, I know where he is,
I know where he is, I know where he is.
If you want to find the lance-jack, I know where he is,
He's . . .

Pause.

. . . scrounging round the cookhouse door.

Laughter. Then the others are joining in the chorus:

I've seen him, I've seen him,
Scrounging round the cookhouse door.
I've seen him, I've seen him,
Scrounging round the cookhouse door.

Sitting up front, Jack smiles to himself. Sitting in the back, Townend scowls. Ingham is looking down at something scribbled in his pocketbook. Blake has his eyes on the long, straight road to Roeselare.

An hour later they are there. The men disembark and go straight to work. Spring grass is growing on the gentle slopes that were in enemy hands for most of the war. A burial officer from the Graves Registration Unit has marked the area to be searched with four white flags; the map he holds has pencilled numbers crammed into each square, indicating the likely concentration of bodies. The platoon splits up and each section takes one of the small pegged-out map squares. Within that the men subdivide the ground themselves so that each soldier has an area of a hundred square yards to himself. Then, if he finds a body, the man in the nearby area stops searching and helps his neighbour with the digging.

'Could be worse, I suppose,' Mac says as the men extract another twisted corpse from the sucking mud of this bulging sector of the Salient.

'I'm not sure how,' says Jack. He is stripped to the waist. Although the April air is still cool he is sweating profusely from the effort of digging. A body, bodies, digging and bury-ing have been his business now for several months, but the effort doesn't seem to get any easier.

Mac, too, is stripped to the waist, braces dangling by his side. The older man's torso – white as the wax of a candle – ends in a vivid tidemark of sunburn round his neck. It might be the head of a different man. They both pause and pull the April air deep into their lungs, feeling the warmth of the sun on their backs and the heat of their own blood pulsing in their veins. Neither man could be any more alive than in this foul field of death, or warmer among the cold remains of extinct life they are exhuming.

'He's been underground a long time, this one. Probably since First Ypres, I reckon.'

Mac squats by the grave to take a closer look. 'Waterloo, more likely. Crikey, Jack, there's nothing left of him but bone.'

'No, hang on,' Jack says. 'Take a look at this.'

Mac winds the wire frames of his spectacles round each ear, then stares at the identity disc.

'Odd that he was, y'know . . .' Jack nods at the ground. 'Odd that he was so deep down.'

'Bloody awkward, more like.' Mac removes his spectacles.

'Aye well.' Jack swings back his arms like a battering ram then slices the spade hard beneath the corpse. 'He's been down here long enough. And he'll be going down below again before the week's out.'

'Aye, but a wee bit more dignity this time.'

'Aye – and for a darn site longer.'

'True enough. Pass the wee laddie up, will ye?' Mac opens a sandbag. 'Let's give the poor blighter a feel of the sun on his bones for the last time.'

'Until t'parson gets hold of him, eh?'

'Aye, and seals him in his little patch of Belgium until Judgment Day.'

'There's just one problem,' Jack says as he passes the first shovelful out of the hole to Mac.

'What's that?'

'Look' – Jack points to the remains of an arm, a crumpled body and a random, gloved hand. A pair of stout leather riding boots gape round the man's leg-bones like a child's oversize wellingtons.

'Summat's missing.'

'By crikey, you're right! I thought you said you'd found his ID disc?'

'Aye, I did. But it was tied round his wrist, not his neck.'

'Hey, fellas,' Ocker calls out from the neighbouring hole. 'Is this what you're looking for? Thought my bloke was a bit on the small side, even for a bantam,' he says as he passes Mac the empty skull.

'Strange,' Jack says, scratching his head. 'He doesn't seem to have copped a shell.'

'Ach, no. It's a bullet wound, laddie – will you take a look?' Mac's finger traces the outline of a jagged hole in the top of the man's cranium. 'He's shot himself. It's as clear as day.'

'SIW?'

'I wouldn't think an officer would have done that to himself,' Mac says. 'Anyway, he's blown the top of his own head clean off.'

Jack takes a closer look. 'Bloody 'ell, Mac, I think you're right.'

By now the rest of the men have gathered round the hole, helping Mac assemble the bones on the tarpaulin and speculating about what might have happened to the soldier.

'I reckon it was a minnie-whiffer did for 'im,' Fuller is saying.

'A minnie-what?'

'A minnie-whiffer.'

'Woofer! Jeez, can't even get the lingo right, this joker. And don't kick the flamin' ground like that, you mongrel, or you'll blow all our heads off the same way. There's grenades and all sorts o' stuff down there.'

'You know, I can't quite work this one out,' Jack says, ignoring the bickering between Fuller and Ocker.

'I can,' says Ocker. 'I reckon I know what's happened here.'

'Oh aye?' Mac raises an eyebrow.

'Yeah. One of our company did this once,' Ocker goes on. 'Four days without so much as a wink o' sleep and he's been put on sentry duty, hasn't he?'

'Never!' says Fuller, still unable or unwilling to believe some of the men's front-line tales.

'Yeah, mate. And that's not all. The week before we've all been lined up on parade to watch a cobber being shot dead for dozing off while he should've been on watch.'

Fuller is silent now, as are the rest of the men.

'So this bloke says to himself, that's not going to be the death of me. And he has a plan. He stands his rifle butt in front of him with the point of the bayonet under his chin.'

'What the bloody hell did he do that for?'

'So if he nods off, his chin will hit the point of his bayonet and give him a shock and wake him up good and proper.'

'So what happened?' says Jack.

'Forgot to put the bloody safety catch on his rifle, the silly bugger. Closed his eyes for a minute, nodded off and jabbed himself under the chin just as he'd intended.'

'And?'

'And then he must've kicked the flamin' gun in surprise, mustn't he? Bang!'

Unsure whether to laugh or cry, Fuller bites his lip and says nothing. Jack lights a cigarette. Mac shakes his head, tut-tutting.

'Poor bugger.'

'Daft bugger, more like. Looks like this chap must've done the same.'

'Ah well. I suppose we'll have to assume that *is* his head?'

'Aye. Let's stitch it up in t'bag, quick!' Jack says.

By the time the grisly jigsaw is complete and the last stitch sewn into the canvas shroud, the men are ready to call it a day. Bone-weary from the day's labour and with their heads hurting from the memories of front-line duty, they are tired and hungry. But as they trudge back across the field there is good news. The driver has managed to park the mobile kitchen just a few yards from their camp. One of the last of the Chinese labour companies has been detailed to set up their tents and a brazier has been lit.

'Bloody luxury,' Ocker shouts as they trudge back up the hill. 'All we need now is some entertainment. Who's gonna start the sing-song?' He takes hold of Fuller's hand and kneels in front of him in the mud.

'If you were the only girl in the world, and I were the only boy . . .'

'Gerroff me, yer daft . . .'

'Oh, come on, Fuller,' says Ocker, pulling himself back up. 'Give us a kiss.'

8

The summer of 1919 is warm and dry. The men rise earlier and work from four a.m. till noon, leaving the stench of the battlefield to the flies and the maggots in the midday sun.

'Sergeant?'

'What is it, Jack?'

'Come an' have a look at this,' says Jack, standing back from the shallow hole he has just dug.

'Ah!' Townend crouches down to take a closer look. 'Fritz dead?'

'I reckon so,' Jack says, looking at the dirty scraps of grey-blue fabric wrapped tightly round the bones. 'What shall we do with him?'

'Well he can't stay here,' says Townend, 'that's for sure.'

'No?'

'No, dig him up, Jack. Check his pockets – if he's still got any. Cop a gander, see if there's any ID.'

'And then?'

'And then we'll take him up to Langemark,' Townend says. 'Drop him off there on our way back home.'

'Sir?'

'What the fuck is it now, Ocker?'

'Another bloody Jerry here, I'd say, Sarge.'

'Oh bleedin' great,' Townend says. 'We must've hit upon a fucking Fritz cemetery. Ingham will be happy.'

'Reckon there's two or three of them in this trench.'

'Never mind,' says Townend. 'Dig the fuckers up and pile 'em on the lorry. Just be quick about it. We'll let the POWs dig the graves and do the burying.'

But the Germans that the men are digging up haven't been buried deliberately; these aren't marked graves, which is why the men have hit on them by accident. Apart from the lone corpse Jack has found, the rest of the bodies lie in a tangled heap of mud-encrusted bones in what might have been a shell-hole or the line of a reserve trench. An explosion, a bombardment, something sudden and terrible, has buried these men alive. And yet, amid the accidentally entombed Germans, one grave, properly dug and marked, seems against the odds to have survived intact. *Ein unbekannter Englander* is carved into the rough wooden cross with a penknife, possibly by the very hand – and the very knife – that killed the man beneath.

'This is the one we've come for,' Townend says, taking the cross out of the ground. 'Don't get this poor bugger's bones mixed up with them krauts.'

'Aye, sir. We're taking care of it.'

Once the bodies have been sewn into tarpaulins and loaded on the motor transport, the men trudge back on foot to the road while the ex-Red Cross ambulance bumps and bounces over the rough ground, shaking up the dismembered, desiccated cargo still further.

'Jeez!' Ocker shouts at the departing vehicle. 'They're gonna be a right flamin' mess when they get 'em there.'

'Don't matter,' Jack says, stepping up into the front of the

Albion. 'All t'Germans do is shovel 'em into a ruddy great pit anyway.'

A short time later both trucks stop at the side of a quiet road just south of Langemark. Grey-uniformed German prisoners – shovels sloping over shoulders – stand smoking on the verge.

'This is it,' says Townend, climbing down from the cab. 'Come on, you buggers.' He bangs with his hand on the side of the ambulance. 'Everybody off. This is your stop.'

The Germans POWs slowly gather round at the back of the truck. One of the guards slings his rifle on his shoulder as he lights a cigarette. The men of Jack's platoon jump down from the back of the truck, keen not to miss the rare pleasure of watching as someone else does all the hard work for a change. But things aren't going smoothly.

'Jack? Jack!'

Townend is having trouble persuading the prisoners to unload the packages of bone and uniform. Standing at the back of the ambulance gesticulating, he points to the bundles lined up on the stretcher shelves. He mimes the action of unloading the truck and carrying the sacks to the German cemetery. But none of the prisoners moves. The escort – a couple of absurdly youthful Canadian privates – shrug and shake their heads when Townend asks them to communicate.

'Jack, Jack? Come over here will you?'

'Sir?'

'Speak kraut, do you, Jack? I can't seem to get the square-headed bastards here to understand.'

'Sorry, Sarge. Bit o' French, bit o' Flemish – that's about my limit.'

'Oh bleedin' hell!'

In desperation Townend climbs into the back of the motor

ambulance, takes one of the bundles off the shelves and tosses it down to the first of the waiting Germans. But instead of catching it, the prisoner steps back, startled, and the wire binding splits. The contents of the bundle spill out at the man's feet. From the back of the group comes the sound of a cigarette being spat out. Several of the POWs remove the shovels from their shoulders, knuckles whitening on the handles of the spades as they stare up at Townend. The muttering – in a language none of the men understands – is getting louder.

'Who the fuck's in charge here?' Townend shouts. He jumps down and turns, walking back to the front of the truck. The clod of earth hits him full force between the shoulder blades and Townend stumbles forward, picks himself up and then scrambles quickly to the cab. He checks that the revolver is loaded, then walks round the other side of the ambulance to where the prisoners are still standing.

Bang!

'Missed the bleeder, sir,' shouts Ocker. But Townend isn't laughing. At least the single shot he's fired into the air has silenced the muttering prisoners. Reluctantly, they make a move and slowly begin unloading each of the remaining bodies.

'We've got a record of their IDs here, you bastards.' Townend waves a handwritten scrap of paper in his hands. 'Not that you're getting it until I'm satisfied. Now' – he picks up a shovel and mimes the action of throwing soil, fast, over his shoulder – 'get bloody digging!'

'Trouble is,' says Mac, stoking his pipe as the prisoners get to work at last, 'none of these fellows thinks they've actually lost the war, you know.'

'You reckon?'

'No, not really. Look at them. They all feel terribly hard

done by. They seem to have got it into their thick, square heads that they're an undefeated army, that they've merely withdrawn tactically from the field of battle . . .'

'That they'll be back?'

'Stabbed in the back, more like,' says Mac. 'But who knows?'

'Well,' Ocker says, 'let's just hope we're not around to find out.' He looks at Jack. 'Unless you were planning on being here for the second half, eh, Jacko?'

Jack shakes his head.

'Yeah, just look at 'em,' Fuller laughs. 'They all fink they should be back 'ome in Berlin, celebrating.'

'They're not the only ones,' says Ocker. 'They think they've got it bad, just look at us. And we bloody won! Didn't we?'

'Quiet in here tonight, love.' As the men gather for a drink in the British Tavern in Ypres later that day, the mood is still subdued. 'Here, Françoise.' Jack reaches inside his tunic pocket. 'Present for you!'

'Chocolate!' the girl's eyes widen. 'Where did you—'

Jack taps the side of his nose. 'I didn't,' he smiles. 'Well, not on me own. Happen you'd better go and say summat to your Uncle Mac,' he nods. 'He was the one who found it.'

'Found it?' Katia hands Jack a heavy, foaming mug of Vermeulen *bièr blond*. The young girl wanders over to the table where the men are sitting. Within moments Mac is patting his knee and Ocker is ruffling Françoise's hair. 'Where do you find chocolate?'

'Aye, well,' Jack says. 'Bit of a story, actually.'

Katia raises her eyebrows. Jack takes a long, deep gulp of his beer. 'Bloody hell, lass, that tastes foul.'

'Foul?' she looks at him, confused rather than concerned.

'Dreadful. Awful.'

'You don't like it?'

'Nay, lass. Not straight away. I don't like owt I drink straight away these days.'

'Owt?'

'Anything,' he translates. 'Everything tastes of bloody petrol, that's the trouble.'

'Why so?'

'That's how we used to get it at the Front,' he says. 'Water, that is. They used to send it up in old petrol cans.'

'That is terrible.'

'Aye, well . . . It certainly tasted terrible.'

Silence. He looks at her as she carries on decanting the beer from jug to tankard, going along each of the mugs in turn.

'You and your *aye, well*,' she says as the ale froths at the top of the mugs. 'What does that mean anyway – *aye, well*?' She stops and looks at him, waiting for the beer to settle, waiting for an answer. Jack shrugs and smiles, then turns away, unsure what to say. 'I am sorry. You have had a difficult day,' she says.

'Aye, well . . . Sorry, lass. I mean, yes. Yes, you could say that.'

'Could I? Why don't you tell me about it, Jacques?' She leans forward, resting her hand on his arm.

'There was a bit o' trouble this afternoon, that's all – with the prisoners,' he says as he wipes the froth from his lips. 'Nowt much, but still.'

'With the Germans?'

'Aye, lass – with t'Germans.'

'What were you doing with the Germans?'

'They were digging graves over at Langemark. A few of 'em got a bit uppity, that's all.'

'Uppity?'

'A bit big for their boots.'

'Their boots?'

'Sorry, lass. They was starting to throw their weight around a bit . . . I mean – look, it doesn't matter.'

'Then why was it trouble? Was it trouble for you?'

'Nay, lass, not for me. I wasn't involved. Well, not with t'fighting.'

'You were fighting the Germans?'

Jack looks at her and smiles. Then, suddenly, he starts to laugh – great, chest-heaving guffaws that leave him wheezing, holding the thin wooden bar for support.

'What is so funny?' The girl looks puzzled, then concerned. But in spite of the pain Jack can't stop laughing.

'I've been fighting . . . t'Germans . . . for t'past . . . three years,' he says at last, once his wheezing laughter has subsided.

'I don't know what you find so funny.' Katia suddenly looks upset.

'No, lass,' he says, striking a match and bringing the flame up to the cigarette clamped between his lips. 'Neither do I.' He rubs the flame out, tossing the stick to the floor. 'But no. I wasn't fighting them – the Germans, that is. Not on this occasion.'

She pouts and flaps the tea towel she is holding at the counter. The bar is quiet. Jack turns and squints through his tobacco smoke at the yellowing, varnished posters – cracked and blistered with age – covering gaps in the walls where panels of the corrugated iron have been joined together. Music hall acts, he assumes. For long-gone performances.

'You don't hate them, do you?' Katia asks at last. 'You don't hate the Germans, not like we do.'

'Why should I hate them?'

'You should hate them for what they did,' she says. 'For who they are. For what they will become.'

Jack pushes back his cap and scratches his head. 'I can't . . . I don't hate anybody.'

'But they would have killed you, Jacques! They killed your friends. These men you dig up every day and bury . . .'

'It were war, lass.' Even though it is all that Jack can think to say, he knows it's not much of an answer. '*La guerre.*'

Katia stops, hands by her side, and looks at him. But she isn't smiling. 'Was it *la guerre* when our women and children were, were . . .' She stops for a moment, struggling in her anger for the correct English. 'When they were *violées* – raped, killed in 1914? Why, some of them, they were no older than—'

No older than her sister. No need to say it. Jack can suddenly see it, see it all so clearly.

'Was it war when *les Allemands* shot our menfolk simply because they were Belgians in their own country, living their lives peacefully as they had always wanted to?'

'Aye, well . . .'

But Katia is angry now, and in no mood for 'aye, well' any more. Jack turns his head. Again the posters catch his eye. He wonders why he's never noticed them before. And alongside gay variety notices there are others – a plump, apron-wearing artisan holding a brimming mug of Vermeulen beer in front of the ruined campanile: *demandez les Bières de la Brasserie . . . Vraagt de Bieren der Brouwerij*, the slogan reads. Jack brings the mug he's holding to his lips.

'Maybe it was only "war" to you,' Katia is saying, watching him, watching his eyes over the rim of his tankard.

Remember Belgium – Enlist Today! Another slogan. And below the call to action is a smart Tommy standing to attention. *Remember Scarborough!* is the recruiting poster Jack can picture when he shuts his eyes. He remembers the bombardment, too – remembers the ripple of fear that had spread through the village at the thought that the Germans were poised for an invasion. Here, in Belgium, that fear was a reality. No wonder they – no wonder she – feel such hostility. He can see it in the figure of a blonde-haired young girl being held by the wrists and dragged off by a thickset, square-jawed Hun in a *Pickelhaube*; see it in the background of the angry fires of a burning Belgian city whose red flames turn the figures into silhouettes. *Schrecklichkeit*.

'You had a gun,' she says, following his gaze. 'But what about the poor citizens of Andenne and Seilles, Tamines and Dinant?'

Is Your Home Worth Fighting For? It Will Be Too Late When The Enemy Is At Your Door. Oh God, please no. But he can see it now – the baby on the floor, an old man seated, mother at the stove, father home from work, the table set for dinner. But it wasn't bayonet-wielding Germans who had come to take his child. No, he doesn't hate the Germans. Jack's enemies are much closer to home.

'Aye, well.' He shakes the image from his head, stares again at the wall. 'Aye, well,' he sighs.

'Aye well, you say. Aye well, aye well. It is easy for you to say. That is all you ever say – aye, well. Well I will tell you something. In August 1914 at Louvain, the German army set fire to the town, destroying the medieval library . . . all of its ancient books. Yes, and killing hundreds of innocent people and forcing – oh, *milliers de personnes*—'

'*Milliers de* what, love?'

'Oh,' she shrieks. 'Thousands – almost the population of the town – they forced them all to leave their homes. And for what? There were no *francs-tireurs* there. It was a seat of learning, a place of art and culture, and the Germans looted and destroyed it all.'

'Franc – what, love?'

'*Francs-tireurs*. Those suspected of resisting the enemy.'

'And did they?'

'Did they what?' she asks, tears now welling in her dark eyes.

'Did they resist the enemy?'

'Katia?' Françoise appears, looking up with concern at her older sister. '*Wat is er aan de hand*?'

'Nothing,' Katia shakes her head. 'Nothing is wrong, Françoise.' She looks at Jack. A cold, hard look. A mixture of hostility and guilt. 'Give Jacques back his chocolate,' she tells the girl.

War Diary or Intelligence Summary: Army form C. 2118

1919

DIVISION MAIN DRESSING STATION—Remy Siding
Map Sheet 28; Grid reference: L.22 d.6.3

September 1st – Party of 4 Officers and 20 O.R.s instructed in the use of the fire pump at Lijssenthoek Fire Station. Remainder of Battalion in ordinary training.

September 3rd – Concert by Divisional Brass Band. Men who did not bathe on 1st inst. bath parade Poperinghe.

September 8th – Salvage operations commenced, ref. sheet 29 & 29 1/40000 Belgium. Court of Inquiry re illegal absence of 18667 Pte. F. REDSTONE, 2905 Pte. V.W. UNDERWOOD & 7742 Pte. R. McGARRY.

September 11th – Parades held under Coy Commanders: Vlamertinghe. Ypres cordon sanitaire reduced to the immediate vicinity of Cloth Hall and St Martin's Cathedral.

September 16th – Guard detail of 1 N.C.O. and 2 other ranks sent to Ypres to enforce cordon sanitaire surrounding Cloth Hall and Cathedral at request of Army Town Major Lt. Col. BECKLES WILLSON.

September 18th – Lecture by 2/Lt. Jenkins in Salvation Army hut – subject 'The British Empire'. Orders received for a party of 50 men to proceed to BRUSSELS to escort a supply train.

September 20th – All Coys at the disposal of Company Commanders. Hockey Match against 3rd Royal Welch Fusiliers, Battn lost 7–3.

September 24th – 'C' Coy ordered to assume escort duties for 121 P.O.W. Coy and to leave immediately.

9

'Come on, you lot, shake a leg,' Townend calls through the door of the half-empty hut first thing the next morning. 'Ingham wants you on parade in half an hour.'

Ocker's boot crashes into the door just as Townend pulls it shut behind him. The other men stir.

'It's still bloomin' dark,' someone grumbles. 'What the hell does Ingham want us up so early for? There's no chance of finding any bodies in the flamin' dark!'

'Aye, and we cleared the last of that debris yesterday . . . eventually.'

'Hey, fellas!' Fuller shouts, returning from an early breakfast. 'How about this then for a bit o' news?'

'We're all ears,' someone mumbles.

'There's only a party of tourists arriving this morning on the first train,' he says, picking bits of bacon from his teeth. 'And Ingham wants us to meet 'em at the station!'

'So that's what this is all about.'

The men tidy up as best they can for the parade, but no officer or NCO checks that boots and buttons have been polished any longer.

'Although,' Ingham tells them, 'some of you might want to smarten yourselves up a bit for this next assignment.' He sniffs the air. As the men shuffle into line and the birds sing, the sky gradually starts to lighten, a blood-red sun rising out of the September mist.

'Why's that then, sir?' asks Ocker.

'Because as far as I can gather, Private Gilchrist, the party seems to consist mainly of former nurses. It would appear that they wish to see for themselves something of what the poor beggars they cared for had to put up with during the Flanders offensive.'

'Bit late for that now ain't it, sir?' someone mutters.

'Well you'd hardly have wanted them with you in the trenches, would you?'

'Oh I don't know about that, sir,' says Ocker. 'Might've, you know, brightened things up a bit.'

Ingham doesn't answer. 'Patterson?'

'Yessir?'

'Clearly there's not going to be any more digging for a day or two. There's a great deal of paperwork to complete and I'm going over to Base Depot to meet with the ASC Commander and to update the maps and complete the burial returns. Sergeant Townend will accompany me.'

'. . . to tell you what to do,' says Ocker from the corner of his mouth.

'And so while we are away . . . Private Patterson?'

'Yessir?'

'Didn't you once have a stripe?'

'Er . . . I don't rightly know, sir. Did I?'

'Ha! Yes, very good,' Ingham nods and smiles. 'Well, according to your record, which we seem to have acquired at last from your previous company' – he looks down at the clipboard that he's carrying – 'yes, you were awarded it in 1917. It also says . . . Yes, it says here that it was revoked following an incident in which you were found to be drunk while in uniform.'

'Tut-tut-tut! That doesn't sound like you, Jacko.'

'I do wish you chaps wouldn't be so awkward.'

'No, sir,' Jack says. 'Sorry, sir.'

'Well, anyway, Patterson, I was thinking – consider it reinstated.'

Townend coughs theatrically, glancing sideways at Jack.

'Thank you, sir!'

'Now, Patterson, take a couple of men with you and give these VADs a good . . . you know, a jolly good—' The rest of the men suddenly burst out laughing. 'A jolly good look around!'

'Yes, sir. Very good, sir.'

'Jesus, Jacko – you get a flamin' stripe for giving a bunch o' British nurses a bit of the how's-yer-father.'

'Gilchrist!'

'Sorry, Sarge!' Ocker shakes his head. 'Jacko, you jammy bugger!'

'I am referring, of course . . .' Ingham blinks, his eyes staying closed for slightly longer than intended. 'I am referring to a proper and respectfully conducted tour of the battlefields and the adjacent cemeteries. These nurses are particularly—'

'Desperate?'

'Quiet in the ranks! They are particularly keen to see for themselves what things were like out here in the Salient. And, no doubt—'

'And no doubt to meet Lance-Corporal *Jack-the-Lad* whose reputation with the ladies goes before him!'

'And, no doubt,' Ingham carries on, 'to pay their respects at the graves of the fallen, some of whom – for all we know – may be personally known to them.'

'Do we know which cemeteries they're particularly wanting to see, sir?'

Ingham looks down at the clipboard. 'I believe they would like to . . .'

'. . . make the intimate acquaintance of the greatest grave digger in the whole of Flanders.' Ocker bends low giving a mock twirl until Townend plants a boot on his backside and he goes sprawling on the gravel. Ingham looks up briefly, squints, then carries on reading.

'Essex Farm and . . . yes, Tyne Cottage are the two cemeteries listed on the itinerary. No doubt there will be others too,' he says, ignoring the commotion. 'I'd ask them when they arrive if there's anywhere particular they'd like to be taken.'

'Or any way,' says Ocker, picking himself up and dusting himself down.

'They'll be arriving on the first train from Hazebrouck, Lance-Corporal.'

'Staying there are they, sir?'

'No, Lance-Corporal. They are boarding at the new Skindles Hotel in Poperinghe, I believe.'

'. . . now offering the luxury of bathrooms and central heating,' Mac mutters to himself.

'Yes – my friend Captain Poyntz has arranged rooms for them there, and I have agreed with the CO that some of my men should be made available to assist the parties as they explore the battlefields. We wouldn't want any more accidents, would we?'

'No, sir. Did you say Captain Poyntz, sir?'

'Yes, Private MacIntyre, that's correct. Captain Poyntz.'

'He's the chap that's running the new battlefield tour company, isn't he?'

'He is, Private,' Ingham nods. 'Your point being?'

'So we'll be getting paid, I suppose?'

'You'll be paid by the Army, of course. As usual.'

'So this is Army business, is it, sir?' asks Jack.

'These are your orders. From me. And as agreed by the CO. We can't have parties wandering across the former theatres of war unattended. So be a good chap and meet them off the train, take them to their hotel and then arrange with the transport officer to take one of the trucks – no, make that a staff car, maybe even two – and give them a good day out.'

'Very good, sir.'

'And Patterson?' Ingham says as he is leaving.

'Yes, sir?'

'Good luck!'

'Thank you, sir.'

'Not at all,' Ingham smirks. 'I think you're going to need it.'

'He's not doing them all himself, is he, sir?' Ocker shouts as Ingham walks away. 'We can share 'em out between us, can't we?'

An hour later there's a party atmosphere on the low railway platform at Poperinghe station. In addition to crowds of giggling girls in hats and coats, men in officers' uniforms are busy shepherding parties of their own out of the station before looking round for transport. Smaller groups of older men and women stand in silence with their baggage, bewildered by the noise and smoke and shouts in a foreign language from porters and the guard. The stationmaster checks his watch. At the entrance Jack stands by the cars while Fuller goes along the platform looking for their designated group.

'I say!'

Without thinking, Jack finds himself standing to attention and saluting.

'I don't suppose we could get a ride out to Hill Sixty could we?'

Jack glances sideways at the young subaltern standing with a group of smiling WAACs. 'I'm very sorry, sir – Major Rennard's orders. We're awaiting a party of VADs. This is their transport.'

'Now look here, Private . . .'

'Lance-Corporal, sir.'

'Really? I don't see a stripe.'

At that moment the party appears and the nurses climb aboard the two open-topped cars. Fuller and Skerritt crank the motors into life as Jack and Ocker pull on the throttles. The young subaltern jumps back as, with a tug, Jack releases the brake and sets the first car bumping forward. Fuller jumps up onto the running board and holds on tight, while the girls reach up to their heads and hang on to their hats as the cars set off on the Switch Road out towards Vlamertinghe.

'Where are we heading for then, Jacko?' Fuller shouts over the noise of the engine. The road is muddy and still pockmarked with holes, the more dangerous for being filled with water and covered with a thin shimmer of oil. 'Somewhere nice and quiet? There's one for each of us back there, y'know.'

'Reckon we'll go to Ypres,' Jack cries, ignoring Fuller's suggestive remark. 'Show 'em the ruins. Then out towards the Yser before we stop at Essex Farm and have a look at the old dressing stations.'

'Yeah! We can get Skerritt to recite "In Flanders Fields",' Fuller laughs. '*In Fwlanders, Fwields duh Ppppppeeessss gruh* . . . just better make sure they've got their umbrellas up, eh, skip?'

'That's not funny, lad.' Jack stares at the road. 'Not funny at all.'

'Suit yerself, skip.' Fuller looks down at his feet before changing the subject. 'Then where are we off to after that, Jack?' he asks, rubbing his hands together.

'Well then . . .' Jack considers for a moment. 'Then, happen we'll take the road up to Gravenstafel. Plenty for them to see up there if the roads is clear.'

'Right-o, skip! You drive. I'll tell the ladies.'

As Jack looks over his shoulder he notices that Ocker – in the car behind – has already settled comfortably into his role as guide and chauffeur. Driving with one hand on the enormous steering wheel and the other, no doubt, between the thighs of the nurse who sits alongside him on the front seat, he is giving what looks like a continuous commentary as the party turns past Talbot House and then through the market square and out onto the Ieperseweg. A short time later they are passing the remains of Vlamertinghe, with what is left of Road Camp and Givenchy Camp on their right and the ragged shape of the Cloth Hall bell tower in the Grote Markt at Ypres just visible on the horizon ahead of them.

As they slow to pass the small cemetery, the nurses fall suddenly silent. The tattered remains of camouflage netting still line the sides of the road. The ruins of Vlamertinghe church abuts a flat expanse of wooden crosses – some tall, some small, some old, some new – each silently marking one of the many hundreds of graves in the military cemetery. A War Graves Commission works team is busy levelling the ground and digging shallow borders along each row of the established graves. To the side, bordering the wartime railway, a flat expanse of earth has been cleared and is now fenced off from the road, the ground divided into squares by neat lines of chalk.

'Is that a playing field?' someone asks.

'Er . . . not exactly, Sheila,' Ocker says. 'Unless you like playing the harp.' A nervous laugh. 'No, that's space for the rest of 'em.'

'The rest? You mean there are more? But the war . . .'

'I know, I know, the war is over. No one gets killed these days. Well, not unless you count daft coolies playing around with high explosives.'

'Or tourists who take it on themselves to go for a wander . . .'

'So . . . ?'

'So, it's for the men that were buried in the field, miss. Smaller cemeteries, and the like. Shallow graves dug in a hurry after a show.'

'A show?'

'A battle. An attack – offensive, miss. Those coves who stopped one were dug in close to where they fell.'

'Stopped . . . what?' asks one of the girls.

'A bullet, miss. Or shrapnel. Or maybe a shell if they was really lucky.'

'I see,' she says. 'I think.'

'And now,' Ocker continues, 'we dig 'em up again and bring 'em here. Or somewhere else just like it.'

'Oh.'

No one else speaks until they cross the Leie Kanaal and enter Ypres fifteen minutes later. 'And this, ladies,' Ocker is announcing to his party, 'is the famous Wipers.'

A brief flutter of recognition at the familiar name is followed by another hushed silence as the cars drive past ruined buildings, open cellars and streets still lined with piles of rubble.

'Why aren't they . . . rebuilding?' one of the nurses asks.

'They is,' Fuller says. 'You should've seen the size of them piles o' stone when we first got here.'

95

'Really?' One of the girls shakes her head.

'I hear Ypres was a magnificent city,' another adds, 'before the beastly Germans came here.'

'They didn't have to come here to destroy the place, miss.'

'But I thought . . . ?'

'Oh aye,' Mac tells them. 'The Germans were here, briefly, in 1914.'

'Oh, really?'

'Aye,' he goes on. 'But for the next four years it was ours, stoutly defended by the British Army. Why, there can scarcely be a man who served who hasn't passed through this place.' Mac turns to the girl on the back seat and takes hold of her hand.

'My fiancé!' She passes him the small portrait she is holding. 'He was here,' she says.

'A fine-looking young man,' Mac says, handing back the photograph.

'He was first here in 1915,' she tells him. 'And then again in 1917.'

They drive on, down the main street, past the skeletal remains of the cathedral and the Cloth Hall. Weeds grow out of the stones. Birds – pigeons – are nesting in the ruins, laying eggs and raising chicks well into September as if determined to repopulate the city on their own.

'Oh, look!' one of the girls says quietly. 'It's just like Fountains Abbey.'

'It's beautiful,' another girl adds. 'I think they should leave them here as they are,' she says, 'as a memorial to the men who died.'

'Don't be silly, Daisy,' her friend says. 'Life does go on, you know.'

'Aye, lassie, for you maybe,' Mac says, softly.

But the girl isn't listening. 'So, who did you book with?' she is asking another member of the party.

'The British Legion,' the girl answers. 'Three pounds eleven shillings and sixpence.'

'Oh,' she says. 'I came here with Thomas Cook.'

'Nice-looking, is he?' They both laugh.

Jack crosses the ramparts at the end of Menin Straat before turning the car left alongside the moat, then turning left again towards the Minneplein.

'There you are,' he shouts, pointing to the neat lines of small huts spreading across the flat area of grass. 'Rebuilding!'

'Oh, Lucy, look at those lovely little houses!'

'Very cosy,' another girl laughs. 'Is that where you live?' she says to Fuller.

'No, miss,' he says. 'We still live in camp.'

'In tents?'

'Oh no, miss. We've got huts now, ain't we, Jack? And a brazier. Them houses – them's for the locals.'

Children play in the space between the small, prefabricated dwellings; a pig squeals from a backyard sty and scraggy chickens scratch and peck the ground.

'They've been given 'em,' Fuller tells the girl. 'By the King.'

'By the King!' the girls shrieks. 'My God!'

'I know,' Fuller laughs. 'They're hardly palaces, are they?'

'They are to the folks that live in 'em,' Jack interrupts. 'They are for them who've had their houses flattened by a thousand German shells. They are for them as have had their lives destroyed by four years of war and who are trying to get things back to normal.'

'I suppose so,' says the girl. 'Why are they building them here, though?'

'Because there's a such lovely view of your pretty ruins, Daisy,' the other girl grins. 'Look at them!' The broken walls of the campanile loom over the neat rows of wooden dwellings like the bleached bones of a long-dead dinosaur.

'Nay, lass. They build 'em here because it's safe,' Jack tells the girls. 'No danger of summat falling down on top o' your head.'

'Or what you've just built disappearing down some great big hole in the ground,' adds Fuller. 'Like an old cellar or somefink.'

'So what was here before the war?' another girl asks.

'Nothing,' Jack says. 'It were just a field.'

'A field?'

'Aye. Where kids played. People wandered. Bit like a park, I suppose.'

'Oh! And does it have a name?'

'T'locals call it Minneplein,' Jack tells the girl.

'And what does that mean?'

'That's the local lingo for *La Plaine d'Amour*,' grins Fuller, winking.

The girl blushes.

10

A little farther out to the north of the town on the road to Boezinge is Essex Farm and one of the smaller dressing station cemeteries. Hidden in their concrete bunkers in the flood banks of the Yser, the Canadians clearly patched up most of the men who made it back here, injured, from the front lines. A mere seventy burials mark the medics' failures – or the enemy's success. Some of the graves are tightly packed where hurried interments under fire were necessary; others are neatly spaced where more leisurely funerals or reburials have occurred.

'Hallo.' Jack nods a greeting to a local woman. She hands the baby on her arms to him and smiles.

'Another of yours, eh, Jacko?'

Jack tickles the thin child before handing it back to its mother.

'Aw,' one of the nurses smiles. 'Look at that!'

'Handsome, isn't he?' the girl's friend teases.

'Who, the baby?'

'Good with children, too, by the look of him.'

'Yes, but look at the other one,' the first nurse frowns, 'over there.'

'Private Skerritt, you mean?' Mac interrupts. The nurses blush. 'Lost his lower mandible at Third Ypres.'

'Careless of him, I know . . .' says Ocker.

'Aye, and we're still looking for it.'

The woman with the baby turns and goes inside. 'Are they . . .' one of the girls asks, pointing to where the woman was standing, 'living there in those concrete shelters?'

'Happen they are, aye!'

'Next to all these graves?'

'Excuse me!' One of the other girls is waving her hand and pointing to the far corner of the cemetery. A group of about half-a-dozen men with picks and shovels appear to have been digging. Fresh earth stands dark against the pale yellow, late-summer grass.

'What are those men doing?'

'Don't rightly know, miss. Stay here a minute,' Jack says to the nurses. 'Ocker? Mac?'

'Coming, mate!'

'Hey, what about me?' cries Fuller. Skerritt mumbles something unintelligible. 'Stay here with the ladies,' Jack tells them both.

'Hey!' Jack calls over as they dodge between the rows of crosses over to the corner where the graves are being opened. 'Hey! *Wat doe je?*' The labourers stop what they're doing and look up, briefly, but don't answer. '*Wat doe jij hier?*' Jack says, a little louder. One of the men shrugs. 'Bloody 'ell, not fucking Walloons are they?'

'What's happening?' One of the girls turns to Skerritt as they see Jack and the others talking to the men. Skerritt makes a sound and points at Fuller. Fuller shakes his head and they stand and watch. Amid much waving of arms and a little conversation, one of the labourers produces a folded piece of paper, handing it to Jack.

'It's all right,' he says as he strides back across the cemetery.

'They're French. They're digging up the French graves, that's all.'

'Digging up the graves?' one of the girls says. 'But . . . why?'

'To take 'em back home I suppose, miss. It's all above board,' Jack says. 'I've seen the paperwork – they've got permission.'

'But what are they . . . I mean, the *bodies*.' She lowers her voice, almost mouthing the word. 'What are they doing in a British cemetery in the first place?'

'This was a French cemetery before we took it over. French are allowed to repatriate their dead if the families want 'em back.'

'Unlike us,' says Fuller.

'Yes,' one of the girls says. 'Why is that?'

'Why don't you explain, laddie?' Mac turns to Fuller.

'I, er . . .'

'Because you don't know, do you, eh?'

Fuller looks confused.

'Which is no doubt why Ingham . . .'

'That'll do,' Jack puts a finger to his lips. 'No need to hang our dirty washing out here.'

'I suppose not.' Mac stokes his pipe and the party breaks up, dispersing into small groups, each wandering informally round the tidy rows of graves. Late swallows gather along telegraph wires recently restored. A blackbird darts about among the earth disturbed by the exhumation.

'Looking for someone special?' Jack approaches a tall girl standing alone by a small cross at the end of the row. She looks round and smiles, momentarily, before suddenly bringing a hand up to her mouth and shaking her head.

'Hey now – don't take on.' Jack looks round for one of the other girls, but they all appear to be following Ocker like the Pied Piper out of the cemetery and towards the canal. Jack raises an arm awkwardly before bringing it down gently on the girl's shoulder. Suddenly she has turned and put both her arms around his waist. He gently folds his other arm around her shoulders and he holds her and they stand, her head buried in this chest, her sobbing gradually subsiding.

'I'm sorry,' she says at last, dabbing her eyes with a lace handkerchief.

'Don't be.'

'No really, I am. I'm not looking for anyone.'

Jack looks surprised.

'There is no one,' she says coldly. 'There never was' – she shakes her head quickly – 'never has been.'

'What?' Jack smiles, looking down at her. 'A pretty lass like you?'

She laughs and looks at her shoes. They are caked in mud and wet with dew.

'Oh my God,' she cries. 'What a mess.'

'No matter, miss.'

'Please, call me Rose.'

'Look, there's a bothy over there . . .'

'A what?'

'The gardeners' bothy. It's a hut they use, y'know – to store their tools, shelter from the rain, that sort of thing.'

'I see.'

'You'll be able to clean yourself up there. There'll be nobody about. And there'll be a kettle. Don't know about you but I could use a cup o' tea.'

The door of the gardeners' bothy at Essex Farm cemetery is locked, but Jack knows where the gardeners hide the key. Having opened the door he steps back, allowing the girl to climb the three steps up into the small hut. Before her eyes have a chance to adjust her nose tells her what kind of place it is – damp earth, tools and empty plant pots; a sharp, pungent tang from a sack of bonemeal.

'So, you chaps have to . . . ?' Rose is tense, sitting on the end of the rough wooden bench that runs along one side of the hut, like a bird perching on a cliff edge. Jack lights the stove and places the kettle onto the flame to boil.

'Aye, lass. We dig the graves.'

'And the bodies?'

'Aye. We dig up the bodies.'

'That must be . . . I don't know. It must be awful for you.'

'Someone's got to do it, lass.'

'I suppose so.'

'And there's still thousands of 'em still to find. They're all over t'place. They're everywhere.'

'Really?'

'Aye, lass. And somebody has to find them.' Silence. The kettle boils quietly. The flame on the small stove burns blue.

'And then?' She looks up at him at last. He can see the whites of her eyes in the darkness.

'And then, we have to bury them.' He spoons tea into an old pot and stirs as he pours on the water. 'Has to be done.'

'And that is what you men do,' she says, 'all day long?'

'Aye.'

The girl lights a cigarette as Jack pours two mugs of tea. The silver strainer that he holds beneath the spout of the teapot swells with black leaves. There is no milk or sugar.

'Sorry, lass.'

'It doesn't matter.'

His hands, large and rough, fold round the tin mug – his palms immune to the heat – and he offers the girl the handle. She smiles. He stands awkwardly, towering over her in the tiny space. 'No room to swing a cat.'

'Come on.' She pats the bench next to where she is sitting. 'Space for one more here.'

He squeezes in beside her and removes his cap. Dust motes settle lazily in the sharp shaft of sunlight shining through a gap in the shed wall. The silence is uncomfortable but she closes her fingers around the warm mug and is glad of a chance to be away from the other girls. She glances sideways at Jack. He is looking at the floor. His short fair hair, with the slightest trace of grey around the temples, catches the single shaft of light and the stubble on his chin shines. She thinks of the hundreds of men like this man that she once nursed; thinks too of the man not unlike him that she once knew.

'I suppose I'd never thought about it before,' she says at last. 'I'd assumed that the men who died were buried and, well, that was that. I know it was decided that no bodies were to go back home during the war. But I suppose I thought that now that it was finished . . .'

'Where a tree falls . . .'

'Where a tree falls?'

'Where a tree falls, there let it lie. It's in t'Bible, so the chaplain tells us. I wouldn't know about that sort of thing myself.'

She looks up at him again, noticing his blue eyes as he stares out of the single, grubby window. Faint lines at the corners of his eyes trace – what? The pattern of a thousand smiles? Or an endless need to squint into the sun to see the enemy? She shudders, momentarily, at the cold, at the thought of what his eyes have seen, at her own secret shame sitting here beside him.

'I'd never really thought of it before today. I suppose I'd just imagined . . .' Her voice trails off and she curls her fingers tighter round the tin mug.

'Nobody does,' Jack shrugs. 'Nobody really knows. And no one wants to, neither.'

'It's . . . surprising really. Rather shameful too, I suppose.'

'Nay, lass,' he smiles and shakes his head. 'War's over for most folk. No one wants to have to think about it any more. Or about us. Or about them.'

Silence. Whatever Ocker's doing, Jack thinks, it's taking him a long time.

'They should dig them all up,' the girl says bitterly. 'Dig them up and take them all back home.'

He is surprised by the hostility in her voice. 'They don't want to be reminded of the past at home,' he says. 'They want to concentrate on t'future.'

'But you've got to deal with the past first,' she says.

'Aye, well – we do plenty o' that,' he nods. 'Clearing away t'rubbish. All that stuff that's left lying around the fields.'

'Stuff?' She looks confused. Surely he doesn't mean bodies?

'Rifles, bullets, bombs – you name it. Mess-tins, ammunition boxes, duckboards, ladders, shell cases. There's scrap lying about everywhere.'

'Oh I see,' she says.

'And the Belgians want to get their land back. They've got mouths to feed.'

'It can't be easy for them.'

'It isn't. And they could do without some o' these daft ideas for . . . God knows what – leaving the towns as ruins; building memorials instead of building shops and schools and houses – grand schemes for ruddy great statues, plinths and sculptures.'

'But the people must remember.'

'Must they? Most of us would quite like to forget.'

'But the world, the people at home, the politicians. This

can't be allowed to occur again. It simply cannot. The world must know what happened here in order to make sure it never, ever happens again. Don't you agree?'

'Aye well,' Jack sighs. 'That's what we all thought when we was fighting, I suppose.'

'You fought?'

'Aye, lass. Of course.'

'Of course,' she repeats, looking down at the floor. 'Of course you did.' The mug the girl is nursing starts to rock as her hands tremble. Tea slops over the rim and drips onto the floor. Jack gently prises the mug from her fingers and puts it down beside her on the bench. As he turns back the girl starts pummelling his chest with her fists – surprisingly hard – her slender body convulsing once again in deep, racking sobs.

'Hey, lass . . .' Jack takes hold of her wrists. 'Whoa! Steady on!'

The tears in her eyes glint as anger gives way to sorrow and the tension in her arms relaxes. She unclenches her fists. He pulls her towards him, his arms enfolding her narrow shoulders, her wet face buried in his sleeve. Instinctively, his hand begins stroking her hair and she digs her nails into the back of his greatcoat. He takes her arms and pushes her back, slightly.

'What were all that about?'

She holds a hand up to her mouth.

'There is someone, isn't there?' Jack asks. The girl looks down, nodding briefly. 'Do you want to tell me about him?'

She quickly shakes her head then says, 'No – he won't be buried here.'

'Oh, aye?' Jack plants a tiny, chaste and gentle kiss on the girl's forehead. She looks up at him, astonishment and incomprehension on her face.

'What did you . . . ?'

'Shhh! It doesn't matter,' he says softly.

She opens her mouth as if to speak and then closes it again. She shakes herself as if trying to wake up from a dream.

'I haven't got the words to say much more,' Jack says quietly.

'No words then.' The girl puts a finger to his lips.

'I, er . . .'

'Yes, I know.'

But she is looking up at him still, not moving away, not getting up, not wanting to release herself from this embrace. She feels the warmth of his skin seeping out through his Army uniform. His breath, held slightly, is gentle on her face. And she is not moving.

'I'm . . . look, I . . .'

'Aye. Me, too . . .'

The words are at odds with what they both seem to be feeling, with what they are doing, what they're thinking. And pretty soon, they both give up talking. His hand rests on her thigh. Her eyes are closed. Her head tilts back and he kisses her neck.

It is over within minutes. In the half-light of the hut, her brief nakedness – his hardness – seems unreal, like a waking dream. They stare at each other. Jack buttons his flies. The wet at the top of her thighs turns cold.

'We best be getting back to the others,' he says as tenderly as he can manage.

'Yes,' the girl replies, replacing her hat. 'We better had.'

'That shouldn't have . . .'

'I know,' she says.

'I'm sorry.'

She looks at him. 'I'm not,' she says.

'Not . . . what?'

'Not sorry,' she says briskly, putting on her gloves. 'Although the floor was a bit hard.'

'Aye, lass,' Jack laughs, 'and a bit mucky too!' he says, brushing down his greatcoat.

She reaches up and holds his face in her hands. 'This is what you were fighting for, Jack. This is what he would have done if he were here . . . what they would all have done.'

'Aye, lass, but . . .'

'We owe it to them, Jack.'

'Aye, I know, but . . .'

She pulls away from him. 'You're married, aren't you?'

'Nay, lass!'

'No? But there is a woman, isn't there?'

'Aye, well . . . I suppose so. Sort of.'

'Sort of?' The girl laughs. 'Sort of? Then you had better "sort of" get things sorted out, Lance-Corporal Patterson.'

'Aye, well . . .'

Outside, the rest of the party has wandered back into the cemetery and is gathering round one of the larger, better-built crosses. Ocker is acting like a tour guide again.

'The grave of Valentine Strudwick,' he announces. One of the nurses stares at the inscription, leaning closer to the tin plate on which the soldier's details have been stamped:

5750 RIFLEMAN

V.J. STRUDWICK

8TH RIFLE BRIGADE

14 JANUARY 1916

AGE 15

She steps back suddenly as if stung. 'Surely . . . ?'

'No mistake, miss.'

'But he was just . . .'

'. . . a boy,' someone else says softly.

Silence. Far off, on the road, a cart passes. The horse whinnies.

'I didn't think that sort of thing . . .'

'It wasnae meant to,' Mac says. 'Especially not when there were some o' them old enough still at home and sucking at their mammy's titties!' Fuller looks down at the ground, and kicks a clod of earth. Jack is suddenly overwhelmed with an urge to thump him, hard.

'But . . .'

'Joined up when he was just a wee lad o' fourteen. Had his last birthday out here in the Salient, before . . .'

The girls all bow their heads. Someone mouths a silent prayer. The French exhumation party walks past carrying a stretcher.

Ocker pauses for a moment. 'Right-o then, ladies,' he says, breaking the spell. 'Time to move on, I reckon. What d'you think, Jacko?'

'Aye,' Jack nods. 'We'll drive over towards White Sheet and have a look at Gravenstafel Ridge. And then we'll stop for a bit o' dinner at Tyne Cottage. What d'you reckon?'

'Dinner?' One of the nurses laughs.

'He means lunch,' says another.

'Oh!' the girl says. 'Is Tyne Cottage a restaurant?'

War Diary or Intelligence Summary: Army form C. 2118
1919

DIVISION MAIN DRESSING STATION—Remy Siding
Map Sheet 28; Grid reference: L.22 d.6.3

December 3rd – Salvage operations resumed in N.36a, M.35b and adjacent battery positions.

December 7th – Church Parade (all denominations) held in Salvation Army hut due to cold weather.

December 8th – Kit inspection. AF3221s completed for all ranks.

December 9th – Battalion selected to send one officer and 16 O.R.'s from Auxiliary Labour Company to assist Graves Registration Unit (G.R.U.) in battlefield clearance and cemetery concentration. Remainder: Drill and P.T.

December 10th – Lecture by 2/Lt. ANKERS in Salvation Army hut entitled 'Birds of the British Isles'. Orders received for a party of 30 men to proceed immediately to LILLE to escort a supply train.

December 11th – Capt. G.R. HAROLD, Lt. T.D. FREEMAN D.S.O. and 23 O.R.'s left Battalion for demobilisation.

December 13th – All salvage and recovery operations suspended due to inclement weather.

December 17th – Snow clearance operations POPERINGHE, YPRES and VLAMERTINGHE.

11

Winter comes early in 1919, and all around the ground is frozen hard. There isn't much digging to be done, and even clearing the remaining iron harvest is starting to prove difficult. Shell cases, guns and discarded ammunition freeze to the ground. The men are restless; some see ghosts. And the devil makes work for idle hands. The CO decides to keep Ingham's men busy by sending them to assist one of the few remaining Chinese working parties.

'Out beyond Tournai,' Ingham says, once the men have fallen in, 'we've been informed that there seems to be rather a lot of stray ordnance – small items, guns and ammunition, that sort of thing. Anyway, the demolition party needs some extra manpower. As we're not able at the moment to do much digging . . .'

'Who's not able to do much digging, sir? You should see Jack hard at it with his pick and shovel!'

'Well, yes I know, but' – Ingham stops and looks at Jack – 'but that's pretty dangerous, isn't it? I thought I'd given orders, Patterson – no mattocks. There are unexploded shells out there, for God's sake!'

'Yes, sir. Very good, sir.'

'Right then, Sergeant Townend and I will take the car.

Private Fuller, you can come with us and help navigate. Corporal Patterson, you and the others will follow in the ambulance. Private MacIntyre will navigate for you and the remainder of the men can travel in the rear.'

'Yes, sir.'

Once they are dismissed the men gather their tools and climb aboard the old, high-roofed ex-Army ambulance, still half-lined with its stretcher-shelves. 'Don't know about you,' says Ocker, knees pressed against the wooden partition that divides the rear of the truck in half, 'but this is giving me the creeps. Couldn't we have travelled in the Albion?'

'No room,' shouts Jack from the front. 'And anyway, I'm not trained to drive it yet!'

'Well, bloody well look sharp and get your chitty for it, Jacko,' Ocker shouts above the engine noise. 'Because I'm not travelling in the back of this bloody body buggy much longer.'

'What d'you reckon?' Jack says to MacIntyre. 'Reckon we can squeeze him in the front wi' us?'

'Aye, why not,' says Mac. 'If the poor wee lamb is afraid of ghosts.'

'You can swap with me if you like,' says Ocker. 'But apart from being bloody uncomfortable – I don't know . . . it's flamin' creepy too.'

'Ach, stop being so windy, will ye. What's the matter with you? There are no bodies in there, are there.'

'No, but . . .'

'And even if there was, what harm would they do ye?'

'Plenty,' Ocker says. 'I can't stand it when a cobber's quiet. Need a bit o' conversation, I do.'

'Aye,' says Jack. 'We've noticed.'

They pull in to the side of the road briefly, waving Ingham

and the staff car past while Ocker climbs into the cab with Jack and MacIntyre.

"Struth, that's a relief,' he says. 'I reckon there's bits and bobs of fellas we've dug up rattling around back there in all the dust.'

The others smile, but no one finds it in the least amusing.

'Seriously, you weren't back there with 'em, mate.'

'There's no one back there now, you daft bugger,' Jack says. 'Not now you're pestering us up front here.'

'Yeah but they've *been* there, mate,' says Ocker. 'Honest, it's like sitting in your own grave back there.'

'Didn't have you down as superstitious,' Mac tells him.

'I'm not,' says Ocker. 'At least, not normally. But this ain't normally, mate, is it? This is . . . weird. I dunno, but this is . . . digging these fellas up day after day. It's worse than war, this is.'

'At least no one's firing at us any more,' Jack says.

'D'you know,' says Ocker. 'I think I'd prefer it if they were.'

'You what?'

'Yeah! I mean, at least then you know who the enemy is, where he is, and what you've got to do to him. But this way . . . Jeez!'

'Someone send for the MO – quick!'

'This way it's as if we've crossed over some flamin' threshold and we're living in a land of the dead.'

'It's not a doctor this laddie needs, I tell ye – it's the priest!'

'Don't you ever think about it? Doesn't it ever get to you?'

'Not me, lad.'

'No. Me neither.'

'Oh yeah?' says Ocker. 'I don't believe you. Honestly, there's more dead every day in this job than the living. I'll tell you something—'

'First time for everything.'

'No, mate. Listen.'

'We're all ears.'

'Well . . . don't you sometimes wonder?'

'All the time,' Jack smiles.

'Mostly about the rubbish you keep talking.'

'No, fair dinkum, mate, hang on a mo. I mean – how do we know the whole world hasn't died, eh? How do we know the whole human race isn't lying out there somewhere, waiting for us to find 'em and bury 'em, fill a flamin' form in for 'em and then go out looking for the rest of 'em?'

'This is getting a bit . . .'

'Deep?'

'Too deep for me, Mac.'

'You ever seen the MO about any o' this, Ocker ol' lad?'

Suddenly, Ocker is very quiet. 'Actually,' he says at last, his voice barely audible above the noise of the engine. 'Actually I did, once. It was only then I had to eat crow and join the daddies unit . . .'

'Does this fella ever speak English?'

'Beats me. Not sure why we even have him in our army.'

'Had an English mother, apparently. Is that not right, Ocker?'

'Ocker had a mother?'

'Turn right at the next junction, Jack!' Mac suddenly calls out, looking up from the map that has spread to fill most of the cab.

'It should be signed to . . . now then, what's that called – *Vaulx* is it?'

'To where?'

'To Vaulx? I don't know how to say it. Vos? Vol? Vough?'

'It's Vouw,' Jack corrects him.

'Look, Jack, I'm no expert, if anything you're the man to get your lips around these Belgian tongue-twisters rather than me. After all, you're the one with more than a bit of help from the locals.'

'And I bet that's not all he gets his lips around,' says Ocker. 'Is it, Jack? Get plenty of action in Ypres of an evening don't you, Jack-the-lad?'

'Aye, well. I'm learning a bit of t'language if that's what you mean.' Jack hauls the heavy steering wheel round, making a left turn.

'That's all, is it, Jack? Language lessons? That's all she gives you, is it?' Laughter.

'Look, lads, I think you've got the wrong idea about me and Katy.'

'Katy is it now?'

'Blimey, Jacko, if that's the wrong idea then I wouldn't mind barking up the wrong tree myself a bit more often.'

'Nay, we're just friendly, like. She's pretty—'

'She's available.'

'Not if de Wulf has anything to do with it, she isnae!'

'And she's clearly good with her tongue, eh, Jacko?'

'She helps me,' Jack smiles, 'if I get stuck on any o' these B—'

'Berkshire Hunts.'

'Give over!'

'That's *la langue d'amour* for you,' says Mac.

'Yeah, and if anyone knows how to say it proper it'll be our Jacques.' Ocker is laughing. 'Isn't that what she calls you, Jacko? That what she whispers in your ear at night is it, mate? *Jacques, Jacques, kiss me Jacques, make love to me, ravish me, have your wicked way with me . . .*'

He leans across in front of Mac and tries to plant a kiss on Jack's cheek.

'Get off me, yer daft bugger,' Jack shouts as he tries to keep the truck on what little of the road is clear of snow. 'You'll have us all in yon ditch.'

For a brief moment, anger flickers across Jack's face. But then suddenly, the other two men are singing. And Jack finds himself smiling slowly to himself, almost against his will.

Mademoiselle from Armentières, parlez-vous?
Mademoiselle from Armentières, parlez-vous?
Mademoiselle from Armentières,
She hasn't been kissed for forty years,
Hinky, dinky parlez-vous.

'Come on "Jacques" – join in, man! You know the words.'
'Yeah, better than the rest of us . . .'

Oh, mademoiselle from Armentières, parlez-vous?
Mademoiselle from Armentières, parlez-vous?
She got the palm and the croix de guerre,
For washin' the soldiers' underwear,
Hinky, dinky parlez-vous.

'Isn't that what she does for you, Jack – *Jacques* – eh? Washes yer underwear, does she?'
'Aye, well . . .'
'At least he's wearing some,' says Mac. 'Unlike you, you filthy wee . . .'
'Give over, mate!'
'I reckon your kecks got so high-and-mighty that they marched off of their own accord.'

'Or disintegrated!'

'Even the chats won't go near Ocker.'

'I'll have you British peasants know,' says Ocker indignantly, 'that I had a bath . . .'

'. . . yeah, we know, Ocker – Christmas 1915!'

'Hey! Pipe down now, lads,' Mac says, pointing to the road ahead. 'Look – Ingham's here already.'

Jack slows down and pulls in at the side of the road. But by the time they've disembarked and joined the others, things aren't going well. The Chinese labourers are squatting at the roadside boiling tea, and Ingham isn't happy. 'Why the devil aren't you fellows working?' he is asking. 'Who's in charge here?'

A little man runs up to him and tries his best to explain. The farmer, he is telling Ingham, has already cleared the scrap. The shell-hole they've been sent to find has been filled in.

'See? No work left for us to do.' The man shrugs and grins.

'What? No work? Then where are the guns?' Ingham asks. 'Where's the metal? Come on, man. Where's the scrap? If you've sold it on to some bloody Belgie bootlegger, then I'll have you shot. D'you hear me?'

But the man is simply nodding, smiling, pointing over to the field where a large patch of brown earth stands out vividly against the snow.

'Right, men,' Ingham says. 'Follow me. We'd better take a look.'

They stamp across the frozen hillside while the Chinamen turn back to their roadside fires and the tea they're brewing. All around them, shell-holes and bomb craters have been smoothed out and softened by fresh falls of snow, but the snow around the hole they have been sent to clear is grimy with soil from a recent excavation.

'This is British government property,' Ingham shouts when they reach the site to take a closer look. 'You have no right . . .'

'*Dit is van mij*,' the farmer shrugs, and carries on throwing splinters of wood and old elephant iron over the top of the hole.

'Dammit, man, stop what you're doing. Stop, I say. And that's an order.'

'I don't think he understands you, sir,' Jack says, stepping forward. Ingham tries again in French, but the farmer carries on shovelling, this time even faster.

'*Niks van aan trekken!*' Jack calls over to him. The man stops digging. 'They speak Dutch now,' he says to Ingham. 'Not French no more.'

'*Spreekt u Vlaams?*' The farmer smiles.

'Er, I understand a bit, aye, but . . . *Spreekt u Engels?*'

'What the devil are you and he on about, Patterson? Tell him we're here on the authority of the King – his bloody King – Albert the whatever-he-is.'

'He says it's his farm, sir. He also says look at the mess you lot made of it.'

'Tell the bugger he'd not have a bloody farm if it wasn't for the mess we've made of it. Tell him he'd not even have a country if it wasn't for the stuff he's so conveniently burying in this field and the men who left it here in the first place. Ask him if he'd prefer to be spoken to in German by some Jerry clearance party instead?'

Jack smiles. Three years in Flanders have given him enough of the language to transmit the basics. And three years in the Army have taught him enough about human nature to calm the current situation. The officer is a pillock, he is saying in his pidgin Flemish. The Belgian farmer laughs. Oh yes, the men do all the work, Jack tells him. But if he wouldn't mind stepping aside for a while he can rest on his shovel, have a smoke and watch the British Army do a morning's unpaid digging for him. Jack offers the man a cigarette. Some of the Chinamen wander up the hill from their roadside camp to find out what is happening.

'Well?' Ingham snaps.

'He says we can get all t'stuff out of t'hole . . .'

'Yes?'

'Aye. But only if we fill it in agin – afterwards.'

'Christ, man, can't you speak English either?'

'Sorry, sir?'

'Oh, nothing. Right, you chaps.' Ingham turns to the Chinamen. 'We need to uncover this hole and collect the, er . . . GUNS AND THINGS,' he shouts. 'And then . . .' he mimes a digging action, 'then we FILL – IT – UP – again and put the soil back. Be careful though,' he adds quietly, careless now about whether they are listening. 'Probably some live ammunition down there.' Ingham stops, looks, shouts 'BOOM!' suddenly and throws his hands in the air. The Chinamen stare back blankly.

'I don't think they understand you either, sir.'

'Speak Chinese too, do you, Patterson?'

'No, sir.'

Ingham pushes his cap back on his head. 'Christ! Bloody Belgians one side, Chinamen the other, and a damn Yorkshireman as my translator. How in God's name did it come to this?'

'I dunno, sir,' Ocker chips in. 'But I reckon you ought to be grateful. Got quite a flair for the lingo has our Jack.'

'If mimicking what you hear and repeating the sounds dumbly like a child is a flair for language, Private Gilchrist, then I'll grant you, Corporal Patterson might indeed have something of a facility for translation.'

119

'Well,' Jack turns and starts to walk away, 'happen you'd like to tek o'er yer sen then, eh, sir? If my effort in't reet enough for thee!'

Ingham shakes his head. Jack mutters something in the guttural dialect of Dutch that the West Flanders locals all speak, and the exotic Flemish cadences are more than enough to fool Ingham. The Belgian farmer laughs. The work begins. And Jack's vocabulary has suddenly expanded.

12

By the time the men get back to Remy Siding that evening it is already dark and the frost is freezing harder by the hour.

'Reckon we'd better stick to Pop tonight, lads,' Jack says when the men stand down. 'It's not a night to be cycling anywhere, least of all to Wipers. Who's coming for a drink?'

'Count me out,' says Ocker, rubbing his hands by the brazier. 'It's brass monkey weather out there.'

'It's not much warmer in here, either!'

'I'm staying by the fire.'

'Fuller, you coming? Blakey? Tell you what, I'll stand you a glass o' water!'

Blake smiles, apologetically. 'There's a talk in the Salvation Army hut tonight.'

'Cheap round, this one,' Jack shrugs. 'Don't you let me down, Mac.'

'Aye, son, why not?' Mac gets to his feet. 'Someone's got to keep ye out of mischief, I suppose.'

'You'll have no worries on that score, Mac,' laughs Ocker. 'Jacko's mischief is stuck in Ypres minding the shop and not even his tallywhacker is long enough to get stuck into her at that range.'

*

A short while later the two men leave camp, turning left past the guardroom to walk the mile or so up the slope to Poperinghe. The night is cold and clear. Although the moon is new, the stars are bright as flares, casting clear shadows. When they reach the town it is deserted; the first *estaminet* they come to is already closed. Another, the one at the end of Duinkerkestraat, is to be avoided. So they turn instead towards the market square, passing Talbot House and the Hôtel de la Bourse du Houblon.

'I doubt they'll want to see the likes of us in there,' says Jack.

'What? In Tubby Clayton's place?'

'Nay,' Jack laughs, 'not there. I'm not that desperate.'

'Aye, well – there's napoo booze in Toc H,' Mac says. 'That's why Blakey's such a regular.'

'Aye, he's lining up a little job there once the Army lets go of him.'

'I thought it'd closed down?'

'For sale,' Mac says. 'Apparently.'

'Oh aye?'

'The owner came back once the war was finished but cannae stand all these tourists and ex-Tommies coming knocking at his door.'

They pause at the imposing façade of number 57 Rue de l'Hôpital or Gasthuisstraat as the locals are now calling it, outside what used to be the Officers' Club.

'Well would you take a look at that,' says Mac, pointing to a sign on the door. 'Skindles Hotel.' He reads the printed notice. 'Now offering the luxury of bathrooms and central heating.'

'Better than t'others,' Jack says.

'Aye, son – but better for whom?'

'For all them battlefield tourists,' he answers. 'Pilgrims.

Widows. Orphans. It's not just the privileged few like us over now, you know.'

They laugh. The street opens out onto Grote Markt, the brooding and ominous outline of the Town Hall looming in the darkness in front of them. They cross the square quickly and head off down one of the narrow streets that lead off from the market square like drains.

'Is Ginger's still "Officers Only", d'you reckon?'

'Dunno, but Ginger's not there no more.'

'Not much point in going, then.'

Turning away from the town centre, the men find themselves in Rekhof. 'There's always Katia's old man's place I suppose,' Jack says.

'I thought he'd packed up now and moved the family back to Wipers,' Mac says. 'What with the war being over.'

'Happen he's hedging his bets,' Jack says. 'Keeping both places open, just in case . . .'

'In case what? In case the Germans decide to do an encore?'

'That'll never happen,' Jack shakes his head. 'Anyway, let's see how much business he's still doing in Pop, shall we? I reckon he might have some more work for us back in Wipers, you know.'

'Oh aye?'

'Expanding, I reckon,' Jack says. 'After all, t'British Tavern's always pretty busy.'

'He's a canny businessman, that's certain.'

'Pretty good barman, too.'

'And with a pretty wee lassie for a barmaid.'

The two men turn and head down Peper Straat. The stars have disappeared behind successive waves of cloud, and rain has started falling on the frozen streets. They hurry on in search of warmth and a welcome.

'Strange,' Jack says as they finally reach Monsieur Steenvan's temporary wartime *estaminet*. 'Why would he be closed tonight, of all nights?'

'Why are they all closed? Is there something they're not telling us?'

'Come on, Mac.' Jack turns and sets off walking in the opposite direction. 'This is no use.'

'Back to base, then?'

'Nay,' Jack calls over his shoulder. 'I'm not sure I can cope with Ocker's snoring, to be honest. I know – how about t'picture house?'

'What are they showing?'

'Don't rightly know,' Jack shrugs, then grins. 'But it's got Lillian Gish in it.'

'*Broken Blossoms*?'

'That's the one!'

'In that case . . .' Mac rubs his hands together.

A solitary truck rumbles past in the darkness as the two men approach the cinema on Vuermer Straat. Neither of them turns to look and it heads out of town, ignored, turning right onto the Switch Road and heading off in the direction of Ypres. By the time the Albion lorry pulls slowly away from the town through the gap in the ramparts half an hour later, heading out on the road towards Menin, it is raining steadily. The dim light from the gig lamps catches the falling drops like sparks in the yellow beams as the truck slowly negotiates the potholed road. It continues east in the direction of the old front line. At Hell Fire Corner the truck turns along the old corduroy road that once fed supplies of men and horses towards the almost certain death that awaited them at Railway Wood.

'Look out, sir!'

Ingham swerves to avoid a crater, but the road is still surrounded by shattered timber. 'Damn coolies,' he grumbles. 'Surely they should've cleared this road by now?'

'So, where exactly are we going, sir, if you don't mind me asking?'

'Never mind, Private Fuller. There's no need for me to bore you with the details. And no need for you to tell the others, either.'

'Yes, sir. Of course, sir. Sir?'

'What is it, Fuller?'

'Pardon me for asking again, sir, but why are we going there – wherever we're going – at night?'

'As I explained, Private, this is a delicate mission. Secret. Top secret.'

'Top secret?'

'Yes, Private. Which is why I have chosen you specifically for the purpose.' Fuller sits a little taller in his seat. 'That's right, Private. I need a man that I can trust. I can trust you, can't I, Private Fuller?'

'Yes, sir. Of course, sir.'

'I thought so, Private Fuller.' Ingham pats him on the thigh. 'And, of course, there'll be extra pay. I can't promise much, but you will of course be compensated for volunteering for extra duties like this.'

'Thank you, sir.'

'Right,' Ingham says, bringing the truck to a halt a few moments later. 'I think this should be it.' He unfolds the map across the steering wheel and shines a torch at the lines and grids and contours, looking for a particular spot.

'It's like a treasure map,' says Fuller. 'Like we're in search of hidden gold.'

'Ha. Well, in a manner of speaking, I suppose you might say

that's exactly what we are doing. Right, come along. And bring the pick and shovel with you.'

The two men climb down from the cab. Ingham, Fuller notices, is carrying a large army haversack across his shoulders. 'Should I bring the rubber gloves an' all, sir?'

'No no, don't be silly, Private. We're not looking for a body.'

'What are we looking for then, sir?' Ingham doesn't answer. The two men pick their way across the wasteland, taking care in the inky blackness to avoid shell-holes and old trenches. 'Is this the field we searched the other day, sir?'

'Er . . . no. It looks a bit like it I'll admit. They all look the same in the dark, don't they, Private Fuller?'

'I suppose they do, sir.'

'Yes. That's right. This is nowhere near where we were the other day. Nowhere near.' Fuller isn't so sure. The mud smells the same, a mixture of cordite, crap and a vague hint of gas. 'Right!' Ingham shines his torch onto a patch of bare earth. 'This looks like the spot. Yes, this is it. Well don't just stand there, man. Get digging!'

Fuller looks at the earth in the dim pool of yellow light. He can't be sure, but the soil looks almost freshly turned. In spite of the rain there is still a hint of frost on the otherwise black earth. Hard, he thinks. Maybe a pickaxe? Fuller hesitates, then pushes the blade of the shovel into the ground. It is soft. Placing his foot on the bar, he presses the blade down a couple of inches, levers back a lump of sticky clay topped – like icing on a cake – with an inch of snow, before setting it neatly to one side. The blade goes in surprisingly easily; soil falls from the shovel without much effort. Repeating the procedure a couple of times, he makes what begins to resemble a shallow, V-shaped moat like the kind a child would dig around a sand-castle.

'Good God, man,' Ingham says. 'We'll be here all night at this rate. Dig, for pity's sake. Get the shovel working.' He snatches the spade from Fuller's hands to show him how it's done. Within a few minutes the metal blade hits something hard. Ingham crouches, shines the torch and, with a gloved hand, scrapes away some of the soil. He smiles.

'Right, Private. Now – get digging around this crate. And digging properly this time. I want that box out of the ground and back on the truck within the next fifteen minutes. Do you understand?'

'Yes, sir.'

Ingham throws the shovel down at Fuller's feet and lights a cigarette.

'Can I . . . can you shine the torch for me, sir? Please?'

'Bloody hell, man!' Ingham turns on the torch and a dim circle of yellow light illuminates the top of what looks like an ammunition crate. 'That bright enough for you?'

'Thank you, sir.' Fuller starts digging carefully around the wooden crate. 'What's in the box, sir?'

'Never you mind,' says Ingham. 'Just keep digging.'

The excavation takes a little longer than Ingham had anticipated, but soon enough, the two of them are manhandling the coffin-sized crate down the frozen slope to where the van is parked. The contents rattle as they stumble on the rough ground. The box is heavy – far too heavy – for its size. Fuller still wonders what might be inside.

Once on board, Ingham covers the box with some of the tarpaulins the men use for wrapping bodies and they set off back to Ypres. Turning the corner into the deserted market square half an hour later, Ingham parks the truck and gets down from the cab, nodding as he does so to a man standing waiting in the shadows. He orders Fuller to remove the crate and they load it into the back of the stranger's car without a word.

'Right-o, Private. Dismiss.'

'Sir?'

'And not a word of this to any of the men, understood?'

'Yes, sir. I mean no, sir.'

Ingham turns on his heels and starts to walk away.

'Sir,' Fuller calls after him. 'What now, sir?'

'What now?' Ingham sighs. 'What now? I don't know "what now", man! Whatever you bloody well want to do "now". Go and knock up some tart. Go and have a drink if you can find a bar here that's still open.'

'Very good, sir,' Fuller says, not moving.

'Well, go on then, man.'

'But, sir,' Fuller goes on. 'How will I . . . I mean, how will we get home? I mean, I haven't brought me bike.'

'Christ, man – what do you think this is for?' Ingham kicks one of the truck's solid tyres. 'I'll be back here in an hour. If you're not in the square I'll assume you are where you are usually to be found when in Ypres – the British Tavern. Isn't that where you men choose to spend your time when off-duty? Yes, go and amuse yourself in what's left of Wipers and I'll collect you in the truck. And remember – not a word of this to anybody.'

'No, sir. You can count on me, sir.'

'Good, good. Ah' – Ingham waves his arm as a car pulls up beside them in the darkness – 'my chariot awaits.'

'Can't I come with you, sir? Please?'

'Out of the question!' Ingham calls out, climbing into the passenger seat of the waiting vehicle. 'You get yourself over to the British Tavern and I'll see you there in precisely one hour.'

Fuller notices something being passed between Ingham and

the driver: an envelope, he'd say, at a guess. But it is too dark to see properly. Then suddenly the man behind the wheel grinds the big car into gear and pulls out of the market square at speed. The noise of the engine fades and the black bulk of the vehicle slowly melts into the darkness. The sudden silence is broken only by the screech of an owl perched high on the ruined campanile.

Fuller turns on his heels and walks slowly back across the cobbles to where the truck is parked. He pauses briefly, one foot on the running board, ready to climb into the cab and wait, before stepping down again. He pulls up the collar of his greatcoat, turns and marches away from the black ruins of the Cloth Hall, turning quickly down Boomgarde Straat towards the Rijkswachtkazerne. There, at the end of Station Straat, he can see that the lights in the British Tavern are still lit. Someone must still be awake, he thinks. And didn't the officer just give him permission to 'knock up' a whore?

13

Moments later Private Fuller is sitting in the middle of the British Tavern with his hands wrapped round a mug of de Snoek Vlaams *bier blond*. He is the only customer.

'You are alone tonight?' Katia asks him as she starts to clear the other tables.

'You too, mademoiselle, by the looks of it. Where's the rest of the family, then, eh? Where's that pretty little sister o' yours tonight then, eh? Not here sweeping the floor for you, is she? Or collecting up the glasses?'

The older girl looks down at her hands. 'She is sick,' she says.

'Ha!' The boy smacks his lips. 'Love-sick, eh? I seen her making eyes at me.'

'She has been doing no such thing,' says Katia. 'Françoise is a . . . er, *une jeune fille*: a girl – only still a girl!' She looks down at the floor, both hands gripping the table she is clearing. 'And she is ill.' Katia looks up. 'She is in bed.' She sees a faint outline of a smirk on Fuller's lips. 'My mother is looking after her.' She glares at him. 'Back in Poperinghe!'

The glasses and beer mugs chink loudly as she gathers them up a handful at a time. 'It is fine,' she says, as he makes a move to help her. 'I can manage.'

Fuller gets up and begins to clear the remaining tables. 'I am sure you can, mademoiselle,' he smirks. 'In fact, I'm certain of it.'

Katia stops and stares at him. 'Shouldn't you be getting back,' she asks, 'to Remy? It is late.'

'Nah,' he says, draining one of the glasses on the table she is clearing. 'No rest for the wicked!'

'The . . . wicked?'

'Special orders for me,' he grins. 'That's why Ingham knocked me up after hours.'

'You are working this evening?' Katia asks. 'But it is going to begin . . . snowing.'

'Yeah, well . . .' He shrugs. 'There's things only me and Lieutenant Ingham can do, y'know.'

'I am sure you are right.' Katia carries on wiping the table she is clearing without looking up.

'Yeah! I could tell you a thing or two, y'know,' Fuller says, draining the last of his beer.

'I am sure you could,' Katia sighs.

'Don't you want to know what we all got up to, then?' – he smirks – 'while we was on holiday over in Roselare in the summer?'

Katia stops and wipes her hands on her apron. 'Got up to?' she says. 'You got up to something?'

'Ah, I thought you'd soon prick up your ears at that little bit o' news.'

'What did you – what news?'

'Wouldn't you like to know!' Fuller taps the side of his nose. 'Or maybe it's more your ol' man's business, eh? Maybe he's the one who'd like to know what Jacko has been up to while he's away from his intended, eh?'

'Jacques has been up to . . . something?'

131

'Or someone!'

'No!' The girl puts her hands up to her mouth.

'Bet you'd like to know who it is he talks about in his sleep, an' all! Whose name do you think he whispers in his dreams, eh?'

Katia closes her eyes and shakes her head.

'No matter, missus. Scared o' what you might hear, I suppose. Certainly don't sound much like "Katia" to me. More like . . . dunno. Anna, maybe? Wonder who she is, eh! Wouldn't *you* like to know?'

'Please!'

'As you wish, miss. My lift'll be here in a minute anyway. I'll get these for you, shall I?' He picks up some more of the glasses.

'Sit down,' the girl tells him, quietly. 'Sit down, please.'

'Well,' Fuller smirks. 'As you was so polite about it – saying please, an' all. How can I refuse?' Dried smears of spilt wine glisten on the table in the candlelight – a sticky mucous pattern like the slime trail of a slug.

'James?' Fuller looks up at the woman. Not unattractive, he thinks to himself. Bit on the skinny side. Not as pretty as her baby sister, but . . . 'Would you like another drink?'

A shy smile creeps across his face.

Whatever he is planning, the older Steenvan sister reckons she is equal to it. After all, Fuller is not much more than a boy. But on the other hand, if he knows anything – if there is anything to know – then Katia wants to know about it. She wants to know so much about the man she can't quite shake from her thoughts, the man she . . . loves? Does she love him? Does he love her? So many unanswered questions. Jack remains too much of a mystery: an intriguing mystery, but she has to know more, to take the risk, to find out even if she hears things that she would rather not know. Fuller sits down at the table and Katia brings him a *bier blond*. 'On the house – is that what you say? On the house?'

'Cheers!' The boy takes a gulp, wipes the froth from his mouth and looks at the girl and grins.

Katia puts her hand over his. 'So what is it that you have to tell me, James?'

He stares for a moment at the back of her hand. 'Ah, nuffink.' He pulls away. 'Don't worry about it.'

'You are playing games with me, James. Don't. Please don't.'

'On yer own are yer, tonight, miss? Behind the bar? No Papa Steenvan here to keep an eye on yer?'

'James, please.'

'Oh dear. Oh, dearie me. Oughtn't to do that, your papa, ought he now? Oughtn't to leave the pretty Katy on her own here wiv all these men.'

'I see no men.'

'Well . . . man, then.'

'No,' the girl looks airily around the room. 'Still nothing.'

'Oh!' He pulls his head back – like a tortoise, she thinks, shrinking back into its shell. 'Like that is it? Playin' hard to get, eh? You should teach a bit o' that attitude to your little sister. Always making eyes at me, she is!' The boy is worried now. Katia knows what he is thinking. She knows, too, now, that there is nothing whatever to tell – no secrets, no tale of betrayal or of infidelity, no skeleton in Jack's closet. She can tell. Fuller senses it as well.

'So what is it that you want to know?' he asks, glancing around the room as if looking at it for the first time.

'I am just curious,' Katia shrugs, 'about Jacques. We feel we know so little about him. He has been very kind to Papa. You all have, helping us acquire . . .'

'Yeah, well, the less said about that the better, miss. You see—'

'We could not have rebuilt our café here so quickly if it hadn't been for all the wood and sheets of metal Jacques – you all – have given us.'

'Ulterior motive, that's what it is,' says Fuller.

Katia can tell by the look on his face what the words mean. She smiles to herself, smiles at the thought of the Englishman she barely knows but somehow knows so well. 'So tell me,' she goes on. 'Tell me what you know, James. Tell me everything you know. Tell me what you think about him.'

Fuller is smiling again now, grinning actually – a silly, schoolboy grin as he suddenly remembers the game he is playing and the strength of his hand. 'That depends' – he takes another swig of beer – 'what it is you want to know about him.'

He narrows his eyes through the smoke of his cigarette and looks at her, more carefully now, more aware of what he thinks might be happening, aware of the cards he's holding. She looks away. It's late. The street outside the bar is emptying. She can hear the last train for Poperinghe slowly puffing from the station opposite.

'I don't know,' she says. 'He has been kind, as I said. But . . .'

'You wouldn't mind a bit more than just kindness, eh?'

She blushes, shakes her head. 'No, no.'

'No?'

She won't look at him. 'We know so little about Jack, that is all,' she says. 'Did you know him? Back in England?'

Fuller laughs. 'Nah. He's a Yorkshireman, isn't he?'

'A . . . Yorkshire man?'

'Yeah, bloody northern peasant, Jacko. They're not much more than savages up there.'

'Savages?'

'Up north, or *oop nerth* as they say, the savages.'

'You don't like him?'

'He's all right. He's a bloody good digger. Reckon that he must've been a sapper.'

'A sapper?'

'Engineer. Or labour corps most likely. Dunno. His battalion was disbanded after the Jerries used it for machine-gun practice at the Somme.'

'In 1916?'

'Yeah. Well, I say disbanded. Wiped out, more like. He was one of the only survivors, apparently. No one seems to know that much about him.'

'He is a mystery?'

Fuller looks at her, sizing her up. She is obviously several years younger than Jack – maybe nearer to his, to Fuller's own age, who knows? The girl's brown eyes are large and dark, and in the dim light of the bar and with his head now full of beer he can't make out the little black pupil in the middle of the iris. Her eyes suddenly seem so large that he feels he's falling into them. She looks away, quickly. Fuller blinks and takes another gulp of beer. 'Oh yeah, he's a mystery all right is our Jack.'

The street outside is silent now. The last of the townspeople have gone home. Doors are closed for the night; windows shuttered against the coming snow.

'I suppose' – Fuller lets out an enormous belch – 'I suppose I'd better be on my way.' But he makes no move to go.

'But there is so much that I need to know.' Katia moves her chair a little closer, leans her elbows on the table and looks up at him, sighing. 'And I thought, I really thought that you might be able to help me.'

Fuller coughs on the cigarette he's just relit. He knows what she wants, or thinks he does. And she knows what he wants.

One of them can give the other what they're asking for and knows it; the other wants the prize but can't deliver.

'I might,' he says at last. 'Depends.'

'Depends? Depends on what?'

'Depends on what I might get in return.' He raises his eyebrows.

'What you might get?'

'Well, information like that don't come cheap, y'know.'

'Wait!' She holds up a hand.

'Oh no, miss, I didn't mean—' Fuller suddenly looks worried, thinking that he may have gone too far. But the girl is simply pausing to make sense of what he's saying, taking time to think about the words he is using.

Downing the rest of the beer, Fuller decides to regain the initiative. While Katia is looking across the table at him, he makes a quick lunge forward. Before the girl can pull away his open mouth is pressed against her lips and she can taste the last mouthful of beer on his tongue. Standing up, she manages to push him off, wiping her mouth on her hands and her hands down her apron as she backs away.

'Telled you I wouldn't do it for nothing,' Fuller slurs. 'And that, mademoiselle ...' He makes another clumsy move towards her. 'That is only the beginning.'

'The beginning, you say?' she shouts, throwing a tea towel hard into his face. 'No! That is the ending. Now go. Please. Leave now. I am sorry to have troubled you and I will ask no more of you.'

'But I wanna ask so much more o' you.' He tosses the towel to the floor and grabs her by the wrist. She twists away but he doesn't let go.

'Don't be like that,' he breathes, pulling her closer, smelling of beer. 'We all know what Jack-the-lad gets up to here of an evening when he's off duty. We know what he does, what you both get up to. And we're jealous, eh? Want a bit o' that ourselves, don't we?'

'Let me go!' the girl shouts. 'Help! *Helpen! Aidez-moi!*'

He pulls her towards him. For a thin, wiry boy he is remarkably strong. She can feel his moist breath warm on her skin. His hands begin to fumble underneath her petticoats; he clearly doesn't know what he is doing. She stamps the sharp point of her heel into his foot but he doesn't flinch.

'Now that's not very nice, miss, is it?' he says.

'Please, James. Stop this madness. This is stupid. Jack will . . .'

'What will Jacko do, miss?'

'He will KILL YOU!' she suddenly screams. As the echo of her voice dies away, there is the rumble of a truck pulling up in the darkness of the street outside. Katia sighs heavily.

'Oh dear,' he says. 'What rotten timing. Well, my chariot awaits.' He lets her go, and his words settle like dust in the silence. And then, suddenly, he's turning to the door. 'Well, it's been very nice, mademoiselle,' he says, 'but I've got work to do, me.' He looks at her. 'You looks tired, darling. Best get back and get some sleep, eh?' He winks.

Katia gets up and smooths her dress; she walks across the bar and then unlocks the door. The cold night air hits Fuller like a punch and as he hears the door quietly bolted behind his back, he has a sudden urge to turn around and put his fist through the glass. But the truck is waiting, its engine running.

Katia picks up the empty beer glass, wipes the tables, turns off the oil lamps and blows out the remaining candles one by one.

War Diary or Intelligence Summary: Army form C. 2118
1920

DIVISION MAIN DRESSING STATION—Remy Siding
Map Sheet 28; Grid reference: L.22 d.6.3

January 1st – Observed as holiday.

The New Year's Honours Gazette contained the following awards: D.S.O. – Major T.H. ROBBINS; D.C.M. – 23378 Sgt. J.K. TOWNEND; 24789 Drummer T. HODGE; 4493 O.L. PARTRIDGE. M.S.M. – 2761 R.S.M. W.R. MITCHELL; 5611 C.S.M. W. TITLEY; Mentioned in Dispatches – Lt. Col. H.K. ANDREWS D.S.O.; Major H.H. HOWELLS M.C.; 2/Lt. M.V. MURRAY; R.S.M. N.H. ATKINSON.

January 2nd – Hockey Match against 3rd Royal Welch Fusiliers. Battalion won by three goals to nil. 'C' Coy ordered to assume escort duties for 121 P.O.W. Coy and to leave immediately.

January 3rd – 22198 L/Cpl. PATTERSON and 34677 Pte. KEEGAN returned from local leave.

January 5th – Further five O.R.s reported sick with Spanish Influenza. Company concert party 'The Sandbags' gave a performance in the recreation hut.

January 7th – Salvage operations resumed in T.7 and T.8 together with dismantling of surplus Nissen huts. Battalion Lewis Gun Officer (2/Lt. H.J.K. MERRICK) inspected Lewis Guns of companies.

January 8th – Arrangements made for isolation wards to be established at the field hospital for the treatment of victims of latest Spanish Influenza epidemic. Lt. J.K. LEVISON and 3 O.R.s admitted to hospital.

January 10th – Companies paraded at Grand Place, Poperinghe and marched to Salvation Army hut for Church Parade (all denominations).

January 15th – The Battalion played the 5th Rifle Brigade at Association Football, winning by 4 goals to 3.

January 20th – Baths parade, Poperinghe.

14

'Shall we give t'pub a miss tonight?' Jack shouts to the men in the back of the van. 'Get straight back to Pop?' There is a loud groan.

'You'll be in trouble, *Jacques* – if yer missus discovers you've been to Ypres without calling in to say hello.'

'Especially as you missed saying *bonne année* in person, what with going on leave to St Omer an' all.'

'Yeah, did you bring 'em your presies, Jacko?'

'Damn! They're back at Pop in me haversack.' Jack slows the truck to a crawl as they cross the moat through the wide gap in the ramparts. 'Right you are then, lads. Just the one, mind. Road'll be like a skating rink if we leave it too long.'

They drive along Menen Straat and park in the open square of the Grote Markt. The thin wire cordon sanitaire has shrunk now to the perimeter of the Lakenhalle and St Martin's Church. Building work is under way on the corner of Dismuide Straat and a forest of scaffolding now clads each of the few remaining walls of the cathedral. Heavy timber buttresses shore up the campanile. They pass a cart loaded with small children, a big oak table, four chairs and several mattresses. Another family returning home.

'Busy here tonight!' There are men everywhere, darting in

and out of shadows or striding quickly down the road, others laughing, talking loudly, hailing friends. 'And there must be a small fortune to be made in scrap,' Ocker says, 'judging by the fancy strides these coves are wearing.'

'Aye – where there's muck, there's brass,' Jack says. 'Wonder where they're all going.'

The bar, when the men arrive, is deserted. Neither of the Steenvan girls is there and the barmaid, Margreet, pours the men their drinks as they huddle round a table in the corner. Someone gets out a pack of cards.

'You in, Jack?'

'Not tonight.' He shakes his head and pushes back his chair. Ocker shuffles the pack and deals the others in.

'So where is she?' Jack asks as he walks back to the bar. Margreet smirks at him and shakes her head. '*Waar is ze vanavond?*' The woman leans her elbows on the bar, cradling her head in her hands and smiles. 'Er . . . *waar is Katia vanavond?*' he says again.

'*Wat is er mis met mij? Ben ik niet goed genoeg?*'

'Nowt, lass. There's nowt wrong wi' you. I just wanted to know—'

'Françoise is not well,' Margreet says in near-perfect English.

'Still?'

'Still,' the woman gives an exaggerated nod and a smirk, then starts idly wiping the surface of the bar, forcing Jack to move his elbow. 'And then there is Katia . . .'

'Katia? What's matter wi' Katia?' Jack suddenly looks worried.

'She is fine.' The woman waves away Jack's frown, keen to carry on annoying him. 'She was . . . how do you say? Digging. Yes, she was digging.'

'Digging?'

'Mm!' she nods her head slowly. 'Digging for information.'

'Information?' Jack pushes his cap back and scratches his head.

'About you!'

'About me? And did she . . . ?'

'Wouldn't you like to know?' Margreet looks down and smiles to herself. The beers, lined up in mugs on the counter, begin to settle. Jack watches the bubbles pop, one by one, each frothy head deflating slowly like so many tiny balloons bursting.

'Ah, well,' he says at last. 'Will she be in later – Katia, I mean?'

'No,' the woman says.

'No matter then,' Jack sighs. 'We'll not be stopping long tonight anyhow. Not if you hurry up with them beers, anyway.'

'Good.' The woman starts adding more beer to each of the mugs.

'Aye, well. I can see how busy you are.' Jack looks round the otherwise empty room.

'Later,' the woman says, 'we will be busy later. When they all come back.'

'Come back from where?'

'Come back from the meeting,' Margreet says. 'They are all there tonight. Monsieur de Wulf is there.' She looks at him and smirks. 'And Katia's father. Maybe they will, you know . . .'

'So what's up?' Jack says.

'Up?'

'What's happening?'

'A meeting,' she tells him. 'I told you. They are having a big meeting at the Nieuwercke.'

'Oh, aye?'

'They are talking about the rebuilding,' she goes on. 'Ieper is rising.' She raises her arms in the air. 'Rising like a phoenix from the ashes of war. That is what they are discussing.'

'Is that so?'

'Yes, Jacques, it is so.'

Jack shakes his head.

'And when it is "so" you will no longer be here, will you? You will soon be gone; you will all be gone. And then we will have the town back to ourselves and one day it will be bigger and better than before.'

'I thought they was leaving t'Lakenhalle as a ruin,' he says to her.

'What would they do that for?'

'As a monument,' he says.

'A monument?' she tuts. 'A monument to what? To German shells?'

'A monument to t'men who died,' Jack says. 'To them who was killed saving the place – them poor buggers we dig up and then rebury every day.'

'How could a broken ruin be a monument to anybody, Jacques?' The woman throws her head back, laughing. 'You are stupid. The English are all . . . stupid. This is our town,' she says, twisting a curl of hair between her thumb and forefinger. 'We saw the English off in 1383—' She pauses, crossing herself and mumbling, '*Sancta Maria Deo Gracias.*' Then she looks at Jack and smirks. 'And we will do so again.'

'Aye, but . . .'

'But?'

'Well, that were a long time ago.'

'So?'

'And, well . . . There wouldn't be much of it left no more if it hadn't been for the likes of us,' Jack says to her.

'Much of it left?' she shrieks. 'There couldn't be much less than this!'

'Maybe,' he says. 'But at least it's yours – not overrun with Germans.'

'Exactly! It is ours – this is our home. And we are now taking back what is ours.'

'Aye, well . . .' Jack shakes his head.

Margreet finishes topping up the beers. 'So why do you not go back?' she asks. 'Back to your home?'

'What's to go back for?' He stares at her, wondering if he has said the words aloud or simply thought them, wondering if they're true or if he merely dreamt them.

'Is there not a woman waiting for you, Jacques?' Margreet leans across the bar and runs a finger down his cheek. 'You need a woman, Jacques – a real woman. Not these, these . . . *jeunes filles*. Not Katia. She is just a girl you know. And you—' She steps back, looking Jack up and down. '*Vous êtes un bon homme*,' she whispers, leaning over the counter.

'Aye, and you're a bloody good linguist.' Jack picks up his beer and turns to join the others. 'When you want to be.'

'Perhaps,' she calls after him whilst studying the glasses she is polishing, 'perhaps there is something there that you do not want to go back to? Perhaps you are hiding, Jacques? What is it that you are hiding from, Jacques? Or who?'

'I'll tell thee, shall I?' Jack turns suddenly and is back at the bar. 'I'll tell thee why I don't go home.' He is leaning close across the counter into Margreet's face. 'I don't go home 'cos there's nowt to go back home to,' he says. 'There's nowt there no more.'

'Nowt?' She moves back from him, startled.

'Nothing,' he says quietly. 'No one. Nowt!'

*

144

The burgomaster is calling the meeting to order. The Town Hall – like most of the buildings in Ypres – is just a temporary wooden hut on the Minneplein, barely large enough to house the municipal furniture recently returned from the safety of a Poperinghe cellar. The burghers and the townsfolk crowd into the single room for the open meeting that the council has convened to discuss the city's future.

'Gentlemen.' Monsieur Colaert calls the room to order. On his left, the city architect, Jules Coomans, is taking several large, rolled-up plans from a long canvas bag and placing them on the table in front of him. At his side, his young assistant, Eugène Dhuicque – who remained in Ypres throughout the war, helping to shore up the little that remained after successive German bombardments – looks down and lights a cigarette. The room falls silent.

'Gentlemen, thank you. Apologies again that we are somewhat cramped this evening.'

'Cramped?' a rather large man interrupts. 'There is more room in my wife's brassiere!'

Someone laughs. Another burgher tuts his disapproval and others roll their eyes and shake their heads. Monsieur Colaert smiles patiently before turning the interruption to his advantage.

'Quite so,' he smiles. 'Quite so. Then maybe this evening, gentlemen, we will see it within us to finally settle the great matters that have been troubling us and come to an agreement on the future of our city. That way we might start rebuilding the Kasselrij and once more have a suitable venue for our deliberations.'

He waves an arm as if to remind everyone that the small wooden barn of a building they are packed inside is not just impractical, but beneath the dignity of the city council. There are murmurs of approval; nods of heads. Everyone in the room agrees that rebuilding should begin. Everyone, that is, except one man.

'Following our last meeting, I think we can at last be reasonably certain of our future here and of the future of our city. Is that not right, Colonel?'

Canadian Lt Colonel Beckles Willson – Town Major for the Army in Ypres until his recent demob – is attending the meeting ex officio. He sighs, looks down at the back of his hands on the smooth, dark wood of the heavy table, then presses down his palms as he rises to his feet.

'It is true,' he begins, allowing his translator to catch up and at the same time giving him more time to choose his words with care. 'It is true that we now believe it right that the people of Ypres should be allowed to return to their homes and rebuild.'

'None of this nonsense about leaving the entire place as a ruin,' someone mutters.

The colonel pauses, turns and glances at the speaker for a moment. 'It is true that some of us have felt that the ruins of the city should remain as a permanent monument to the dead—'

'. . . a monument, more like, to the efficiency of German guns!'

The translator whispers into the colonel's ear. He smiles, resignedly, then carries on. 'We nevertheless believe, Monsieur le Maire, that there should be left a zone of silence, to include the sacred sites of the Cloth Hall and the cathedral, and that these ruins should remain untouched.'

The burgomaster rises to his feet. 'I will remind you gentlemen that the government in Brussels—'

Someone in the crowded room makes a loud spitting noise.

'The government in Brussels,' Colaert continues, 'has agreed that the area to which the colonel refers – together with the Meninpoort and the ramparts – should indeed remain untouched for the foreseeable future, at least until such time as the British government decides on what it wishes to build by way of a suitable memorial to its war dead.'

'But we cannot simply leave the Lakenhalle as a ruin,' shouts someone from the floor. 'It is the symbol of our city, of its commerce and of our proud history as a centre of the cloth trade.'

'Why, even our very name . . .' another voice trails off, the point made to all except the colonel.

'Icper was the name given to a particularly finely woven cloth, Colonel,' the burgomaster explains, 'traded in the Lakenhalle.'

'The city must be restored,' shouts another burgher, 'and we should not be obliged to wait on the whims of a foreign government!'

'There are a great many from among our own community who agree that this is the most appropriate course of action,' Monsieur Colaert argues.

'Then what have we been fighting for these last four years?' someone else shouts out. 'If we are not free to rebuild as we choose, then we might as well have just surrendered the town to the Germans.'

'At least then there would be no need for the rebuilding,' someone laughs. There is a rising murmur in the room as conversations across tables turn neighbouring burghers into friend or foe according to their views. The translator struggles to make himself heard above the noise as he tries to keep Beckles Willson informed about what has been said.

Slowly, as the words sink in, the colonel's face reddens, and he suddenly rises to his feet and in the voice of the parade ground bellows: 'You would not have a city to rebuild if it wasn't for the dead of the British Empire, gentlemen. Let no one here forget that fact.' The room instantly falls silent.

Colaert, afraid that this would happen and now embarrassed, struggles to return to the agenda of the meeting. 'Please, gentlemen, let us confine ourselves solely to the business we have come here this evening to discuss. I will permit no further interruptions. This is how matters now stand: there is to be a moratorium on rebuilding in the areas I have already mentioned. But I must emphasise' – he turns to Beckles Willson – 'that this is at present merely a temporary arrangement, to be reviewed as and when the British decide on where, and in what form, their memorial should be built.'

Murmurs of approval from the assembled burghers.

'In the meantime, gentlemen, we can be certain that Ieper will rise in triumph from the ruins of destruction. We have faced down the many challenges – both from foreign governments and, I must point out, from some among our own people . . .'

'Count d'Alviella is a Walloon,' someone interrupts. There is laughter. Monsieur Colaert looks down and smiles, then holds up a hand for silence.

'Nevertheless,' he continues, 'there were many voices, persuasive voices, noble voices, speaking for the idea that the city should remain a ruin and, as such' – he nods towards Beckles Willson – 'should serve as a memorial to the men who bravely fought and died.'

'What about the living?' someone shouts. 'Our duty is to the living, not the dead.'

'That is correct,' Monsieur Colaert agrees. 'But we also have a duty to honour the memory of those without whom there would not be a living population waiting to return to their ruined city.'

'Or a free population!'

'Quite.'

'So the question now before us is one that concerns the nature of the reconstruction – not the principle of whether to rebuild, but what to rebuild, and where, and how.'

There are loud murmurs of approval.

'Gentlemen, this is a great task and a unique opportunity. We have it in our hands to do great things for our city, to rebuild a municipality worthy of the sacrifice of so many Belgian lives, as well' – he turns to Beckles Willson – 'as well, of course, as the lives of those from so many friendly nations.'

'Hear, hear,' someone calls. Others nod and someone bangs the table in approval.

'I have therefore invited Monsieur Coomans to present to us this evening some provisional drawings, an outline of some of the possibilities that lie before us, so that we may properly consider the way to proceed, for the good of the city of Ieper.'

The burghers relight pipes and take cigarettes from silver cigarette cases. Matches are struck, lights are shared. Smoke rises and gathers, curling high into the wooden roof of the temporary council chamber.

'Gentlemen.' Monsieur Coomans rises to his feet, unrolling the first of the architect's plans. 'Were it solely my responsibility,' he begins, 'I would have no hesitation in recommending to this meeting the wholesale reconstruction, brick by brick, of what was lost. That seems, to me, to be by far the most acceptable, desirable and popular solution.'

Monsieur Colaert nods his approval, scanning the room as he does so, registering which of the assembled burghers is in agreement, noting possible dissent and mentally preparing specific arguments for future use with individual burghers.

'Nevertheless, as Monsieur le Burgomaster has pointed out, as a nation we are no longer in agreement over certain matters.'

'We never were,' someone shouts from the back of the room. Others laugh.

'The government-appointed architect, Professor Dhuicque, is keen that we should explore the options now made open to us by modern methods of construction – new materials and even bold and innovative designs. Here' – he unrolls the first of the plans – 'is a suggestion for the new Kasselrij, for example.'

He holds up the architect's drawings, turning them slowly to give each side of the room a better view. 'Or this' – he carries on – 'for the Gendarmerie.' Again he carefully shows selected plans to the assembled burghers. But several are now turning away. Others look down as he unrolls government-approved plans for the Fire Station, secondary school and, finally, the Post Office.

'But the Post Office,' someone shouts as the last plan is unrolled, 'is one of the only – in fact, the only – building left standing in Ieper.'

'Yes, but not in any habitable state,' someone else says.

'Nevertheless,' the man continues, 'it is the only one of our cherished buildings to have survived, no matter that it has survived in such a state of dereliction. It stands. It can be repaired. It must be repaired and not – not – rebuilt. Especially not in this . . . this . . .' He waves a dismissive hand over the plans and then sits down. 'It is ironic, no, that a professor of medieval architecture should be so keen to see Ieper rebuilt in the German modernist style?'

'Gentlemen.' Monsieur Colaert calls the room to order once again, although it seems clear now that further progress will be limited. Cigarettes are being lit and pipes stoked. Soon afterwards, the meeting adjourns once again and the burghers depart into the quiet streets and the shadows of the town whose future they are planning.

15

'Jeez, I'm sorry, Jacko.' The men all stare. Mac shakes his head. Ocker reaches out and puts a hand on Jack's shoulder. There are tears welling in Mac's eyes, and all of a sudden Skerritt lets out a wail. From outside the hut come bursts of laughter. Snatches of song and other sounds of gaiety intrude as the others return from the evening show by 'The Sandbags' in the recreation hut.

'I don't understand. I just don't understand.' Jack sits on the bunk with his head in his hands. On the floor, his haversack is still packed with the cigarettes, chocolate and newspapers he bought in St Omer while on leave.

'Katia came over, Jack.' Blake hovers over him, trying to pace the remainder of the news. 'She left a message at the guardroom.'

'But . . . when?'

'Françoise took ill a couple of weeks ago, just after Christmas. They took her to Poperinghe for her mother to look after her.'

'That must have been . . .' Jack looks at Mac.

'Aye, laddie. No wonder they were closed.'

'I assumed you knew.'

'Of course I knew! Just haven't seen much of 'em for a couple of weeks, what with Christmas and then me leave.'

'She went downhill rather quickly, Jack. Apparently Doctor Holeurt called the other day and gave her an injection. He said if she was no better next day she'd have to go to hospital at Hazebrouck.'

'They could have brought her here,' Jack cries. 'They needn't have gone to Hazebrouck.'

'They didn't,' Blake says.

'They wouldn't have been able to bring her here anyway, Jack, you know that.'

'Ah, we could've wangled it somehow. Someone could've bribed Ingham. He's always ready for a backhander is that bastard . . .'

'No, Jack. They wouldn't have brought her here whatever Ingham did or said.'

'Or however much you paid 'im.'

'She'd not even have been sent to Hazebrouck in her condition. You know how damned contagious this disease is.'

'But she were so young,' Jack is saying, 'so strong.'

Mac sits down beside him. 'That's how *la grippe* likes them.' He shakes his head, slowly. 'Lord alone knows we've lost so many of our own men to it since 1918 – all good, strong, healthy fellows too.'

'Would you like . . .' Blake hesitates. 'Would you like me to say a prayer?'

'Oh God!' Jack puts his head in his hands. 'Oh God! Christ Jesus!'

Next morning Jack rises early, smartens up and goes before the CO, hopeful of being granted at least a few hours' compassionate leave.

'I'm not exactly family, sir.'

'You aren't even engaged to the girl's sister are you, Corporal?' Major Rennard is asking.

'I know, sir. Not yet, sir. But—'

'With respect, sir,' Ingham interrupts. He glances sideways at Jack. 'The men aren't being used for digging at the moment, what with the snow and ice.'

'No, no. Quite. Twenty-four-hour pass, Corporal.' The CO pushes back his chair. 'Dismiss!' Jack salutes as smartly as he can, turns on his heels and marches straight to the guardroom with the signed chitty.

Half an hour later, after walking into Poperinghe, he is standing before the dark door of the little *estaminet* in Peper Straat, waiting, cap in hand, listening to the sound of children on their way to school, to women with baskets on their way to the weekly market, to the deafening screaming in his head. His eyes close and he steadies his breathing.

Never come back no more, boys. Never come back
     no more.
The camp is becoming a bore, boys. It is becoming a
     terrible bore.
Shut up the old shop window. Put a notice over the
     door.
We're packing our kits for the jolly old Ritz, and we
     ain't coming back no more.

Eventually, the cold becomes unbearable. He lifts his arm, closes a fist, knocks at the door. He knocks again. And again. After several minutes of blowing on his hands, he hears movement in the small café. A shadowy figure appears at the door.

Bolts are being drawn back and a handle turned. The door opens and there she stands, looking up at him.

'Jacques!'

'I'm sorry, lass. I'm so sorry.'

'Come in,' she says, stepping to one side. 'My mother is . . .' The girl gestures towards the open door behind the counter. Jack walks past empty tables, round the chairs, and goes through the door.

Monsieur Steenvan appears, still wearing his apron. '*Priester!*' he whispers, putting his fingers to his lips. Jack strains to listen to the low mumble of strange words while following Steenvan into the tiny back room as silently as his Army boots allow.

A priest, black as a crow, looks up briefly as he enters. Katia, following them into the room, walks past Jack and takes her father's hand. Madame Steenvan kneels by her daughter's body, laid out in an open coffin on the kitchen table.

In nomine Patris et Filii et Spiritus Sancti.

The priest's hand hovers over the dead girl's face, the family all lift their right hands, touching first their foreheads, then breastbone, then the left shoulder, then the right.

Amen.

Jack stares, transfixed, at the girl's body. Katia's sister Françoise looks so much smaller, so much younger, than she did when she was . . . when he last saw her. She looks so peaceful, too. This isn't death as Jack knows death. The girl is asleep, surely? She is sleeping, merely sleeping.

De profundis clamavi ad te, Domine: Domine, exaudi vocem meam.

Out of the deep . . . the deep . . . *de profundis.* The steep walls of a deep grave, closing in at all sides, pressing slowly against Jack's chest and making it difficult for him to breathe.

Fiant aures tuae intendentes: in vocem deprecationes meae.

Oh hear the voice of my supplication . . . the thin, desperate pleading, the silent screaming: Oh God! Oh God!

Si iniquitates observaveris, Domine, Domine, quis sustinebit?

If Thou, Lord, shouldst mark our iniquities, O Lord, who shall stand? Jack steadies himself against the jamb of the door. The room spins; he can feel his legs buckle; he grips the door frame with both hands.

Quia apud te propitiatio est: et propter legem tuam sustinui te, Domine.

But there is forgiveness with Thee . . . Is there forgiveness? Is there really forgiveness? Can Jack be forgiven for what he has done? Can anyone?

Sustinuit anima mea in verbo ejus: speravit anima mea in Domino.

The priest goes on. The remaining words are a blur. Jack can't take his eyes off the girl: her hair, unpinned, is combed in long, dark waves over her shoulders. It is so much longer than he could ever have imagined. Françoise's lips are open slightly in a ghost of a smile; her eyes are closed, but seem barely to be closed at all. In fact Jack can clearly see the little bump of her cornea through the tissue-thin skin of her eyelids and her long, dark eyelashes are restless, moving – are they moving? She is sleeping. Dreaming. A sudden hard spasm in Jack's throat makes him gasp. He tries desperately to stifle a cough.

Anima Christi, sanctifica me.
Corpus Christi, salva me.
Sanguis Christi, inebria me.
Aqua lateris Christi, lava me.
Passio Christi, conforta me.
O bone Iesu, exaudi me.
Intra tua vulnera absconde me.

Ne permittas me separari a te.
Ab hoste maligno defende me.
In hora mortis meae voca me.
Et iube me venire ad te,
Ut cum Sanctis tuis laudem te
in saecula saeculorum. Amen.

The priest stands, gathers some things together in a small bag and unwinds the thin silk scarf from around his neck. Monsieur Steenvan leads him out, past Jack, through the empty shop and out onto the street. Madame Steenvan goes on weeping quietly by her daughter's body.

'Thank you, Jacques.' Katia looks down at the floor, tears in her eyes. 'Thank you for coming.'

'I . . .'

She puts her hand on his. 'I know how you must feel,' she says. Jack shakes his head.

'If there's anything I can . . . well, you know.' She nods. He makes a move.

'Actually.' She looks up, taking hold of Jack's sleeve. 'Actually, there is one thing, Jacques.'

'Aye, lass?'

'There is one thing you can do.'

'What is it?'

'I don't want to ask you, Jacques. It is too much to expect.'

'What, lass? What is it?'

'My father,' Katia says. 'He is not so strong. And the ground is so . . . hard. It is frozen solid.'

'Aye, lass?'

'He will have to dig the hole.'

'Eh?'

'There is no one else to do it. Papa, he will have to dig the hole.'

'What – the grave, you mean?'

'Yes, yes, the grave. Please, Jacques?'

'Aye,' Jack puts his hand on top of hers. 'Aye, lass, of course I will.'

'Thank you, Jacques.' Suddenly the tension drains from her shoulders and her head drops. 'Thank you so much, Jacques. You are a good man.'

'I'm not . . .' Jack slowly shakes his head. 'I'm not the man you think I am.'

16

In the middle of the communal cemetery in Poperinghe, a small row of British military graves marks the final resting place of some of the earliest British casualties of the war. Here, and at the far side of the cemetery, is a total of twenty-one Allied burials all dating back to 1914.

'*Goedemiddag,*' Jack calls out as he wheels his barrow along the gravel path. The man stops hoeing briefly and touches his cap, but doesn't answer.

'They're ours,' Jack says as he walks past the line of simple wooden crosses. Crowding in on all sides are elaborate stone and marble vaults, graves fenced off with rusted ironwork chains and railings and the crosses – explicit, tortured, brightly painted Calvaries and crucifixes. 'And they're in a darn site better shape than yourn. Happen you'd better spend a bit o' time tidying your bit of t'cemetery and leave them graves to us.'

'You what?'

'You English?' Jack stops, surprised.

'Why wouldn't I be?'

'Well, I don't know,' he says. 'You're not Army.'

'Not now.'

'You used to be?'

'Aye, of course. And before anyone starts making judgments about what's smart and what's not, you could do with a bit o' spit-and-polish yourself, Lance-Corporal.'

'Sorry,' Jack says. 'I didn't realise. And I'm not at me best just now.'

'Who is, these days?' the man says. 'Jim Ashbury, by the way. Sergeant Jim Ashbury.'

Jack nods. 'Patterson, sir. Jack Patterson.' The men shake hands. 'So you're no longer in t'Army, then?'

'Not any more.'

'But you're tending Army graves?'

'That's right,' the man says. 'War Graves Commission – gardener, second class!'

'Lord Wargraves's Regiment!'

'What's that?'

'That's what we all call you fellas,' Jack laughs. 'Lord Wargraves's Regiment. Don't rightly know why . . .'

'Probably some dig at the ol' Major-General,' the man says. 'Fabian Ware. Used to be a Red Cross volunteer, searching the battlefields for stragglers and survivors.'

'Not many o' them left these days,' Jack says. 'It's all about finding bodies and burying the dead now.'

'And making sure their graves are cared for,' says the man. 'That's what Ware – Lord Wargraves – wanted. And that's why I'm here.' He offers Jack a cigarette. Jack gives the man a light.

'Anyway,' he says, puffing smoke into the cold air, 'I ought to be asking you what you're doing here. I'm tidying the graves of soldiers. That's my job. But there are no more soldiers buried here. The cemetery closed in 1915.'

'To us,' Jack says.

'So you're digging graves for them, now?'

'You could say that,' Jack nods. 'It's their turf, after all.'

'I suppose so . . . apart from this little bit that I'm tending.'

'Some corner of a foreign field, eh?'

The man says nothing.

'Makes you wonder, doesn't it?' Jack goes on. 'I mean, did they really think that local cemeteries like these would be enough? That there would be space enough to bury all the casualties of this bloody great war?'

'I suppose, at the time, they hoped they wouldn't have to dig many more.'

'If only . . .' Jack sighs. 'Have you seen Lijssenthoek?'

'Seen it?' the man replies. 'I'm based there. We all are.'

'What, at Remy?'

'That's where we're all billeted,' the man replies. 'And Lijssenthoek – that's our playground.'

'You what?'

'That's where we get to experiment with shrubs and plants,' he says.

'So you really are a gardener?'

'Hardly,' the man laughs.

'But . . .'

'Oh, I can do this,' he says. 'Dig, plant, sow. I can even propagate now. Got our own nurseries at Remy Sidings . . . you must've seen the greenhouse.'

'Aye, yes, aye.'

'It's a big affair.'

'You're telling me!'

'Chap even comes across from London, no less.'

'What – to make sure they all stay put?'

'Who?'

'This lot.'

'No, no – don't be daft. Chap from Kew Gardens. Comes to give us instructions, teach us what plants to put where.'

'Oh, aye?'

'Yes. They're thinking *Papaver rhoeas* should do well in this local soil – you know, 'In Flanders Fields' and all that.'

Jack shakes his head.

'Poppies!' the man says. 'And then maybe calendula and one or two dwarf polyanthus – to brighten the place up a bit, you know.'

'Aye, well,' Jack smiles. 'That sounds well and good, but it's all Dutch to me, I'm afraid.'

'Latin, actually,' the man laughs.

'Oh aye?' Jack says. 'Heard a bit too much o' that just lately . . .'

'Really?'

'Funeral,' Jack says. 'Well, start of it. I didn't go with them to t'church.'

'No?'

'No. There were the priest spouting the usual claptrap . . . except it wasn't this time 'cos it were in Latin.'

'Not a religious man yourself then, Jack?'

'No. Not me. Not for me, all that life after death and stuff.'

'No?'

'No. Seen a bit too much of it, I have.'

'Haven't we all?'

'And as for the bloody padre . . . *Glorious Resurrection*?' Jack sniffs. 'I do that every day wi' me blinkin' shovel!'

'I must say I don't envy you chaps.'

'I'll tell you one thing, though.' Jack's voice is shaking now. 'Vile bodies – the Holy Joe's got that bit right. Oh, Jesus Christ!'

'Steady on, soldier. Pull yourself together.'

'I'm . . . sorry.' Jack takes out his handkerchief. 'Anyhow, this won't get the grave dug, eh?' He blows his nose and tries to laugh, tries to forget, tries to imagine that it's just another hole to dig, another trench, another sap.

'That's all these things are anyhow,' he says to himself as much as anyone.

'You what?

'Holes in t'ground.'

'Oh, aye.'

'You dig a hole, you dig another, join the two together, meet up with your fellow digger – trench, sap, graves. They're all just cold, wet ways to hide, to keep your head down for a while.'

Or for her, for Françoise, now, for ever.

'Come on then,' says Jim, picking up Jack's wheelbarrow. 'Let me give you a hand.'

17

The snow melts and then it rains, continuously, rains for days, filling up old trenches, overflowing shell-holes and making the mud cling more jealously than ever to the sticky corpses that the search teams are exhuming. The greedy, green-black Belgian earth with its bitter harvest is transformed into some shape-shifting monster from the marsh, jealously possessive of the lives it swallows. It refuses to yield up even the smallest bones without a struggle. And there are many, many struggles.

Jack is struggling himself, even in sleep. Struggling waist-deep in the green slime, or struggling to get a foothold on the sodden Menin Road marching towards the front line; struggling to pick his way through the piles and piles of horses, smashed wagons and the scattered debris of extinct men and beasts. Struggling too, once he awakes, to come to terms with what has happened.

He stops to light a cigarette. A small 'thud' in the distance is the signal that another unexploded shell has just been detonated – by the ordnance teams? Or by the enemy? One of ours or one of theirs? Jack could never tell. Not like the other men who seemed to know by the sound of the bang whether it was coming for them . . . or for the enemy. Yellow-green smoke curls against a boiling sky bubbling with black-grey clouds.

On the far horizon, darker plumes drift high into the heavens like the clouds of incense burning by the open coffin in the Catholic church in Poperinghe.

Silence.

Birds sing again now – the first sign of spring. But Jack no longer hears them; his ears are shelled to near-destruction. But he remembers them; he can remember their song. And when he sees them, chest feathers ruffled, beaks wide open, he can hear them, hear them in his head. So the songs still exist.

When he sees her, too, he can hear her. When his eyes close, he can feel her, smell the mix of soap and sunshine on her skin. When he wakes in the morning at Reveille, for a blissful moment she is there and he can feel what the world was like when she was still a part of it, imagine a world with her walking at his side, her small hand in his hand, her shy smile, her blue eyes. And then he feels again the fear of losing her. His eyes close and he sees her leaving, getting smaller and smaller. In the worst of his nightmares she lies dead, in her mother's coffin. And in the morning, when he resumes his digging, all the corpses, every empty shell of a skull, will wear her face whenever he lifts them on his shovel.

He is dreaming again. A barge floats past, the water gently slapping the sloping, wet, black sides of the boat. Jack knows that he should be getting back to camp, but the river just here is filled with eels; the black waters teem with slick silver slivers of life. A ration-barge passes slowly in the darkness, water slap-slapping at the stern. Once it's safely out of sight Jack creeps back to the reedy riverbank to collect the bounty from his baskets. Dawn breaks, and in his head he hears the fluting of a blackbird; then the big thrush that always sang as night fell near the rest camp safe behind the lines at Heilly Station.

Was he really deaf to the dawn chorus by the time he was rebadged and sent back here to Ypres? Hadn't his ears recovered from the pounding of artillery bombardments during those few brief weeks back home on leave after the catastrophe of July 1916? Had his nerves not been soothed listening to the rattling murmur of the River Ure over moss-covered limestone, catching the whine of the curlew on the breeze like the sound of a minnie-woofer echoing across endless, empty moors or the swifts screeching overhead like shrapnel shells? Had he not closed his eyes and heard her again and felt the sound twisting like a bayonet in his guts, seen her tears as she is taken from him, taken away, taken from the lifeless body of her mother almost twenty years earlier? He can see the small, red mouth opening and closing like a fish. But he cannot hear her cry.

A barn, a warm, dry barn. Jack curls up each night of his last leave like a fox on a bed of fresh straw. Listening, even in his sleep; hearing the sound of anything at all that is unfamiliar, quick to wake and to make good his escape, should it be necessary. But he is running out of hiding places.

One last week at home before returning to the Front, this time, for ever. One last listening to each tiny rustle of nocturnal activity in the fitful, restless sleep of the great silences of hillsides and of moorland, hemming him in on all sides. The scratching of rats in the rafters; the foreign tongue of jackdaws and crows carried on the breeze from the enemy trenches.

It is night. Out hunting, Jack's senses are balanced like a trigger, responsive to each snap of paw on old twigs, each soft pad, pad, pad of a rabbit on dry leaves. He hears the sleeping breath of a pheasant, roosting in the low branches of a tree. Suddenly, the bird is exploding with the noisy energy of shrapnel just above Jack's head as he pulls the wire noose tight around the scrawny neck of his next meal.

No. Jack's ears aren't the problem. He can still hear; it is listening that is troubling him. He hears everything. Just like he sees everything, has seen everything. But his mind is editing, selecting, amplifying and modulating every tiny airborne vibration. Like now, like the slop, slop, slop of water on the improvised punt floating in the small bomb crater he is searching.

'Watch yourself, Jacko!' he hears as he scrambles onto what is little more than a floating door, pushing himself clear of the steep sides. Ocker hands him the pole. The idea, of course, not being to use it to move as much as to prod, prod, prod the murky depths of this man-made pond until it touches something, something less yielding than the mud, something reaching out from years ago for rescue.

'Take it easy,' Ocker says, paying out the rope. 'Might be an unexploded shell down there.'

'Well it's not gonna go bang after being under all this water,' Jack says.

'I wouldn't be so sure, mate.'

Jack hears him. He hears the slop, slip, slop of the water, the bump, bump, bump of the bargepole. And he feels the sudden, yielding crush of bones as the pole crashes through the ribcage of a sunken body.

'Oh, bloody hell.'

'What is it, mate?'

'There's summat here, that's what,' Jack shouts. 'Get us back to t'edge, will yer. I've had enough.'

The two men carefully record what they have found, record where – complete with compass bearings, map references and descriptions – and then rejoin the rest of the company. And then comes the ambush. The enemy is suddenly all over them, and quickly advancing.

One of them slips. Or has he been hit? A boy, the battalion baby. What was his name? What *was* his name? He tumbles down the chalky slope, bouncing like a doll. Another shell bursts above them. Shrapnel. Burning metal on the back of Jack's hand. At least they've escaped the sudden burst of machine-gun fire, Jack is thinking. But artillery fire is landing right at the bottom of the shell-hole where they are both heading.

'Come on, yer bugger!' Jack is shouting at him. 'Let's get out o' here.' But the boy cannot hear him. And anyway, where are they going? Out there to where the 9.2s are bursting, yards away? Out there to where the rat-tat-tat of enemy machine guns is raking up the ground and making the dead dance one final, fatal flourish? Out there to where the dead and the soon-to-be dead are all lying, waiting patiently for what is coming? He opens his eyes and stares at the boy. The boy's lips are moving but he's saying nothing. Shells are exploding all around them but they're making no sound. The corpses in the shell-hole are already black with flies.

'Christ!' The boy is twisting round now, writhing in his own blood. 'I'm hit, Jack. I'm fookin' hit. Oh Christ Jesus!' Jack flattens himself on the ground and closes his eyes. He could stay here – out of reach of the guns – until the futile attack on Fricourt is called off. But from the bottom of the shell-hole comes a whining, like the bleating of a lamb. 'Help me, Jack. Help me.'

As much as Jack desperately wants to help, he is desperate to advance. This isn't duty; he is not doing this for King and Country. Nor is it obedience to the sergeant's orders – 'If they're wounded leave 'em for the bearers, lads. Press on with the attack or before you know it, Jerry'll be here and you'll be for it. And if it ain't the Alleyman,' the sergeant twists his mouth into a smile, 'it'll be the Battle Police. And let me tell you lads – they take no prisoners.' No. This is not courage or obedience. This is not cowardice or fear. This is it. This is the end. This is the moment Jack has been waiting for. This is what he enlisted to do.

But first, there is the boy. He cannot leave the boy here. Jack feels responsible for him. Why wouldn't he?

'Come on, yer bugger.' The farmer is standing over them, muttering. 'Come on!'

Midday. The sun is blinding. Suddenly he is no longer in the shell-hole but on the hillside. It is not the boy's bloodied fingers but the hot grip of a ewe's last uterine contractions clenching round his wrist. And the elastic tightening of the animal's cervix closes painfully around his arm. Jack closes his eyes, gives one more enormous heave – all his strength, the young boy shepherd straining all his sinews. But now the numb, aching, sleepless fatigue of another night awake on a bare hillside listening for the familiar low, grunting, bleating of an animal in labour is against him. And the earth is stronger. The pull of the earth is always stronger . . .

Jack suddenly opens his eyes, expecting to see cloven hooves, slimy-wet, spindly legs and blind, black sticky eyes – a comical red tongue, too, pushing through clenched jaws in readiness for a first, whining bleat. But the staring, terrified eyes are blue, the water in the bottom of the hole is black. And the smoke and fog is a French dawn in the heat of battle. There is no sound – no low panting, groaning, and no high-pitched bleating; no shells screaming, no gunfire cracking – just the slurp, slop of water as the soft earth underneath the boy's feet sucks and sucks. In one last, ghastly heave of a convulsion it will all be over.

Then suddenly, from nowhere, he has an idea. He is hurriedly unshouldering his rifle, checking the bolt and clicking the safety catch. The boy stares, blue eyes wide, into the endless black barrel of the dull Lee Enfield. Somewhere in the black tunnel of darkness, in the chamber, lies a bullet. The knowledge that he is now about to die, that this is how it will be, that there is nothing more now to be done, that he is drowning, that he will drown, that he will choke on this thick green slime or else this man will pull the trigger that will explode the sharp, lead tip from the polished brass case, sending the bullet spiralling down the rifle and out of the barrel and into his skull, and that will be that – that certain knowledge and the sudden sight of the blue-black gun barrel inches from his nose suddenly, instantly, stops the boy from moving. No more churning, no more straining. Nothing.

The water in the shell-hole suddenly stills as the final ripple hits the muddy sides. Jack looks at the face, over the sights of his rifle. The boy squeezes his eyes tight shut and waits. Jack waits . . . And then, suddenly, someone's arms are enfolding him in the darkness, soft and warm, though he is wet with sweat and cold with shivers at the same time . . .

'Jack,' his mother whispers gently in his ear. 'Jack . . . Jack.'

And his hair, tangled and damp, is being stroked gently as she cradles his head in her bare arms, cradles him just like the baby he has suddenly become, like the sobbing infant at her warm, bare breast, bleating for life like a newborn lamb, bleating for milk, bleating for air, for love, for life, for warmth . . .

*

'Jacques,' the whore says softly in the small, damp bed in the maison tolérée. 'Monsieur Jacques, réveillez-vous!'

He hears a knock at the door. Another customer. He turns and places a hand on the girl's soft breast and feels the nipple harden. 'À bientôt!' she smiles and the madame bustles in to change the water in the washstand. Jack gets up, gets dressed and leaves the room, pushing his way past the queue and down the staircase. The fresh blue morning air washes over him like a cool Dales stream in summer. And suddenly, there he is again, in the fields, beside her, the midday heat of the sun bursting through his thumping head . . .

'Jack.' He can feel the woman's chin nestling in his hair. Her arm is supporting him as he sinks deeper in the darkness, into her naked softness. A hay cart bumps along the track high above them on the hillside. He starts to breathe more slowly. The afternoon gradually begins to reassemble all around him. Even with his eyes closed, the river by their side, the drystone walls, the fields, the sheep in the valley all vividly take shape. A dove is purring gently in the trees above their heads – *torr-torr; torr-torr.*

> *Rise up, my love, my fair one, and come away;*
> *For lo, the winter is passed, the rain is over and gone.*
> *The flowers appear on the earth, the time of the singing*
>   *of birds has come,*
> *And the voice of the turtle is heard in our land.*

And now the padre. Church parade. And the sudden shock of a Bible reading – could it really be a Bible reading? – that Jack seems instinctively to know by heart. He is asking about it afterwards, months, even years later. And as Blake reads from the Song of Solomon, Jack can still remember every word:

My dove, my undefiled is but one;
She is the only one of her mother,
She is the choice one of her that bore her.

'I'm pregnant, Jack,' the girl says. She is smoothing his hair and soothing his head as he lies in her bare arms, in the shade of the tree, by the river. He is afraid. He is not much more than a child himself and she, maid of the lady of the house and daughter of the foreman. But his fever subsides, and he hears her words as clearly as if she were there by his side. 'I'm pregnant, Jack. I'm gonna 'ave a baby.'

War Diary or Intelligence Summary: Army form C. 2118
1920

DIVISION MAIN DRESSING STATION—Remy Siding
Map Sheet 28; Grid reference: L.22 d.6.3

March 5th – The Battalion played the Middlesex Regiment (12th Battn) at Rugby Football and were beaten 21 points to 7.

March 6th – 2/Lt. N.V. FITTON proceeded to UK for demobilisation. The Commanding Officer inspected Billets.

March 7th – Church Parade – all denominations.

March 9th – Major J.L. COSGRAVE proceeded to St Omer as President of a Field General Court Martial. 5 O.R.s reinforcements arrived.

March 11th – Companies (strength 30 O.R.s per Coy and HQ 15) paraded at Lijssenthoek for inspection by the CO. The R.S.M. delivered a lecture to all N.C.O.s in the Recreation Hut.

March 13th – Captain R.J. ABBOT commenced series of lectures entitled 'Homer and the Age of the Hero.'

March 15th – 2/Lt. I.T. NORWOOD proceeded on leave to UK. Lt. A.C. CAMPION and 2/Lt. E.F. ANDERSON to XIII Corps Demobilisation Camp CAMBRAI as Conducting Officers for demobilised personnel.

March 18th – Clearance operations commence at Tyne Cottage Military Cemetery, Zonnebeke.

18

As early as 1920, Tyne Cot Cemetery has begun to assume the epic proportions that will soon see this bare Belgian slope transformed into the largest concentration of Empire war graves in the world. No trace exists of the houses that were once scattered along the Spilstraat. Debruyne's farmhouse, Markey's bakery and myriad other small dwellings that once formed part of the Rozeveld estate have long since vanished. Surrounding fields remain drilled with shell-holes, each one filled with stagnant, oily water. The old stone roads that once led up the hill are little more than dust covered in a layer of mud. Only the cemetery is growing, spreading slowly like a bloodstain down the slope from the crest of Passchendaele Ridge.

The Albion lorry struggles up the narrow track to the cemetery entrance and is forced to slow to a crawl behind a man pacing, head down, up and down the lane, scanning the ground as if searching for a pin.

'Christ Almighty, Blakey! Give the daft cove a blast or we're going to drive him into the mud.' Blake squeezes the big, black rubber ball on the end of the brass trumpet horn. The man looks up momentarily, turns and eventually faces the truck, but remains – transfixed – in the middle of the road.

'Oh bloody hell,' Jack grumbles. 'If we 'ave to stop here we'll bloody well sink into the mud.'

'Come on then – run the bastard over,' Ocker says. 'Put your foot down, Blakey – one less yokel won't make much difference. And we've all got our shovels in the back. We'll soon bury the critter.'

'Aye, but that'd upset his conscientious principles, wouldn't it, Blakey?'

By now the heavy wagon has slowed down to a crawl, and the old man steps aside just as it passes. The men in the back shake their fists.

'Daft bugger,' says Jack.

'Come on, we're going to find out what the bloody hell he thinks he's doing,' Ocker shouts as he jumps down from the cab once the truck stops moving.

'This sounds like fun,' Jack says as Blake cuts the engine. 'I'm coming with you.'

The others disembark, shake stiff arms and legs loose and begin unloading tools. Jack, meanwhile, strides back down the Vijfwegenstraat, catching up with Ocker just as he reaches the old man who is still bent, head down, studying the ground.

'Hey!' he shouts as they get within earshot. 'Cooo-ee!' It takes a hard tap on the man's shoulder to get his attention.

'What do you think you're playing at? There's plenty o' room for us both here, y'know, and your boots'll keep you upright in that field.' Jack points a finger at the muddy slope that stretches for a mile back down to Ypres. 'You'll not sink, you know. But we will.'

'Look, mate!' Ocker takes hold of the man by the arm. 'You see that thing over there?' He nods towards the truck. 'Weighs a couple o' hundredweight, that does. And if we come off the road we're done for.'

The man looks bewildered. 'Ah, come on, mate.' Ocker turns to Jack. 'We've found the village idiot here. Let's not waste any more time.'

'*Ik ben op zoek naar mijn boerderij.*' The man smiles as the men turn to leave.

'What?'

'He says . . . hang on a minute.' Jack asks the man again what he was doing, this time struggling to put the question into Flemish.

'What's he saying?'

'Says he's looking for his . . . farm, I think. I think he said his farm. He's certainly looking for summat.'

'What? In the middle of flamin' nowhere?'

'Well it's not much now, is it?' Jack says. 'Hard to tell t'road apart from t'fields, if it comes to that.'

'Suppose not,' Ocker says. 'So anyway, Jacko, has he found what he's looking for? Go on, ask him.'

'Says there's no trace,' says Jack.

'Is that a fact?'

'Not even a ruin.'

The old farmer ends the short exchange by vigorously shaking both men's hands and thanking them for everything they've done for him, for his country and for his family. Finally, he leans to kiss them, but the two soldiers make it clear that won't be necessary.

'Blimey,' Ocker mutters as they walk back to the cemetery. 'That's a bit rich, isn't it?'

'What? Givin' us a kiss?'

'No. Well, yeah – that too, sure.'

'What, then?'

'Thanking us like that, for what we did.'

'He's very grateful,' Jack says. 'They all are.'

'Maybe,' Ocker nods. 'But it was probably our flamin' guns that flattened his farm in the first place.'

'Aye,' Jack adds, 'along with t'rest of this bloody place.'

'The only things our fellas couldn't flatten round here were those bloody German blockhouses.' Ocker stops and puts his hands on his hips. In front of them, amid several hundred graves, between the marked burial plots and the ground already levelled to receive several hundred more, the remains of four concrete bunkers sit like full stops on the German Flandern Stellung. A series of great, grey machine-gun posts clustered close to the crest of the ridge, it is these – rather than any heavily manned enemy trenches – that successive waves of Allied troops were sent to capture back in 1917. The concrete blockhouses are chipped, but the three-foot-thick protective walls managed to withstand everything that Allied artillery could throw at them. Unlike the houses and the farm buildings that once stood close by.

'Can't quite believe we did that, y'know, Jacko. Can't quite believe we let 'em get away with such a daft idea.'

Jack narrows his eyes. 'An' which particular daft idea were that then, lad?'

Ocker laughs. 'Plenty to choose from, eh, mate?'

'Aye, and each time we went along with 'em. We must've been daft.'

'Like a load o' flamin' sheep.'

'Aye, lad.'

Ocker shakes his head. 'The mud was bad enough, Jacko, without these things waiting for you once you arrived.'

Jack laughs, but he isn't smiling. 'Used to take us hours just to tramp a couple o' hundred yards on bloody duckboards.'

'Yeah, and God help you if you fell off,' Ocker says.

'Aye, but He didn't, did he?' Jack adds quietly. 'Oh no. He were far too busy.'

Both men can vividly recall struggling up this wet slope, their comrades being picked off or blown up in their hundreds. One remembers emptying a revolver through the sinister, black firing slits.

'Still gives me the shivers,' Ocker rubs his arms. 'Looking into them black holes.'

'Aye,' Jack says. 'Although, once you lot had captured 'em, well . . .' He wipes a hand across his face. 'We was actually quite glad of 'em then, weren't we?'

'Once you knew it was our fellas inside, eh?'

'Aye.'

'Especially that one.'

Squatting on the hill surrounded by weeds and random, scattered graves, one blockhouse in particular – the famous 'Tyne Cot' itself – sits brooding like a giant spider in the middle of a tattered web, in which are trapped some of the earliest Allied burials in the cemetery.

'They're gonna move these, aren't they?' Ocker says, Army boots crunching on the gravel path as they join the others. 'I mean, they can't just leave 'em here like this, surely?'

'That one looks pretty hard to shift to me,' Jack says.

'I'm sure the engineers could do the job,' says Ocker. 'Few sticks o' dynamite, we all go for a brew and – BOOM! Napoo blockhouse.'

'Oh aye – and napoo all the poor wee beggars lying all around them too.' Mac tuts as the others catch up. 'It's a wonder you weren't given a job on the staff, laddie. Brains like that.'

'Well why didn't they think of that in the first place?' Fuller says. 'Why didn't they just clear the ground before they started burying bodies?'

'Look,' Jack points to one of the crosses. 'Look at the dates, lad.'

SERGEANT LEWIS MCGEE, VC,
40TH BATTALION AUSTRALIAN INFANTRY,
KILLED IN ACTION 12/10/1917

CAPTAIN CLARENCE SMITH JEFFRIES, VC,
34TH BATTALION AUSTRALIAN INFANTRY,
KILLED IN ACTION 12/10/1917

PRIVATE JAMES PETER ROBERTSON, VC,
27TH (MANITOBA) BATTALION CANADIAN INFANTRY,
KILLED IN ACTION 06/11/1917

'That's why they didn't clear these places first.'

Fuller opens his mouth, then thinks better of whatever he had thought to say.

'These poor buggers was here long before the likes of us appeared and decided to bring in a couple of thousand other folks to keep 'em company.'

''S'pose . . .'

'Anyhow, lad.' Jack takes out a folded piece of paper from his tunic pocket. 'I've got good news for thee!'

'Yeah?' Fuller sounds unconvinced.

'Look here . . .' Jack points to the instructions Ingham has given him. 'That's our job. Plot Forty-five, Row G.'

'What – where there's a bloody great lump o' concrete?'

'You are kidding, aren't you, Jacko?'

'Never more serious.' He tucks the paper back into his pocket. 'That's our job, right over there.'

'But it's a—'

'It's a blockhouse, aye. And we're about to bury it.'

179

The ground in the distant corner of the cemetery falls away sharply. A nearby shell-hole has already turned this particular pillbox forty-five degrees; one half has already sunk beneath the mud.

'Abandon ship!' shouts Ocker.

'Aye, she's sinking fast.'

'Too right.'

'And we're going to help it on its way by shovelling a few hundredweight of Belgian shit on top of it. So come on – let's get cracking.'

'Jeez, this job gets better by the hour,' says Ocker. 'Why can't we do some bloody flower arranging like those guys at Remy was this morning?'

'You'd not catch me doing that,' Fuller says, bending to grab the handles of a wheelbarrow.

'Really? Thought it'd have been right up your alley, mate.'

'You'd think they'd have had enough of this shithole, wouldn't you?' Fuller goes on. 'Think they'd know better than to come crawling back here to plant some pretty flowers.'

'Have you tried finding a job back home, laddie?' The sudden force with which Mac throws the shovels in the barrow Fuller is holding makes his knees buckle. 'No – of course you haven't. Because there aren't any, that's why.'

'He's right you know, lad,' Jack says, picking up another wheelbarrow. 'Why on earth do you think we're all still out here digging graves, eh?'

'Plenty o' work back home for me,' says Ocker. 'Got thousands of sheep need shearing . . .'

'Bet that's not all the sheep'll be getting, neither,' Fuller sniggers.

'Don't mutter, Fuller,' Ocker says, clipping him round the ear.

'Ow!'

'You know I don't like it when I can't hear what you're saying. If you want to make some tame reference to sheep shagging or something then just come right out with it, OK?'

'I didn't mean . . . sorry.'

'No, son, of course you didn't mean it. You never do. You want to play the man but you don't quite want anyone to hear the quips, not properly, just in case anyone gets shirty.'

'Leave it, Ocker lad. We'll have a little chat with him later.'

'What?'

'Just a few things me and the other lads need to discuss.'

'Not wi' me you ain't,' shouts Fuller.

'Look, sonny boy.' Ocker grabs him by the collar. 'Seeing as Jacko here is protecting you from the pasting you so richly deserve, you little shit, the least you can do is tell us all about them little secrets Ingham trusts you with, eh?'

'Secrets?'

'You know – the ones the whole camp knows about.'

'To say nowt about de Wulf.'

'De who?'

'Fatso. The bloke with all the big brown envelopes. Don't pretend you don't know what we're on about.'

'But I don't!'

'Later, lads.' Mac holds a finger to his lips. 'Look!' He points to a group of pilgrims arriving at the cemetery – women in black hats picking their way along the muddy duckboards, men wearing black armbands and a few with medals on their chests. One of the party is carrying a wreath. Ocker nods as they pass. The others tip their hats as the ladies tread carefully between the graves.

'Come on,' Jack says once they're out of earshot. 'Best get

this muck shifted. But no singing today, lads. Not with t'visitors so close.'

The men set to work digging a three-foot channel round the exposed corner of blockhouse, banking the soil and filling the void with successive wheelbarrow loads from the heaps left by the builders excavating the foundations for the boundary wall. The plan is to fill the hole and slowly level this sunken corner of the graveyard, burying the blockhouse into the bargain.

'Excuse me?'

Jack removes his cap. 'Begging your pardon, miss.'

'I'm sorry to bother you, but my parents . . .' The girl points up the hill to where the visitors are standing, a little way off. 'They're having a bit of trouble,' she says. 'We're looking for my brother's grave.'

'You from Ozzie, miss?' Ocker touches his cap.

'Yes,' the girl smiles. 'We've come here from Melbourne.'

'And not for the weather either, I'll wager.'

'No.' She smiles and shivers. 'We've come over to find my brother's grave. We've got a letter. Here' – the girl opens her handbag – 'it's from the Imperial War Graves Commission.' She hands them a typed sheet of paper creased thin by the number of times it has been opened and read. 'They sent a photograph too. My father's got that – he's using it to try and find the cross.' Jack follows her gaze as the girl looks back to the group of women, huddled together like frightened birds, then across to a tall man striding over puddles and peering at the tin plates nailed to the wooden crosses. 'Finding the right one is a nightmare.' She looks down and sighs, then tries her best to smile again. 'There are so many here, aren't there?'

'Aye, lass,' Jack says. 'Ocker, why don't you give the lady a hand finding her brother?'

'It would be my pleasure,' says Ocker, putting down his

shovel. 'Right, miss,' he says looking at the letter. 'I can tell you straight away that you're looking in the wrong place.'

'Oh no!' The girl looks horrified. 'But they definitely said Tyne Cottage Cemetery. Look – it says here in the letter.'

'No, miss. Sorry. You misunderstand. You're in the right cemetery, just the wrong part of it. And, as you've already found out, it's pretty big.'

'Ye-es.' She gives another nervous laugh. The two of them walk off along the duckboard path and the others get back to work, raising the level of the soil a load at a time until it slowly begins to cover the blockhouse roof.

'Taking time, this, isn't it?' Mac says when they stop for a breather half an hour later.

'Aye,' Jack says, squinting into the low sun. 'And so is Ocker. Looks like he's giving 'em the full guided tour now.'

'And this, ladies and gentlemen,' Ocker is busy telling the group, 'is the famous Tyne Cot.'

'What?' the man says. 'This lump of concrete?'

'That's right.'

'Why is it called . . . I mean, why Tyne Cot?'

'Nickname given to it by the Northumbrian Fusiliers. They were the coves who first had a go at capturing it.'

'But why did they call it that?'

'Short for Tyne Cottage, miss,' says Ocker. 'Must've reminded them of home back in Newcastle-upon-Tyne I suppose.' He laughs.

'Have you ever been to Newcastle-upon-Tyne, son?' The father narrows his eyes.

'Not flamin' likely,' Ocker says. 'And I never will if this is what the place looks like. Anyway, just for the record, folks, I should point out that it was the Aussies who made it here eventually. It was us that captured the place and took it from the Jerries.'

The man stands a little taller, smiles and turns briefly to his wife. The woman looks down, shaking her head. 'Told you, Dee.' He grips her hand a little tighter.

Jack leaves the others scattering grass seed on the thin layer of soil now covering the concrete roof of the German bunker and wanders across to see what is keeping Ocker.

'I can't quite tell if your friend is having us on,' the girl whispers as Jack appears at her side.

'Aye, well,' Jack smiles. 'It's a good story.'

'Not true, then?'

'Probably not, no.'

'Odd name, though,' the girl says. 'It seems a strange thing to call a German . . . what is it? Blockhouse?'

Jack pushes back his cap and scratches his head. 'Aye, lass. We used to give names to 'em all. There was Cheddar Villa, t'Viking Ship, Goumier Farm . . . well, actually that one were built inside the farmhouse itself.'

'I see,' the girls says. 'So why *is* this one called "Tyne Cot" then – if it isn't to do with Tyneside?'

'Truth is no one really knows,' Jack says. 'But I reckon it has more to do with what was here before t'war.'

'There was something here before the war?'

'Aye, lass. Though you wouldn't think so looking at it now.'

'No.'

'And there weren't much then, either. Just a few houses, the odd farm.' He points to the spot where the man had been searching, but the road is now empty. 'Matter o' fact we met one of t'farmers earlier.'

'Oh really?'

'Aye. And locals,' Jack goes on, 'well – they reckon it comes from t'Flemish.'

'Flemish?'

'Aye, that's what they speak round here.'

'I thought they all spoke French.'

'They do,' Jack smiles. 'Well, they used to. Still do, too, o' course. When they have to.'

'I still don't understand,' the girl shakes her head.

'Well,' Jack says. 'It don't much look like a chicken coop now—'

'It most certainly does not!' The girl laughs.

'But that's what they reckon was here, once. A *t'Hinnekot* – that's the local lingo for a chicken coop.'

'I think I prefer your friend's version,' the girl smiles.

Jack looks down at his boots. 'Did you find your brother's grave, lass?'

'We did, thank you. Thanks to your comrade. I'm glad you could spare him, we'd have struggled to find the grave on our own.'

'It's not easy,' Jack says. 'Not now.'

'There are so many of them, aren't there?'

'Aye.'

'And all so neatly laid out.' The girl looks up and down the field. 'Well, apart from these.' She turns to the handful of scattered graves east of the blockhouse. 'Why aren't these graves in rows like the others?'

'They were buried where they fell, lass. Where a tree falls, there let it lie.' The old lie, he thinks to himself.

'But the others,' the girl says. 'They're are all in such straight, neat rows.'

'Aye, lass. But we don't dig 'em up again unless we have to.

That's Army policy. Anyway there's enough digging to be done without tidying these graves.'

'So the others . . .' She looks along the rows of wooden crosses, neatly spaced, and beyond to a dozen new, open graves dug with mathematical precision. 'My brother . . .'

'He was likely buried somewhere else shortly after t'battle where he was, er . . .'

'Killed?'

'Aye.'

'You can say it, you know.'

'Aye.'

'So he was moved here afterwards?'

'Aye.'

'I had no idea,' the girl says. 'I don't think my parents would be too keen to hear that, either.'

'Don't worry, lass. Ocker's been keeping 'em entertained. But I'm afraid we've got work to do and I'm going to have to take your tour guide back. There's a shovel with his name on it.'

'Of course.'

'Private Gilchrist?'

'Jacko?'

Jack nods his head and Ocker jumps down from his perch on top of the central blockhouse. 'Sorry, folks, duty calls.'

'Listen, son.' The man presses some money into Ocker's hand. 'You've been very helpful.'

'Oh no, look—'

'No, son – I insist.' And the man closes Ocker's fingers round the crumpled notes.

'Nice work,' says Jack as they wander back. 'You could get a job doing that if you wanted. Mind you, you'd have to stop giving 'em that cock-and-bull tosh about t'Northumberland Fusiliers.'

'It's a good story, matc.'

'Aye, but that's all it is.'

'You're right. Anyway,' Ocker says, 'I reckon I'd be better off with sheep. They don't go travelling halfway around the world to put flowers on a cobber's grave.'

'Or have such attractive sisters?'

Ocker smiles. 'You'd get on well down under, mate, I reckon. You've sheared a few sheep in your time, I'll wager.'

'Aye, I have that.'

'Thought so. There's plenty out there, Jacko. Plenty of work for men like you down under. There's loads to be done.'

'Then why are you still here then, eh?'

'I wish, Jacko, that I knew the answer to that question. And I also wish it wasn't flamin' true. Perhaps it isn't. Perhaps it's a dream?'

'Well you can dream on if you think we're going to pack up all your tools for ye, laddie.' Mac says, handing Ocker back his shovel. 'Come on – the sooner we get this done the sooner we can make our excuses and . . .'

'. . . and quench our insatiable thirst. Good thinking, Mac!'

'Come on, lad,' Jack says to Fuller as the men begin to clear up. 'You too.'

But for once, it isn't the thought of a shovel, and of tidying after an afternoon of digging, that is making Fuller hesitate.

19

The truck rumbles along the Menin Road and through the gap in the medieval ramparts heading towards the Grote Markt, then comes to a halt beneath the shored-up remains of the ruined campanile. The walls of both the Cloth Hall and cathedral are now clad heavily in wooden buttresses and scaffolding. The shadows cast by the ruins are already lengthening.

Burying the remains of one of the smaller German pill-boxes has taken the men longer than expected, and now, courtesy of Captain Harris, they have a crate of identification discs and other relics to deliver back to Remy HQ. Their visit to the British Tavern is already going to be shorter than expected. Then, just as Blake wrenches up the handbrake, the men come face to face with Lieutenant Ingham leaning up against a staff car, apparently waiting for them to arrive.

'Oh, heck! Here's trouble,' Jack calls to the men in the back, quickly buttoning his tunic as he jumps down from the truck. 'Get thinking of summat, quick!' he shouts. 'It's Ingham.'

'Ah, Patterson!' Lieutenant Ingham strolls across, squeezing out a thin smile as he does. Jack stops, salutes as smartly as he can, then waits. 'On your way back to Pop with Captain Harris's box, are you?'

'Yes, sir.'

'Just thought you'd stop and admire the view here, did you?'

'No, sir!' Jack's mind is racing. Then Blake jumps down from the cab with a lifeline.

'Come on then, Jack – are you going to check those brakes for me or aren't you? The men are almost passing out in the back of the wagon.'

'Ah! Some trouble with the brakes, eh, Patterson?'

'Oh, I am sorry, sir,' Blake says, standing briefly to attention. 'I didn't see you there.'

'Yes, sir.' Jack winks at Blake. 'Just, er . . . stopping to check 'em, sir. Felt a little slack coming down from the ridge, didn't they, Blakey?'

'Yes, well, quite,' says Ingham. 'Anyway, I thought I might find you here and I've been proved right, haven't I?' Ingham smiles, another frugal tightening of the lips. 'Sergeant Townend informed me you'd been sent to Tyne Cot for the day, and so I thought I'd save you the trouble of taking the crate they gave you back to camp.'

'Sir?'

'Yes. I've come to pick it up myself.'

'Yes, sir. Very good, sir.'

'Yes. And I, er . . . I'll need one of the men to assist me, of course, as it's bound to be rather heavy. Private Fuller?'

'Yessir!' The moment he hears his name spoken, Fuller is climbing out of the back of the truck and thanking the gods above for a narrow escape from whatever Jack and the men have been planning.

'Dreadfully sorry to, er . . . well, deprive you of the spectacle of seeing Jack stripped to the waist and crawling underneath the truck.' Ingham gives him a wink. 'But needs must, I'm afraid.' He points towards the car. The men hand Fuller the

189

crate and he struggles across the cobbles to where the open-topped Ford is waiting.

'Do hope you get those brakes fixed before too long.' Ingham waves as he and the boy drive past.

'Cheers, Blakey,' Jack says as the car turns along Rijsel Straat. 'I appreciate that.'

'That's all right, Jack. I'll have to do penance for it, though.'

'Sorry, lad. I'd buy you a drink,' Jack smiles, 'if you'd take one.'

'Never mind that, Jacko.' Ocker and the rest of the men jump down from the wagon. 'Come on, mate. It's your round.'

'Och! They're all the same, these Yorkshiremen,' says Mac. 'Short arms and deep pockets. It's a well-known fact.'

'Funny!' Ocker says. 'And I thought that was the Jocks.'

The men order their drinks and sit at one of many empty tables in the British Tavern. The only other customer is an old man hunched over an empty glass of Sint Bernardus. Katia isn't at the bar, but Jack thinks better than to ask her father where she is. He believes he already knows the answer. It doesn't matter. He'll ask her what he wants to ask next time he sees her. And then he realises with a sudden, sharp ache, that he wants that to be very soon.

'Jeez, pretty dead in here today, ain't it?' Ocker shouts. 'Hey, *patron*! What've you done to kill off all your customers?' The men stop in their tracks and stare at Ocker.

'Oh, Jeez! Sorry, Jacko. Sorry, er . . . *pardon*, Monsieur Steenvan.' Ocker bows his head then turns and sits down quickly. 'Blimey, that was a close shave,' he says, picking up his beer. 'Think I got away with it, though.'

'You and your bloody big mouth!' Mac shakes his head.

The others sip their drinks then sit and look at one another uncomfortably. Monsieur Steenvan, a grubby tea towel in his hands, continues to polish the glasses. His moustache twitches as he watches the men gather round a table, but his eyes don't seem to register what he's seeing any more than his ears hear what the men are saying. His hands go on twisting the same glass in the tea towel, holding it up to the light periodically, before repeating the procedure over and over.

'He's taking it bad, isn't he?'

'Well how the bloody 'ell would you take it, losing a daughter so sudden like that?' Jack whispers.

'Dunno, mate. Haven't got a daughter. Not that I know of, at any rate.' He shrugs. 'None of us have if it comes to that. Have we?'

'Maybe not, laddie,' says Mac. 'But we can imagine what it must feel like. And we can be a darn sight more sensitive, too.'

'I'd better go an' have a word with him.' Jack pushes back his chair. 'Make sure the ol' boy is OK.'

Jack walks to the counter as reluctantly as if attending his own court martial. He can't think of anything worth saying but feels he must say something. 'Sorry, sir.' Steenvan carries on turning the tea towel, looking down at the glass he's polishing. 'I mean . . . *Ik – ben – droevig – over – er, over hem? Over hem. Aye.*'

'Who taught you your Dutch?' Steenvan suddenly looks up. 'It is filthy!'

'Well . . .' Jack's eyes widen. 'Your little lass, actually.' Steenvan nods, smiling even as the tears start welling in the corners of his eyes. 'She weren't such a bad teacher, neither.'

The two men watch each other for a moment. Then Steenvan slowly starts to look around the room, as if searching for something else to say. Jack follows his gaze, but the eyes flit like flies from one object to the next. Eventually, Monsieur

Steenvan turns and places the glass he's been holding back on the top shelf before looking at it, taking it down again and polishing it some more.

'*Ma fille était très friande de vous, Jacques.*' The tea towel stops moving for a moment and Steenvan looks Jack in the eye. 'I am sorry,' he shrugs. 'Sometimes it is easier in French.'

'Aye, well,' Jack sighs. 'I was very fond of 'er an' all.'

'*Mais elle était jeune, Jacques – trop jeune pour savoir ce qu'elle voulait au fond.*'

'She was, aye,' Jack shakes his head. 'She was too young. Much too young.'

Jack leans an elbow on the bar and turns, watching the men sitting at their table, drinking beer. Ocker is shuffling the cards and they are talking loudly to one another, waiting for the game to begin.

'They are . . . what is it that you say?' Steenvan looks across as the cards are dealt, the conversation never stopping. 'They are . . . chatting?'

'No,' Jack smiles. 'Not since we had us new uniforms.' The mere memory of lice-infested khaki makes him itch. 'No, we're all clean now. No more scratching or running candles up and down the seams of us shirts.'

Steenvan shrugs.

'Chats,' Jack explains. 'Little white fellas living in your clothes.'

'Chats?'

'Lice,' Jack says. 'Sorry, it doesn't matter.'

A wagon passes, iron wheels bumping on the cobbled road. Steenvan suddenly stops moving. 'I thank you, Jacques. I am very grateful for what you did for us, for Françoise.'

Jack looks puzzled for a moment.

'*Non*, no – it was a great help,' Steenvan goes on. 'And I, er . . . I do not have the strength, *n'est-ce pas?*'

With a shock, Jack is suddenly aware of what it is that Monsieur Steenvan is expressing gratitude for. 'I wish to thank you properly,' he says after a while. 'You and the men – you have always been so helpful to me, to us. And your Captain Ingham too, of course.'

'Aye, well. We didn't do too bad with this place, did we?' Jack says, looking round at the tin roof and wooden walls before with a jolt Ingham's name suddenly registers.

'You what?' Jack stares across the bar. 'Who did you just say?'

Steenvan shrugs again. 'All of you. You, Jacques, you and the men have helped build this place with the materials you have given us. And of course you are all good customers too,' Steenvan laughs.

'But Ingham,' Jack narrows his eyes. 'He isn't a regular, is he?'

'*Non*. No, no – of course. But he has . . .'

'What? What has Ingham done?'

Steenvan's expression changes from bewilderment to fear.

'You in, Jacko?' Ocker calls across the room as he shuffles the cards. Jack makes to answer, but then notices Fuller sneaking in and quietly joining in with the other men.

The boy looks at Jack then quickly looks away and goes to sit down. 'I'm in.' He rubs his hands together, trying not to catch Jack's eye again. But he isn't what Jack is thinking about right now.

'You are aware, I think, Jacques, of what we are trying to do. What we want to achieve.'

'Achieve?' Jack is puzzled now.

Steenvan places both his hands flat on the bar. 'Has my

daughter ever spoken to you about her . . . of *son frère*? Her brother?' He looks at Jack. Slowly, Jack shakes his head.

'Killed,' the man goes on. 'In 1916.'

'I had no idea.'

'I thought not, *peut-être*. He was my son,' Steenvan goes on, 'from my first marriage. So, I suppose, he was not – what is it you would say? – her true brother.'

'Half, we would call it. We'd say her half-brother.'

'*Demi-frère*,' Steenvan nods. '*Oui.* And of course, he was so many years older than the girls. They hardly knew him.'

Jack slowly shakes his head. 'I know . . . I mean, I can imagine how that feels.'

Steenvan closes his eyes and holds up his hand. 'He served south of Dixmude.'

'Trenches of death,' Jack nods.

Steenvan smiles. 'He was a brave soldier.'

'Aye.'

'But . . . But he wasn't killed by the Germans.'

Jack can't quite think what to say. He shakes his head.

'He is buried in the churchyard,' Steenvan goes on. 'In Poperinghe.'

'So how . . . ?'

'How did he die?'

Jack stares at Steenvan for a long time. 'No,' he says at last, quietly.

Steenvan nods, slowly. 'He was an intelligent boy, Jacques. Very clever. He could have been an officer . . .'

'But for the fact he didn't speak French!'

'Or wouldn't,' Steenvan shakes his head. 'He was always, er . . . I don't know how to say it? *C'était un jeune homme très décidé.*'

'Determined?'

'Determined, *oui.*'

'But more than that?'

Steenvan nods, thinking. 'He was a headstrong boy, even when he was *un tout petit gosse*. He was angry . . . no, that is not the word. How would you say? Outraged – he was outraged by the injustice in the Belgian Army. So many proud, brave Flemings were treated as no more than . . . cattle. As food for guns.'

'Cannon fodder,' Jack adds. 'Well, we can tell thee summat about that.'

'I am sure you can.'

'So he . . . your lad. What did he do? Nowt stupid, surely?'

'Stupid?' Steenvan shrugs. 'That depends what you mean by "stupid". Whether you think that joining the Flemish Front is . . . stupid?'

'Ah,' says Jack. 'I see.'

'Do you? Do you see?'

'Well, I see that . . . I don't know. I mean – well, I know they was sponsored by the Germans.'

'In the occupied zones, yes. And there were some of them – the Young Flemings in particular – who were very, I don't know how to say it . . .'

'Pro-German?'

'*Oui.*'

'But not—'

'No, not him,' says Steenvan. 'Not my son. He was a proud and patriotic Belgian. But he believed in freedom for the Flemish people. And the Germans . . .'

'Aye,' Jack lets out a sigh. 'It's a complicated business, that's for sure. At least—'

'At least?'

'I mean, it's over now, all that.'

'Is it?'

'Well, aye. Fritz is finished. You've got your country back. You're free.'

'Free, Jacques? Are we free? Are the Flemings free?'

'Well, I . . .'

'Let us just say that we mean to be.' Steenvan looks at Jack and pauses. 'Free, that is. And we are making sure we are prepared.'

'Prepared?'

'In case we have to fight, Jacques. For our freedom.'

Jack is suddenly distracted by angry shouts behind him. A heated argument appears to be on the verge of getting nasty.

'Hey!' Fuller is standing up and shouting.

'What's that, mate?' Ocker, standing over him, is dangling something right in front of Fuller's face.

'Me watch!' The boy swipes at the spinning jewel.

'Your watch?'

'My fuckin' watch . . .'

'Anyone round here seen Fuller's watch?' Ocker looks around the room.

'Anyone know the laddie even had a watch?' says Mac.

'Anyone even know that Fuller could tell the flamin' time?'

'You're just . . .'

'Just what, mate? Green? Wet behind the ears? Nah, not us, mate – you! You're just a bad loser.'

'Give him back his watch, Ocker.'

'Not likely, Jacko. I dealt fair and square and Fuller wanted in. He didn't have a stake so he put his watch down.'

'I was tricked,' moans Fuller.

'I'll trick your bloody arse!' Jack grabs the boy's wrist, twisting his arm back sharply.

'Ow! Argh!' Fuller is forced to stand and turn, trying to

unwind from the pain, but Jack pulls, hard, and holds the boy still tighter.

'Never mind your watch, lad.' Fuller is so close now that he can feel the tiny flecks of spittle on Jack's breath as he speaks. 'You won't have a wrist left to wear it on unless you start to come clean about what's been going on.'

'Goin' on? Arrgh. You're hurting me, Jacko.'

'That what Ingham does, is it, lad? Hurt you? Is that how he gets you to—'

'Get's me to what? Let go o' me arm!'

'*The time has come*, the Walrus said, *to talk of many things.*'

'Thanks, Mac, but I don't reckon Fuller's gonna tell us about sealin' wax . . .'

'Or cabbages!'

'Or kings.'

'I don't know what you fellas are talking about. Let me go, Jacko. Please!'

'Sit down.'

Ocker sweeps the cards from the table. The others pick up their beer. Jack pushes Fuller down hard onto an empty chair and then sits next to him, close. Mac draws closer on the other side, wedging the boy between them.

'Right-o, court of enquiry . . .'

'Eh?'

'Shut it, prisoner!' shouts Ocker. 'Court of Enquiry into illegal – and unnatural – activity by 567211 Private James Fuller.'

'Eh?'

'How do you plead?'

'Guilty or not guilty?'

'We all know he's guilty!'

'Guilty o' what? What the fuck 'ave I done?'

Rain has suddenly begun beating hard on the tin roof of the

British Tavern, driven by sudden gusts of wind, making a noise like falling shrapnel.

'You know what Steenvan were just telling me?' Jack suddenly loses interest in Fuller and turns to look over his shoulder.

'I'll have the abridged version, Jacko, if it's all the same to you.'

'Well, you know we've helped the ol' man out a bit with scrap and stuff.'

'As well as helping him use it to rebuild this place in our precious free time.'

'Aye, that an' all.'

'Yeah, and we know why you're so keen on doing it, too. Got to have a table to get your feet under, eh, Jacko? With the lovely Katia?'

'Aye, well. Seems I might not be the only one wi' an ulterior motive.' Jack eases the pressure on Fuller a little and the boy frees his arm.

'No – lost me at "ulteri—" whatsit, Jack.'

'Are we gonna put the screws on Fuller here or not?'

'Maybe not,' says Jack quietly.

'Let me go, Jacko,' Fuller pipes up. 'I didn't mean nothing.'

'Aye, lad,' Jack says. 'Happen you didn't.'

'Would somebody please mind explaining what on earth is going on?' Mac moves his chair and Fuller suddenly crashes to the floor. Jack rises and stands over him.

'You're a pathetic little bugger, Fuller. But I don't reckon you know what you've got yourself mixed up with.'

Fuller is trying to crawl away on his back, kicking his feet like a frog on the stone floor. 'I dunno what you mean, Jacko.'

'Ah well.' Mac cups his hands around his tankard and shakes his head. 'That's that, then.' Skerritt – eyes wide – twists what remains of his mouth into a smile. Blake gets up from the table and walks over to where the frightened boy has shuffled blindly forward, nose now flat against the bar. Monsieur Steenvan continues polishing the glasses.

'Reckon Blakey'll bust his nose?' Ocker is rubbing his hands together. 'I'll give odds that Fuller doesn't even raise a lily-white hand in his own defence.'

'Nuffink happened, honest, Blakey. Jacko, listen . . .'

'Listen to what, lad? To you?' Jack drains his tankard. 'Reckon I've heard enough to last a lifetime.'

'I'm sorry, Jacko. Jacko, please . . .'

Jack bangs the empty mug down on the table. 'Come on,' he says to the others. 'Best be getting back.'

'What about me?' Fuller whines.

'You can walk.'

The men get to their feet and follow Jack to the door. Only Fuller, still on the floor and cowering against the bar, remains where he is. It is raining harder now – the noise on the corrugated iron roof is almost deafening. As Jack opens the door, leaves from the street blow inside and swirl around the bar.

Jack pauses on the threshold. He looks round, stares at the boy, then nods almost imperceptibly. Fuller scrambles quickly to his feet and hurries after them.

20

Back at the Sidings next morning the sun is clear and bright in a pale blue sky. Last night's rain has passed and the wind has dropped.

'Parade in ten minutes,' a voice calls into the darkness. Light from a hurricane lamp illuminates a disembodied orange face peering in at the door. Ocker groans, turns over, pulls his blanket higher and then starts snoring even louder.

'Come on, lad!' Jack gives his backside a gentle kick. But the Aussie doesn't stir.

'This is yer lance-jack speaking. Parade in ten minutes, Ocker lad. And that's an order!'

'Well I'm staying here,' a muffled voice protests from underneath the rough brown blanket. 'You'll do fine without me.' Jack pulls back the cover like a conjuror revealing his finest trick, but Ocker springs up, snatches it back and holds it close to his chest. 'Look, mate – if I hadn't been woken by you snoring like a train at two in the flamin' morning I might've had a bit more of a spring in my step.'

'Aye, well, I had a bad night,' says Jack.

'Aye, we heard,' says Mac.

'Heard?'

'Son, you sometimes have more to say when your eyes are closed than when you're wide awake.'

Ocker suddenly sits up in bed and rubs his hands together. 'So what did I miss?'

'What do you think?'

'Oh well,' Ocker sighs, lying down again and pulling up the blanket. 'Nothing worth getting out of bed for, then.'

'Leave him be,' Mac says, pulling on his boots. 'Let him suffer the wrath of Ingham.' A comic burst of snoring starts up loudly from the bunk.

'Aye well.' Jack turns, straightening his own bunk. 'Some of us didn't have any sleep last night and we still manage.'

'Yeah, but you were tucked up nice and warm in the lovely Katia's arms, laddie.'

'Bet that's not all of hers he was tucked inside, neither.'

'Watch it, Ocker. Not in front of the children.'

Fuller, red-eyed, snotty-nosed, looks up briefly but knows better than to say anything.

The men continue getting ready before sauntering out onto the parade ground, avoiding groups of workmen pushing wheelbarrows, and gardeners with their arms full of flower-pots shipped across from Britain ready for the planting season.

'Look at that,' Jack mutters as they pick their way through the melee. 'No parades for them chaps. They get their orders and just get on with t'job without all this bloomin' fuss.'

'Fancy joining them, do you?'

Jack looks down at his fingers. White flakes of skin crust like sugar on the brown, mud-stained surface of his hands. 'Need to get these greened up first,' he says, turning them one way, then the other.

Across at the other side of the camp, in the nursery, Commission gardeners are already busy potting shrubs and pricking seedlings and getting on with the business of preparing for the second post-war spring and the work of planting and tidying the cemeteries the War Graves Commission is creating and the Army is filling. The first batch of a delivery of bright white Portland headstones to replace the rows of makeshift crosses is being unloaded from a train which has that morning pulled into the railways sidings.

'I reckon I could get the hang of it, you know,' Jack says at last. 'I've got the hang of this job, after all.'

'Aye, but they're not Army, are they, laddie?' Mac swells with all the pride of an Old Contemptible.

'I know. The lucky buggers!'

The men shuffle into line in shabby uniforms, buttons dull and caps askew. Their boots are permanently caked with mud. The uniform the search teams wear is little smarter than the corpses they uncover. But parade they must. King's Regulations.

'Atten-SHUN!' Jack calls his section to order.

'So where is Private Gilchrist?' Ingham asks in a thin voice as he walks along inspecting the platoon.

'He's . . . not well, sir.'

'The MO seen him, has he?'

'Not yet, sir, no.'

'You've sent for him though, naturally?'

'No, sir.'

'No? Oh dear! Oh dear, oh dear.'

'He was . . . only just taken badly, sir.'

'Ah!' Ingham nods. 'So what, precisely, is the nature of this . . . illness, then?'

'I'll bloody tell you what it is, sir!' Ocker's voice calls out across the parade ground. The colour drains from Ingham's face and his mouth falls open.

'He's bloody gone an' done it this time,' Jack whispers from the corner of his mouth. Mac slowly shakes his head as Ocker – tunic open, braces hanging loose and boots undone – appears before them.

Ingham somehow manages a tense smile, showing his teeth like a monkey. 'Ah, Gilchrist!' He tries to sound as casual as possible. 'Feeling better now, are we?'

'All the better for seeing you, sir.' Gilchrist raises his hand in quick salute. 'Because, you see, it's time we got one or two things sorted out, I reckon.'

'Sorted out?'

'Yeah, mate – sorted out. Now shut your clacker and listen up, Ingham ol' fruit. As the boys here have just told you, I'm sick.'

'Well, they said—'

'I'm bloody sick, "sir" – sick to bloody death of the Army and sick to bloody death of . . . well, death, to be quite honest with you. We're all flamin' fed up with poncing around like soldiers all the time. In fact, we're bloody fed up wi' being soldiers, and that's something I'll come to in a minute. We're not fighting any more, there's not a war on, and even the flamin' enemy has been sent home.'

'Well, yes, but . . .'

'All we do is fight the flamin' mud. And we're flamin' fed up with it.'

By now the attention of men in several other units has been aroused, including Captain Harris. 'Spot of bother, Ingham?'

'No, no, not at all, Harris old chap.' Ingham waves his stick. 'Just letting the men get their grievances off their chest, y'know. Important for morale to let them have their say and for them to know their voices are being heard.'

'Ah.' Harris looks genuinely interested. 'Capital idea. Very brave of you, mind. Not sure it's in King's Regulations but then, most of what we do isn't in the book these days, what?'

'Exactly.' Ingham grits his teeth.

'Yes. Don't want any more mutinies in the British Army, do we?'

'Good Lord, no!' Ingham's eyes widen.

'Calloo Calais, eh?' Harris sniggers.

The rest of the men watch in silence. Gardeners are skirting the perimeter of the parade ground, some studiously ignoring what is happening, others stopping to enjoy a moment's entertainment. Beyond the huts, one of the big green Albion lorries is being cranked, the engine first spluttering then shaking as the heavy truck shudders into life.

'So what is it that you men want?' Lieutenant Ingham asks at last.

'No parade,' says one.

'Better food,' says another.

'And we all want to go home,' Ocker says at last. 'We want out o' the Army.'

'Really? All of you?'

Jack looks down at the floor.

'Well I'm warning you,' Ingham says after a while. 'There's really very little I can do. I'll pass on your grievances to the colonel, but until then you are subject to the King's Regulations. You must do as instructed by the sergeant and you must obey orders.' There is a murmur among the men. 'Although,' Ingham carries on, 'some of you may be interested to know that a number of our fellows are now nearer to getting their wish granted than they might have realised.'

Jack looks up. Ingham unbuttons the breast pocket of his tunic and takes out a letter.

'Yes, yes, I have it here.' He opens up the folded piece of

paper, smiling to himself. 'We may not be finished here,' he says. 'And our work may not be over—'

'We're still finding bodies, sir,' Jack says. 'Only t'other day a farmer out at Langemark called us out because he'd found some poor Tommy lying in a ditch.'

'Quite,' says Ingham. 'And given the numbers of men still missing, what would you expect?'

'Most of the men who are missing won't be in any fit state for us to bury, sir,' says Ocker.

'. . . or for anyone to find,' adds Mac.

'The Directorate of Graves Registration and Enquiries is satisfied that we are doing what we can. They appreciate that the work we do—'

'We, sir?'

'They appreciate that the work is dirty, difficult and sometimes dangerous. And you'll be pleased to know that from now on the task of maintaining the cemeteries is to be transferred to the Imperial War Graves Commission. Major-General Ware – fine chap – and his men will be taking over the running of all the battlefield and concentration cemeteries from now on.'

'And good luck to 'em,' somebody is saying.

'Indeed, indeed,' Ingham nods. 'All of which means there is in point of fact very little left for us to do now the concentrations are largely over and the battlefields have all been searched.'

'But there's thousands on 'em still out there, sir – unaccounted for.'

'Yes, well. Be that as it may, that element of our work is drawing to a close. Dammit, I thought you'd all be pleased.'

'Pleased, sir?'

'Yes. Isn't that one of the things you've just been grumbling about to me? There's no satisfying some people . . .'

'No doubt most of t'lads would be more relieved if you telled 'em they was going home soon, sir.'

'Most, Lance-Corporal Patterson? Not including yourself in that number then?'

'I think what Jack is trying to say,' Mac interrupts, 'is that "pleased" is not quite the most suitable word for the end of the work that we've been doing, sir.'

'I don't see why not. We've done a fine job, a damn fine job.'

'Some of us,' someone mutters.

'I see!' Ingham turns to face the speaker. 'No, I see.' He nods. 'I understand perfectly, and I sympathise – really I do.' The sudden change of tack takes the men by surprise. No one speaks. And Ingham slowly takes another letter from his tunic pocket, glances down for a moment, then looks back at the men. 'You think I'm not in sympathy with the serious and solemn nature of what we do here, don't you?' he says. 'You men think that because I'm back here filling in Army forms rather than out there getting my boots dirty, you think I don't understand. You think me unfeeling. You regard me as cold-hearted. And yet' – he jabs his finger at the letter – 'it may interest you to know that it is to me that requests occasionally come from the living, from the bereaved, from the families of the men we're burying.'

Jack and Ocker both glance at each other. Mac slowly shakes his head. Only Fuller stands alert, waiting on Ingham's every word.

'You know' – Ingham screws up his eyes – 'there are those who feel it very keenly that these poor fellows can't go back to their homes, their families, their loved ones.' He looks carefully at each of the men. The nearby truck has driven off, the remaining sections of the platoon have been dismissed. The gardeners are all at work.

'What if you, not they, had fallen? Would your families prefer a grave that they could visit?' Ingham walks along the line. 'Would your loved ones be helped by having a headstone in a place of their own choosing, where they were able to lay flowers, and to stand and grieve?'

'Fine words, sir,' says Fuller, before a surreptitious kick from Ocker shuts him up. Jack studies the horizon with renewed interest.

'I will read you a letter,' Ingham says. 'It comes from the relative of one of the soldiers we happen to be burying today. This elderly gentleman lives in Canada. As he says, he has little hope of ever visiting his son's grave. He writes:

I beg you, please, to do what you can for a father. My boy is gone for ever. My only son now lies in a country I know nothing about nor will ever visit. I long for a grave where my wife and I may stand and weep. I need to be close again to my son, even if cold earth should separate us. Please, I beg of you, as King Priam begged for the body of Hector – please, do what you can.

'What do you think to that, then, eh?'

For a long time, there is no sound. A train hisses steam. The engine of another wagon fades to a distant hum as another party of Commission gardeners sets off for a day's planting, tidying, landscaping. Birds sing; skylarks rise from behind the spreading acres of rough, wooden grave markers down the road at Lijssenthoek, the sound of their song headed straight for heaven. In the far distance, gunfire: a hunter shooting rabbits.

Mac eventually breaks the spell. 'And did he,' the Scot begins, 'did the laddie's father write to you personally, did he?'

Ingham looks down at the letter. 'Ah, no. This was passed to me by . . . well, by one of the locals, shall we say.'

'We all know who that'll be, then,' Jack whispers.

'Oh aye, aye,' Mac nods, then pauses, looks at Ingham squarely in the eye. 'And why you, sir?'

'Why me?' Ingham stuffs the letter back into his tunic pocket. 'I, er . . . I don't know. I assume . . . I mean, I believe de Wu—' He stops suddenly.

'Told you,' Jack whispers.

'Well, as I said, Monsieur de – the name is immaterial,' Ingham carries on. 'This gentleman—'

Jack coughs. 'Sorry, sir!'

'This person approached me as a representative of His Majesty's forces, having received communication from the father of one of our Dominion troops grieving for the loss of his only son.'

'Knows him, does he?' Mac asks. 'Does de W . . . this "local person" . . . know the grieving father?'

'Well how the devil should I know?'

'Well, sir, don't you think it's a wee bit . . . I don't know—'

'What are you trying to say, Private MacIntyre?'

'It's a little bit suspicious. I reckon that's what Mac's getting at,' says Jack. 'Some bloke in Canada contacts Fats – I mean, this gentleman o' yours, out of the blue and starts asking a lot o' stuff about his son—'

'His *only* son.'

'Who's this Priam bloke anyway? That's what I want to know,' says Fuller.

'It's not that we aren't sympathetic, sir,' Jack goes on. 'We know all about the sacrifices, the pain o' loved ones back home—'

'And I don't?'

'I'm not saying that, sir. I'm just—'

'Well, I can see this isn't going to get us anywhere.'

'Certainly not going to get this poor fella back to Canada,' says Fuller. 'Or answer my question for that matter.' Silence.

'You weren't, by any chance, thinking that I was asking you to assist in the illegal repatriation of this body, were you, men?'

'Course not, sir. Whatever gave you that idea?'

'After all, that would be disobeying Army orders, wouldn't it?'

'Quite.'

'Because we all know – don't we? – that both French and British armies have strict standing orders forbidding the repatriation of bodies.'

'During the conflict, sir.'

'Aye, in 1915'

'The Frenchies are taken their fellas home now though.'

'But not the British.'

'No.'

'Too right,' says Ocker. 'I mean – can you imagine what would have happened if the folks back home caught sight of this lot?'

'I don't think that is the rationale for their decision.'

'Maybe not,' Mac says. 'But I wonder how long the war would've gone on if the docks had been stacked up wi' our dead.'

'Can you just imagine the effect on morale that would have,' says Ocker. 'Passing crate loads o' corpses as you disembark from the troopship.'

'Almost as bad as marching to battle past mass graves, freshly dug,' says Jack.

'Yes, yes,' says Ingham. 'I appreciate all that, men. Nevertheless—'

'Nevertheless, sir?'

'Nevertheless I merely thought that it would interest you to know some of the complexities as well as the emotional sensitivities of the situation we find ourselves in.' Ingham turns, without a word, then stops. 'Interesting, too, to note that they are the same concerns the ancients had for their dead. Even Achilles eventually relented. He surrendered the body of Hector.' He looks back briefly, nods at Fuller, then walks away.

'Reckon your luck's in there, mate.' Ocker digs an elbow hard in Fuller's ribs. 'But if Ingham's Achilles, then who's—'

'Patroclus?'

'Company – DISMISS!'

Blake is waiting for them when the men finally get to the canteen a few minutes later. 'I knew the question of whether men should be returned would raise its ugly head again,' he says, as they explain what kept them.

'It's natural enough, I suppose,' Mac says, passing his mess-tin to the orderly. 'You know – people asking why, if the living can return home, why the dead can't be sent back to where they came from.'

'Well, they could've sent me back a darn sight quicker,' Ocker says as his mug is filled with tea.

'Of course, this is a unique situation,' Blake says, as they move off to find a space on one of the tables.

'You don't say!'

'What I mean' – Blake hacks a knob of butter with his knife – 'is that it's the first time that the country has, I don't know, taken responsibility like this, on a nationwide scale, for burial and remembrance.'

'He's right,' Mac nods. 'The treatment of the Boer War fallen was a national scandal.'

'And in the Crimea,' Blake adds, 'and Waterloo. For most of our glorious history the dead were simply piled up in mass graves.'

'So we should all be grateful, is that what you're sayin'?'

'No—'

'—for letting 'em kill us and then giving us a state bleedin' funeral for nothing?'

'I'm only saying,' Blake shakes his head, 'that it's what these men deserve. They gave their lives. It's the least a grateful nation ought to do.'

'Aye, but Ingham's got a point, hasn't he? Why shouldn't a grateful nation show its respects for them back home?'

'They are already raising funds for memorials and monuments,' Blake says. 'There isn't a town or a village in Britain that won't be doing something.'

'Except for burying.' Jack carries on chewing.

'Och, man – but can you imagine it?' Mac puts down his fork. 'They don't want this lot under their noses—'

'Or under their feet.'

'Do you think so?' Blake takes another bite of toast. 'Do you think that's the only reason?'

'Mac's right. Can you imagine what it'd be like back home if they saw for themselves the size of these cemeteries?'

'Mm,' Blake nods. 'I take your point, Jack, but—'

'They don't want to know, back in Blighty. They want it all neat and tidy—'

'And they want it over here,' adds Mac.

'Aye, so that they can all get on wi' their lives and pretend the whole thing never happened.'

'Well, I'm not quite sure where this little chat is going,' Ocker says. 'But it ain't helping my stomach. Are you not eating that bacon?'

'Here.' Blake passes his mess-tin across the table. 'You have it.'

The men finish the rest of their breakfast in silence, till Jack says: 'Come on,' and drains the last of his tea. 'This isn't digging any graves, is it?'

'Or burying any bodies.'

'Yeah, look sharp – time to shift some more o' this soil.' Ocker picks up his mess-tin and takes it to the washstand. A short time later the men cross the road and walk the short distance down to Lijssenthoek Military Cemetery.

'Right,' Jack says when they arrive. 'This looks like our job. Twenty-four graves to dig, Plot Thirty-one.'

The men dig without a word until they call a halt just before eleven.

'Come on, lads,' says Jack, climbing out of the grave. 'Time for a break. We don't have to dig 'em all in a day.'

'Got the whole summer for this sort o' thing, ain't we, Jacko?'

Jack doesn't answer. He starts walking, then running up the hill. 'Last one to t'caff buys the tea.'

'You're on,' says Ocker, sprinting between the rows of crosses.

'That's not fair,' shouts Fuller. 'He's got a head start.'

'Then you'd better get a move on laddie,' Mac shouts as he jogs past.

A small whitewashed hut by the entrance to the cemetery is just another example of the little local amenities now opening across the Salient for the comfort of the growing stream of visitors. And the men see no reason not to take advantage. Fuller – bringing up the rear – orders the teas and the men drink sitting on the wooden bench against the outside wall of the hut, enjoying the warmth of the early summer sun.

'Ocker?'

'Yeah, mate?'

'Why do you always stand like that?' Fuller squints, as if narrowing his eyes might make sense of what he's looking at.

'Stand like what, mate? On me feet?'

'Nah – slanted.' Fuller leans his body over, demonstrating. 'Leaning like you was holding up the walls or something.'

'Kind o' habit, I suppose,' says Ocker, closing his eyes and turning his face to the sun.

'Habit?'

'Yeah, mate. Habit born o' being shelled from above and shot at by rifle and machine-gun fire from below.'

'Habit born o' madness, I reckon,' Jack laughs.

'I don't understand.' Fuller shakes his head.

'Reduces the chance of being hit, doesn't it?' Ocker says, turning and propping one arm against the outside wall of the hut.

'Really?' Fuller's eyes widen. 'How?'

'Minimise the target area from both angles,' Ocker says without opening his eyes.

'You bloody daft bugger.' Jack swats at Fuller with his cap.

'What? What's so funny?'

'No one's firing at him any longer, are they?' Jack says, recovering. 'He's safe now, isn't he? T'bloody war's over!'

'Is that a fact?' Ocker, the only one not to have been laughing, opens his eyes. 'You think so, do you, Jacko?'

'Yeah, Jack's right, in't he? Course it is. No one's firing at you no longer, Ocker, are they? No one's sending no more shells over!'

'Maybe not,' says Ocker, winking. 'But how do we know they'll not kick off again when it suits them, eh? They don't think they've lost this fixture, after all.'

'They don't?'

'No, mate, they don't. And they'll be back, just wait and see. They'll be back before much longer. And there'll be a whole lot more holes in the ground for some other poor buggers like us to dig before it's finally over.'

War Diary or Intelligence Summary: Army form C. 2118
1920

DIVISION MAIN DRESSING STATION—Remy Siding
Map Sheet 28; Grid reference: L.22 d.6.3

November 1st – Battalion parade under R.S.M. Remainder of day spent cleaning equipment. C.O. inspection of billets.

November 2nd – Clothing parade held in presence of Orderly Officer. Lt. J.K. ADAMS D.S.O. proceeded on short leave to Lille.

November 3rd – Inspection of billets. 2/Lt. INGHAM and 1st Labour Coy resume battlefield searches N. 36.a., M.35b.

November 4th – Fatigue party under Captain A.J. HARRIS and 2/Lt. O.R. DENNIS proceeded by motor lorry to Rosnay for purpose of securing wood for fuel. Lt. J.K. ADAMS D.S.O. returned from leave.

November 5th – Secret orders received from Brig-Gen. L.J. WYATT D.S.O. (see appendix) concerning single re-exhumation of unknown British soldier for relocation to St Pol. Baths parade, Poperinghe.

November 6th – Educational classes given in reading, writing, arithmetic, history and geography; book keeping, shorthand and commercial subjects taught by 2/Lt. L.T. JARVIS.

November 7th – Church parade: all denominations held in Salvation Army hut due to inclement weather.

November 8th – 2/Lt. INGHAM and 1st Labour Coy proceed to assist in re-exhumation as instructed and to undertake additional duties specified in secret orders received on 3rd inst. (see appendix).

21

Autumn 1920 has been fairly mild, but wet. Two years after the Armistice was signed, battlefield clearances are slowly coming to an end and most of the work now consists of exhumations and cemetery consolidations. The muddy fields of Flanders have been searched now four, five, even up to six times – each time the land divided into map squares, the ground picked over, finds collected and recorded and remaining graves consolidated. But the bitter harvest is now dwindling. There are fewer rewards than when they first began, and those that remain are harder to find.

The few souvenirs the men do still discover are being scrutinised more carefully and their position plotted ever more minutely. All this slows the remaining work considerably. But the men who get their boots dirty – those who do the walking and the digging, the finding and the burying – are still here, queuing to have their finds checked by an officer at the end of each day's searching. Lining up like schoolboys waiting to have their homework marked by the headmaster.

But the beak is in jovial mood today. 'Right, men, what kind of omnium gatherum have you got for me today, then?' Ingham rubs his hands together rapidly. The men turn out their canvas bags, handing over badges, buckles, brass buttons, shoulder titles and scraps of fabric that are very likely all that remains of the men they once belonged to.

'Excellent, men, excellent.' Ingham seems genuinely excited by the finds, like some eager young archaeologist studying relics from an ancient tomb. Hard and mud-encrusted fingers pass new finds across the table; Ingham's delicate white palms receive the offerings and cradle each fragment carefully.

'Jeez, just look at those hands,' Ocker whispers. 'Sheila's fingers, those – just like the bloody devil dodger's.'

'Bet he never saw no action,' Fuller mutters.

'Someone did once say he'd been on the Somme,' says Mac. 'In 1918.'

'Well if he was there at all it would have been a couple o' miles behind the lines, I reckon.' Ocker shakes his head. 'That man's as big a base rat as I ever saw. If he was anywhere near the flamin' Somme then he was on a cushy number back at HQ, tucked up in some comfortable billet with the notion that guns firing and keeping him awake at night was his share of the Great War's hardship.'

'Let's see what we can make of all this then, shall we?' Ingham puts on his spectacles and studies each of the finds in turn.

'Welch Fusiliers, cap badge, sir. Map reference 28.J.19b.95.90.'

Townend writes the coordinates in the ledger and records brief details of each find. 'Hermitage Château, that, sir!' He leans across the table, pointing out the location on the trench map. 'Only Duke of Wellington's Regiment items found there so far.'

'Really, Sergeant, really?' Ingham marks the spot with a blue pencil. 'Fascinating. That really is very interesting.'

A wagon passes. On the far side of the camp a train pulls slowly out of the sidings. Someone cycles past the Nissen hut whistling 'I Belong to Glasgow' out of tune. A car whines and bumps in the opposite direction.

'These bits look Australian to me, sir.' Ocker puts a handful of decayed remains down on the table.

'Location?'

'Er – Sheet 28. J.7.b.7.9 I think, sir,' Townend says. 'If I can read this proper. Is this a J or an I, Gilchrist?'

'J – there's also a Lancashire Fusilier cap badge, same place.'

'Splendid, chaps, splendid.' Ingham's eyes light up at the sight of each of the muddy remnants. An old biscuit tin now serves as a shrunken ossuary for the buttons, badges and bone-fragments the party have been out collecting. Only a few months ago old wooden ammunition boxes, two or three or more per day, were being filled. The battlefield's grim bounty is growing thinner.

At the end of the day's reckoning the men are, as usual, eager to stand down and leave the camp, to go and relax in the town that some of them are even starting to regard as home. But today Ingham needs to speak to them about a very unusual mission.

'Gather round,' he tells the men. Somebody lets out a groan. 'Now today, we have received some special orders,' he begins. 'Very special orders indeed.'

'We're going home,' Ocker whispers. 'This is it, boys – bloody demob here we come!'

'Silence in the ranks!' Townend steps forward and stands eyeball-to-eyeball with Ocker for a moment.

'We have today received orders from Brigadier-General Wyatt,' Ingham goes on. 'As General Officer Commanding British Troops in France and Flanders, he has a very special request to make.'

'British Troops, sir?' Ocker says. 'Did you say British Troops?'

Ingham laughs nervously. 'And er, Empire troops too, of course.'

'Well I'm glad you made that clear, sir,' he says. 'Otherwise I might've had to have a word or two to say to General Wyatt.'

'Well, as I was saying' – Ingham looks down at his clipboard. 'We've been given something quite unusual to do. Unique, in fact.'

'Don't tell me, sir,' says Ocker. 'We're going to dig a grave so deep I get to go back home!'

'Not quite,' says Ingham.

'Not quite? Not going to tunnel to bloody Kiwi are we?'

'No, no, no. Now pay attention. This is a solemn and serious undertaking.'

'We've been undertaking – solemnly and seriously – for the last two years,' says Mac. 'I reckon I know more about Funeral Directing—'

'Hey, pay attention, lads,' Jack says.

'On a promise are you, Jacko?' Ocker laughs. The men shuffle feet as they settle to hear Ingham explain the details of their latest mission.

'Our orders are to exhume an unknown British – that could, of course, be Empire too, Gilchrist, given that he will be an unknown—'

'Might even be a sheila too,' says Ocker. 'The other day them gardening fellas was showing me the grave of a young nurse buried at Lijssenthoek.'

'Unlikely, Private Gilchrist. The few English girls buried here are, of course, in marked graves. And we are being specifically ordered to select an unmarked grave. Other parties will be performing a similar duty in each of the other three main theatres of war – the Somme, Aisne and Arras. We have been selected to locate and remove one brave soldier from our sector, one man who may be chosen to lie where the Kings and Queens of Empire lie. There – if chosen – he will be buried with full military honours and laid to rest in perpetuity in Westminster Abbey.'

'So we're digging him up and then shipping him home?'

'Not quite,' Ingham replies. 'The body will be transferred to St Pol, where it will lie along with three others draped in the Union Jack and from among which one of the bodies will be chosen at random to be given this symbolic honour.'

The men say nothing. Nothing the Army or the War Graves Commission asks of them comes as a surprise any more.

'Right-o then, chaps – here's the plan.' Ingham proceeds to issue careful orders about which of the recent graves they are to open, how the body is to be treated and what provision will be made for its onward journey. 'We are to remove an early burial from Bleuet Farm Cemetery near Elverdinge. The precise grave has already been selected and I will be accompanying the exhumation party to ensure that everything is carried out to the letter. But otherwise, you may consider it just like any normal exhumation.'

'Except . . .'

'Private Gilchrist?'

'Except you don't normally come along when we're digging men up, do you, sir?'

'Maybe not. But as I have already said, this is an especially important mission. This isn't any old exhumation.'

'Thought you said it was an *especially* old exhumation, sir?'

'It is an old burial, yes.'

'And we won't be looking for signs, though, will we, sir?'

'Signs?'

'Badges, effects, that sort of thing. As we do with any ordinary exhumation.'

'My goodness me, no – certainly not!'

'It's just that you said it was to be just like any normal exhumation, but it seems to me—'

'Dammit, man, don't take things so bloody literally! What I meant was that the body – the unidentified body – will be removed in the usual way and wrapped in a canvas sack. Except that this time the soldier will, I believe . . . just let me check, ah yes – this time the man will be given a box.'

'A box, sir?'

'A coffin, man, a bloody coffin! Good God, it's like dealing with a group of schoolchildren.'

'Enter clowns with spades and mattock,' Blake smiles to himself.

'So not a sack, then?'

'No,' Ingham sighs. 'Not a sack. Any more questions?' He narrows his eyes.

'Yes, sir,' Jack says. 'Just the one.'

'Speak up, man,' says Ingham. 'What is it?'

'Well, sir, I was wondering . . . If the body we dig up isn't the one that's chosen, what happens to it afterwards? And what happens to the others from the Somme and Arras and so on if they don't get the nod?'

'Those not selected are to be interred at the military cemetery at St Pol. That will be their final resting place,' says Ingham. 'Well, in the case of the three not chosen, that is. The corpse selected by Brigadier-General Wyatt will be sealed in an oak coffin and transported by boat to England on its final glorious journey to the Abbey.'

'Very good, sir. But, sir?'

'What is it this time, Lance-Corporal?'

'Wouldn't it 'ave been easier just to pick a grave at random, you know – rather than digging up all four of 'em first?'

'Perhaps,' Ingham says. 'But these are our orders. Well, most of us, anyway.'

'Sir?'

'You, Patterson' – Ingham smiles like a snake – 'you have a very specific task.'

'Oh, aye?'

'Yes. Your job is to be slightly different from the rest of the men. You will be filling six barrels with clean soil from the Salient. I suppose you had better take somebody along with you to help with the lifting. MacIntyre, Skerritt and . . . maybe Gilchrist as well. But you are to do the digging. Is that understood?'

'Yes, sir. Very good, sir.'

With that, the men are dismissed.

The exhumation party takes the old RAMC ambulance with Blake at the wheel. Jack and his men load six empty barrels into the back of the Albion, then climb aboard the truck and squeeze together in the cab.

'We can't just stop anywhere and dig up any old field,' Mac is saying as the men set off. 'So I hope you know exactly where we're going.'

'Aye,' says Jack. 'We're going to have a bit o' fun, I reckon.'

'Well, as long as you don't forget it's you that's to do the digging. Ingham was most particular about that.'

Jack frowns, crunches the truck into gear and then hauls the steering wheel round, heading east out of Poperinghe and then out onto the road towards Ypres. 'Thirsty work tha' knows, digging,' he shouts above the noise of the engine once they are out on the Switch Road.

'Is that a fact?' Mac says.

'And who's to say you can't slake yer thirst beforehand – prevention's better than cure, don't they always reckon?'

'You crafty old devil!'

Half an hour later they are coming to a halt by the Rijks-wachtkazerne. Getting down from the truck, they head back along De Mont Straat before turning into Station Straat and making straight for the British Tavern. Once settled at a table with their beers, the men inspect the map to determine a suitable location for digging.

'Why don't we head down towards Polygon Wood?' says Mac.

'Yup. Nice light, sandy soil over towards Gheluvelt,' Ocker adds.

'I reckon the railway embankment,' Jack says. 'It's nearer – and the soil'll be drier there.'

'Aye, but won't we end up digging a barrelful of gravel?'

'Not if we're careful.'

The barmaid, Margreet, refills the men's mugs as they are talking. Jack looks up, distracted for a moment, in the way you only notice a clock once it stops ticking.

'So where is the lovely K-K-K-Katy this morning?' Ocker asks, as if reading his thoughts.

'Don't know,' Jack shrugs.

'And you didn't ask the barmaid?'

'I'm not about to ask that old trout!'

'Why's that, then, mate?'

'Interfering ol' bitch, that's why!'

'Ach, she's probably jealous,' Mac says.

'Jealous of Jacko.' Ocker shakes his head. 'The poor woman must be desperate.'

'She is,' Jack laughs.

'Can't see what they see in you, myself,' says Mac.

'Well I'm bloody glad about that,' Jack says. 'Now come on, drink up. We've got work to do.'

'We?'

Back in the truck, Jack heads north past the Minneplein. The old open playing field and park is now covered from corner to corner with neat little temporary houses – Albert Houses, paid for by a special fund provided by the Belgian king.

'A man could really grow to love a little house like that.' Mac winks at Skerritt. 'Especially if a man had a wee lassie there to share the bed with him of a night and to keep him warm.'

'He's working on it, aren't you, Jacko?' says Ocker.

'Don't you lot ever give up?'

'I'm sure he is working on it. And why wouldn't he be? She's a grand lassie, man. Belgian, mind. But a grand wee lassie all the same.'

Skerritt mumbles something, but the noise is drowned by the rumble of the truck as Jack changes gear and heads off along Weverstraat.

'You see?' Mac says. 'Skerritt agrees with me too, don't you, laddie?' Skerritt nods vigorously, salivating like a dog. 'And her father, well . . . He's certainly a canny businessman.'

'He is that,' Jack says. 'Made a small fortune out of us in t'war.'

'And he's not letting peace stop him, either.'

'It was certainly a shrewd move, opening up in Poperinghe like that as soon as Wipers was evacuated.'

'The only place Tommies could quench their thirst without Fritz spoiling the party.'

'Wonder if he'll keep the two places going,' Mac says. 'Now he's opened back in Wipers again.'

'Reckon that's your job, Jacko!' Ocker grins. 'Minding the shop – one of 'em – for him.'

'Might as well,' Jack smiles. 'We as good as built British Tavern for him after all.'

'Fair dinkum, mate,' says Ocker. 'It was for our benefit, too.'

'Aye, we needed a place to wet us whistle!'

'It's just that some here,' Mac smiles mischievously, 'stand to benefit a little more than the rest of us!'

They travel on for a while without saying anything. A weak sun is starting to break through, low cloud, flashing in the puddles on the road. Suddenly, from out of nowhere, in a thin ghost of a voice the men at first can hardly hear, Skerritt starts to whine the words of a familiar song to the tune of 'The Sailor's Hornpipe.'

'Well done, Skerritt lad! By God, tha's found thee voice today,' Jack says, beaming.

'That's the most noise he's made since Third Ypres,' Mac adds. Smiling broadly, and with just a hint of a tear, the others join in with gusto, drowning out the engine noise, silencing their doubts and fears and gaining strength as they remember the rest of the words.

> *Do your balls hang low?*
> *Do they dangle to and fro?*
> *Can you tie 'em in a knot?*
> *Can you tie 'em in a bow?*

'Well done, big fella, well done.' Ocker slaps him on the back. 'Didn't think you had it in you!'

'Neither did he, did you, Skerritt lad?'

'Haven't heard that one since we gave Haig his own personal recital!'

Skerritt sits in silence, a twisted smile fixed like a mask to his face.

By now the men are well out of the town and far along the Menin Road, passing Hell Fire Corner. Turning left down the Cambridge Road to the line of the old Ypres–Roulers railway, Jack decides to bring the truck to a halt.

'This'll do, I reckon.' The men roll the barrels down the long path and upend them at the chosen spot.

'Right, Jacko.' Ocker passes him a shovel.

'Come on,' Jack says. 'You an' all.'

'No, mate! Ingham was most particular wasn't he, fellas? Said it was you had to do the digging. Isn't that right, Mac?'

'Oh aye,' Mac says, lighting up his pipe. 'We'll stand here and make sure no one interferes, won't we, Skerritt?'

'Like heck, you will.' Jack throws them both a shovel. 'Come on you lot – get bloody digging.'

With mock reluctance the others slowly pick up their tools and set to work. Before long they've dug a small trench, shallow so as to collect only the drier, cleaner topsoil near the surface. But so far they have filled only one of the barrels. The early November rain has made the rest of the ground sticky and wet. Eventually it becomes easier to slice out brick-sized chunks like peat and then bag each one before placing it in the remaining barrels – leaving it to the journey and the Abbey to dry out the soil.

Meanwhile, across the Western Front as far apart as the Somme, the Aisne and Arras, and all the way back to Elverdinge, four bodies are now en route to St Pol on board four old ex-RAMC motor ambulances. Arriving at their destination, each truck is met at the gates by the padre. The men unload the stretchers, draping a Union Jack over each of the bodies. And inside the small cemetery chapel waits a single huge oak coffin.

'Our fella'll rattle around a bit in that, won't he, sir?' asks Fuller. 'If he's chosen, that is.' Ingham doesn't answer. Townend is thinking they could probably get all four men in the enormous box. But at midnight tonight, 9 November, Brigadier-General Wyatt will enter the chapel by candlelight and place a hand on one of the stretchers, after which the load it bears will be placed in the coffin and the lid sealed and secured for its final journey.

Forty miles away, Jack is driving away from a Flanders field with six barrels of the soil that will be used to bury the chosen warrior in Westminster Abbey.

'Don't know about you,' he says, as they drive back through Ypres with the barrels bouncing and rolling in the back of the truck. 'But I could do with a drink.'

'I reckon you're after more than just a drink, Jacko,' Ocker jokes as Jack brings the truck to a halt outside the ruins of the campanile.

Halfway down Boter Straat the men pass a local loading rubble onto the back of a wagon.

'Hey!' Jack shouts. 'That stuff's ours. Hands off.'

'Technically, of course,' says Mac, 'it belongs to the Germans, doesn't it? They made it, after all.'

'That's stretching t'point a bit isn't it, Mac?' Jack says. 'It belonged to the Belgies long before Fritz started using the place for target practice.'

'Well either way it's just a heap of flamin' rubble now,' says Ocker.

'Aye, but will you just look at it!' Mac points to the jagged outline of the ruined tower, silhouetted against the darkening sky. 'Never saw it, did you, Jack? Never saw it in its heyday?'

'It was in already in ruins when I arrived, Mac. Not totally destroyed, but still in a pretty bad way.'

'There was scaffolding up around that tower well before the war, y'know. Before the Germans ever fired a shell.'

'Oh, aye?'

'Yes. Restoring it, they were. Like so much of the town, even then.'

'Got a bit of a bigger job on their hands now, I'd say.'

'You're not wrong there, mate!'

'Hallo,' Jack calls as they walk into the bar. The room is quiet, but empty glasses on the smeared tables suggest a busy lunchtime session.

'Not as many of you here as usual?' Katia turns to fill a jug of beer as soon as she gets the nod from Jack. 'The others are all right, are they – yes?' She looks up at him over her shoulder.

'Aye, lass, they're all grand,' Jack says smiling to himself as she straightens up and turns round, jug in one hand, the other tucking loose strands of her hair behind her ears. 'They've gone over to St Pol with a body, that's all.'

'A body?'

'Aye, that's right.'

'Where are they taking it?' she asks.

'Home,' Jack says, looking at her. 'Why?'

'I don't . . . Oh no! Jacques – no!'

'Got a big funeral planned for him in Westminster Abbey.'

'Oh my God, Jacques.' She holds up her hand to her face. 'Jacques, Jacques – what have you done?' Big tears are welling in the girl's widening eyes.

Jack shakes his head. 'What's up, lass?'

She shakes her head quickly. 'You must not . . . I never

thought you would also get involved, Jacques. Please. Monsieur de Wulf and the others, yes . . . but I never thought . . . no, not you.'

'What are you on about, lass?'

She turns abruptly and makes her way into the small kitchen behind the bar, holding a handkerchief to her mouth.

'Played a blinder there, Jack, ol' son.'

'I wish I knew what that were about,' Jack shrugs.

Out of sight of the men, her back to the wall in the small kitchen, Katia closes her eyes and tries to slow her breathing. A wagon passes in the square outside. A train sighs in the station. In her mind the street beyond the window, the ruined town of Ieper and the pockmarked road to Poperinghe all slowly emerge from the turmoil of her mind.

At the door of the bar, the dark silhouette of Monsieur de Wulf briefly blocks sight of the street as he pauses for a moment on the threshold. But none of the few regulars, hunched over beers and glasses of petit rosé, looks up. Jack turns away to avoid catching the man's eye. Only Skerritt is staring, mouth open, with what's left of his lower mandible mouthing words he'll never utter.

'Ah, the Tommies!' de Wulf raises his arms. 'Tommy Atkins!'

'Come on, lads, let's get a seat.' Jack nods curtly at de Wulf, and the men sit down, turning their backs to the bar. 'Don't want ol' Fatso to hear what we've been up to, do we?'

'Has a habit of turning up like a bad penny, that man,' Mac says.

'Can't stand the fat bastard,' Jack adds. 'And have you noticed he seems to hang around more and more these days?'

'Really?'

'Aye. Fuller says it was de Wulf who took Ingham back to Remy the other day after they'd been out on their little *nocturnal expedition.*'

'Ah!' Mac taps his nose. 'You mean the *top-secret mission*?'

'Aye, the one half the camp knew about afore Ingham was even tucked up in his bunk.' The men laugh.

'Christ, laddie, did you not get Skerritt a straw!' Mac suddenly gets to his feet, breeches covered in beer.

'Don't laugh wi' yer mouth full, will you, Skerritt? Waste of good beer, apart from owt else. Shall I get you another one, Mac?'

'No,' Mac says, flapping at the damp patches on his trousers with his tartan handkerchief. 'As a matter of fact I think I'm going to turn in. We ought to get this soil back to the sidings before too long. Coming, Ocker?'

'I'm done in, mate. I'm with you.'

'Jacko?'

'No, lads. Not yet.'

'Daft flamin' question.'

'Aye, but take Skerritt with you an' all, eh?' Jack says. 'Ocker – you can drive the Albion, can't you? I think I might need to stay on here a bit.'

'Got some explaining to do, eh?'

'Summat like that.' He glances at de Wulf. 'Though I'm blowed if I can think what for. Oh, and lads' – the men turn before opening the door – 'cover for me, will you, if you have to. I'll walk back later if I can't find a bike.'

'Or something else to ride on, eh, laddie?'

'Private MacIntyre, that is beneath your God-fearing Scottish dignity.'

'Away, who ever said I had any?' Mac laughs. 'I've been a soldier far too long, son.'

'I know. You never stop reminding us. Now bugger off back to base and get to bed, grandad.'

'Come on then, Skerritt,' Ocker calls. 'You can fire her up for me.'

The men pull up their collars as they open the door. Rain has started beating hard against the corrugated iron roof and there is a brief rush to the door as the regulars, too, decide to turn in early. Even de Wulf seems preoccupied as the rain suddenly gets harder and the wind blows stronger. Pretty soon he's rushing out into the night, and at last Jack finds himself the only customer.

'So it's just me and thee then, lass!' He stands up and starts gathering the empty mugs and glasses.

'You don't have to do that.' Katia shakes her head. 'I can manage.'

'I'm sure you can, lass,' he smiles at her. 'But it's no bother.'

'No bother,' she repeats, another linguistic note, a nuance to be stored away for future reference. The glasses and beer mugs chink loudly as he gathers them a handful at a time. Katia clears the remaining tables then – as Jack puts the final glasses on the bar – she reaches out a hand and places it on top of his. 'Sit down,' she says to him softly. 'Another drink?'

'Why not?'

She pours a mug of de Snoek Vlaams *bier blond* from the pewter jug and sits down opposite him across the small round table in the middle of the bar. Her hair, dishevelled after an evening running the bar on her own, surrounds her face in loose strands. She looks tired. The shadows beneath her eyes are darker; whites still bloodshot from her earlier tears.

'I don't know why I thought . . .'

'Neither do I, lass. In fact, I'm not right sure what you

thought. But whatever it was, it wasn't owt to do with what we've been doing today.'

She looks down and smiles.

'So, where's everyone else then tonight? Why are you on your own?'

'I am not alone.'

Jack frowns. Then suddenly the noise of glass clinking as the cellar boy brings up a crate of bottles. 'Mademoiselle!' the boy shouts. '*Êtes-vous là?*'

'*Oui, Michel, je suis ici. Je viens.*' She smiles at Jack. 'I have to go and help Michel for a moment. I won't be long.'

'Who's Michel?'

'The new cellar boy,' she answers. 'I told you I was not alone.'

'You did,' Jack nods. 'You're playing games wi' me!'

'I am not, Jacques.' She puts her hand on his. 'My father has taken him on to help me here, since Françoise . . .'

'Aye.'

'He is strong. But he is young. He will wish to go home now. He has school in the morning.'

'Aye, well.' Jack drains his beer and gets to his feet. 'Now t'rain seems to have slowed down a bit I suppose I'd better do t'same . . . Go home, I mean.'

'I did not think you also would be going to school,' Katia laughs.

'No.' Jack gets to his feet and looks at his boots, ashamed at his sudden change of heart. Outside the bar the street is deserted. The last train in the station opposite begins to gather steam for Poperinghe. In spite of the recent rain, in spite of the walk, in spite of his plans for the evening, Jack now feels a desperate need to get out into the night air, to be alone. 'Plenty more graves to dig in t'morning, love.'

'Still?' She puts out her hand to delay him. As he leans towards her she draws him in a little closer. He can feel her delicate, warm breath on his face like the wingbeat of a tiny bird.

'Oh, aye.' He turns towards her, wanting to turn away. 'There's thousands of them all over t'place. They're everywhere.'

'I suppose so.'

'Aye. And someone has to bury 'em.'

'And does that someone still have to be you, Jacques?'

'Aye, lass. It does.'

'But why?' She reaches for his free hand. 'Jacques!' He allows her to take it, but he won't turn to face her. She holds on tight, covering the hard, spade-calloused skin with her delicate fingers. 'There is other work,' she says at last. The stubble on the side of Jack's neck reflects in the light of the candles, like tiny grains of sand in the sun. 'My father, he is weary – he is finding things so difficult now.'

'Aye,' Jack turns at last to face her, to properly look at her, her brown eyes large and dark in the dim light of the bar. 'I know.'

'He is thinking he can no more run l'estaminet in Poperinghe.'

'No?'

'Not without help, Jacques.' She closes her eyes and shakes her head. 'And there is going to be more and more for him to do here in Ieper, with the rebuilding.'

'What is it you're saying, love?' he asks. He knows what she is saying, though. He knows he should be pleased, flattered even. But he knows too that that is nothing like what he is feeling.

'Nothing.' She shakes her head. 'Don't think about it.' Katia covers her mouth with her hand as if trying to push the words back in. Tears start to prick at the corners of her eyes. 'It is just . . . it is so much more difficult since my sister . . .'

'You were close.' He draws her to him, opening his arms. 'You and your sister.'

'We were,' says Katia. 'We were – we are – we are a close family.'

'I know,' he says. 'I know.'

Katia lifts her head. 'You were . . . fond of her too, Jacques. You liked her too?'

'Aye, I . . .'

'I know . . .' Her bottom lip is trembling. 'How does the world keep on turning, Jacques? How can the sun keep shining every morning?'

'Shhhh . . .' He holds her, holds her close to him. He feels her sobs.

'How can things go on, Jacques, as they did before?' She rubs her nose with the back of her hand. 'Why is not the whole world dressed in black?'

The rain returns and settles to a steady rhythm on the tin roof of the bar. Jack's heart beats against Katia's face. Her lungs rise and fall in the warmth of his embrace.

'Game goes on, I suppose, lass. We're still . . .'

'The game?' She looks up, puzzled for a moment. 'Are we, Jacques . . . Are you still playing? Are you . . . are we all just playing a game?'

'Aye, lass!' He shakes his head. 'Reckon we are.'

'Don't go, Jacques. Please. You don't have to go. Not tonight.'

'I know.' He looks down, neither pleased nor surprised.

'Please!' she cries. 'Please wait, just a moment longer, Jacques. Let me send the boy home first, at least. Please?'

Slowly, Jack goes back to the table as the girl gives Michel brief instructions. The boy asks – in French – about the barrels, and whether he should fetch another crate of bottles. But she is already helping him into his coat and shepherding him towards the door. Unseemly haste. The cellar boy turns and looks at Jack – a strange, curious smile curling at the corner of his lips – before pulling on his hat and walking out into the rain. The noise flares as the door opens, then subsides again as the girl replaces the latch and slides across both bolts.

'You can't go out in that, Jacques.' She wipes her wet hands on her apron. 'You will catch your death . . .'

He looks at the bolts on the door, then looks at her, then smiles. Then slowly, starts to laugh. Suddenly, great, chest-heaving guffaws that leave him wheezing and in pain echo round the empty bar.

'I don't know what you find so funny.' Katia looks puzzled, then annoyed, and then concerned. And then slowly she, too, begins to smile. 'I see,' she says at last.

'Yer do?'

She nods. Picking up Jack's empty glass, she stoops, wiping the table, blowing out the candle with a gentle 'pfft'. In the dim light of the oil lamp Jack sees the outline of her hips, the neat bow tied at the back of her apron, and imagines the gentle tug that it would take to loose the ribbon. His mind moves to the strings of her stays, the laces round her stocking tops, the taut elastic of her petticoat, the waistband of her drawers. Without warning he leans forward, turning her head and kissing her first on the cheek, then full on the lips.

'Not here,' she whispers, taking him by the hand and leading him across the bar and through the small kitchen, pulling back a curtain to reveal a tiny area at the back of the building complete with single bed, washstand, chest of drawers and mirror. The floor looks familiar. Jack recognises the bare outline of the room from a time months, even years earlier, when it had been no more than chipped flagstones within sight of the ruined campanile. Someone had been sweeping the floor while he dug post-holes with a pickaxe ready to erect the building's temporary timber frame. Wooden walls, a window overlooking a bare yard; the dark, jagged edges of the Cloth Hall just visible in the darkness through a curtain of steady rain.

An old blanket has been neatly placed across the stone floor. Dried flowers in a vase give off the scent of roses. Katia turns, undoes the buttons of Jack's tunic and rubs her hands against his chest. The smell of sweat, soap and stale smoke leaches from his pores. She drinks in the scent like the most refreshing draft of clear spring water.

Just as he imagined, the apron strings untie themselves at the merest tug of his thumb and forefinger. Her blouse is trickier. He fumbles with the laces at her neck but she helps, holding up her arms – eyes closed – for him to pull the garment up and over her head. The loose stays fall easily to the floor. Her bare breasts have suddenly nothing but his cupped hands to support them, and his mouth, his lips, his tongue to caress, to kiss, to tease, to nibble the hard brown nipples. Her skirt, then petticoats, fall to the floor and his hand is sliding down her belly underneath the waistband of her drawers, between her legs. She moves backwards, to the bed, undoing his belt, the buttons of his flies, letting his breeches fall to his ankles, pulling him over on top of her and feeling his hardness against her groin and then suddenly inside her, moving slowly first, then faster as she brings her knees up high and digs her fingernails into his buttocks.

War Diary or Intelligence Summary: Army form C. 2118

1921

DIVISION MAIN DRESSING STATION—Remy Siding
Map Sheet 28; Grid reference: L.22 d.6.3

January 1st – Observed as holiday. The New Year's Honours
Gazette contained the following awards: D.S.O. – Major B.
KEANE; D.C.M. – 23378 Sgt. J.K. TOWNEND; 24789
Drummer T. HODGE; 4493 O.L. PARTRIDGE. M.S.M. –
2761 R.S.M. W.R. MITCHELL; 5611 C.S.M. W. TITLEY;
Mentioned in Dispatches – Lt. Col. H.K. ANDREWS D.S.O.

January 3rd – 7 O.R.s reinforcements arrived. Coys at the
disposal of Coy Commanders for drill and inspection. Capt.
S.J. JAINS departed for demobilisation. 2Lt G.R.
UNDERWOOD to Lille for 3rd Army Rifle Training.

January 8th – Rugby versus 12th Sussex Pioneers. Lost 18–6. 18
O.R.s attested for Regular Army under Short Service
Scheme. Conference of Company Commanders and OC 5th
Labour Battalion concerning ongoing salvage work.

January 10th – Following Warrant Officer and N.C.O.s awarded
M.S.M. 4566 FOX. J.; 78443 WOOD, R.G.; 3455 CQMS
JENKINS, K.N.

January 17th – Capts SNELL and HARRIS return from leave.

January 19th – Salvage and clearance operations hindered by bad
weather. Battalion bath parade Poperinghe curtailed due to
water being cold owing to scarcity of fuel for heating.

January 20th – Battalion was employed chiefly in clearing the
streets of snow. Men desirous of going before the Divisional
Advisory Board were interviewed by the Commanding Officer.

22

'I don't know what the devil he was doing out here,' Ingham is shouting. 'How the hell would I know?'

'But how did he get here,' Ocker says, 'without his bike?'

'Without his bike?'

'Yeah, without his bike. His bike's back at the local, next to mine, right where he left it. When you came screeching up the road like one o' the Bentley Boys and rushing into the bar like the Jerries was attacking, first thing I do is check my bike. And Fuller's is still there, propped up against the wall by the door.'

'Yes, well. Look – I don't bloody well know how he got here, do I?' Ingham shouts. 'All I know is he's out here now and he's hurt.'

'How, sir?' Jack says. 'I mean, how do you know?'

'How do I know what? That he's here?' As the noise of the engine stops, the men hear Fuller's cries of pain like a wounded animal in the darkness.

'How do you know that he's hurt?'

'Ah ... I, er – heard the explosion, Lance-Corporal Patterson. And then I did what any decent officer would do and came out here to investigate.'

'Funny,' Ocker says, 'I never heard any explosion.'

'The state you were in when I found you it's a wonder you

can still hear anything, Private Gilchrist. You realise I ought to have you on a charge.'

'Really, sir?'

'Yes, Private – drunk whilst in uniform.'

'But you're not going to do that, sir. Are you, sir?'

'Am I not, Private Gilchrist? Am I not?'

'No, Lieutenant Ingham, sir.' Ocker leans forward, looking directly into Ingham's eyes. 'No, sir. You are not, sir.'

'Oh shit! Oh, fucking hell!' Jack's voice suddenly breaks like glass. 'Come on, Ocker, come here – give me a hand.' Ocker sprints across the mud to where Jack is kneeling by the boy, cradling his shattered face.

'I want me mum,' says Fuller quietly. 'Mum?'

'Yer mam's here,' Jack says, holding the boy's head together in his hands. 'Here's yer mam now, hush, hush!'

'Jacko?'

'Aye, lad?'

'Jack? Is that you?'

'Aye, lad, aye, it is. It'll be right, lad. It'll be right. Shush now.'

'Jesus Christ!' Ocker whispers.

'Get us some o' that dressing will yer? In t'kitbag, over there.'

'Dress that, mate, and you'll be here till next Christmas. He's a goner, mate.'

'Shut up, will yer! Shut the fuck up or lad'll hear yer. Here, pass bag to me.'

'This one?'

'Aye. Unwrap that. And I'll need a lint pad and . . .'

'Jack?'

'What is it, lad?'

'Am I going to die, Jack?'

'Nay, lad. Don't talk daft.'

'There's a . . . pack o' . . .' Suddenly Fuller retches a bowlful of blood and filth from his mouth.

'I know, lad. Them cards. I know. I'll see it to it for yer. I'll see to it.'

Jack is fumbling in Fuller's breast pocket. He knows, of course, exactly what he's feeling for. But the sensation of rummaging for a pack of dirty postcards against the warmth of soft, living flesh beneath the fabric of the tunic pocket, rather than the cold, damp stiffness or the sticky, smelly bones of an old corpse, is unnerving.

'Here.' Jack hands the postcards to Ocker. 'Get rid o' these, will yer?'

'Jeez!' Ocker winces, shining the torch on the first of the pictures. 'Didn't have Fuller down as one o' them.'

'Christ, man, don't you ever give up? Here, shine that bloody torch over here.'

'Sorry, mate.' Ocker kneels at Jack's side. The two of them listen for a moment to the crackling, gurgling, spluttering noises that Fuller is making.

'Shhh, lad, shhh . . .' Jack whispers. Suddenly, and without thinking, Ocker reaches out and starts to stroke the boy's head. A ghost of a smile starts to spread across his bloody lips. The crackling sound of Fuller's breathing rises for a moment. His eyes dart in the darkness, searching for something. His remaining hand grips hard onto Jack's long fingers.

Then the noise stops.

Ingham is the first to speak as they bump along the road back to Ypres.

'Thank you, chaps,' he says eventually. 'Thank you for that.' Then, after a short silence, adds: 'I think we'd better say as little about all this as possible.'

'Suits me,' says Ocker.

Jack says nothing. Suddenly they see the fat man waiting by the roadside in the shadows by the gap in the ramparts. Newly excavated trenches have been dug, exploratory foundations for a planned memorial arch.

'What's he doing there?' Jack asks, turning his head.

'Ah,' says Ingham. 'Leave this to me. I won't be a moment.'

He drives across the moat and into Ypres, parking the truck about 100 yards down Menen Straat. The engine shudders to a halt. 'Remain here,' Ingham says, stepping down from the van and walking back towards the gate. A short while later, in the silence of the night, the two men can be heard talking.

'Napoo weapons this time,' Ingham is holding out his hands. 'Napoo anything.' But the fat man is arguing, a finger jabbing in the darkness. Jack can't quite hear what he is saying. Then, suddenly, Ingham's voice is raised. 'Look, I've lost one of my best men this evening,' he is shouting. The fat man is turning, retreating into the darkness. But Ingham takes a step towards him and pushes him – hard – in the small of the back. Jack sees a reflection in the truck's enormous wing mirror – the shadowy figure is stumbling over; a flash of moonlight glints like a sudden spark as Ingham unclips his revolver.

'Oh Christ, no!' Jack and Ocker sprint from the van, but by the time they reach the two men, Ingham is already replacing the gun in his holster. The fat man is crawling through the dirt. But there is no blood.

'What the . . . ?'

'Oh don't fret, man,' Ingham sneers. 'I was only warning him off.'

Jack helps the frightened victim to his feet. He feels the man's fat sausage fingers close round his hand as he takes the weight and pulls him upright.

'Thank you!' says the man, brushing the dirt from his clothes. Then he looks at Jack and smiles, suddenly. 'Ah, Tommy! How are you, Tommy?'

'Come on, men,' says Ingham. 'Back to the camp.'

By the time Jack reaches the van and turns again to check, the man has gone – vanished into the shadows of the shattered trees that line the Menin Road.

Next morning, at Parade, Major Rennard informs the company of its most recent casualty. 'The chaplain is already on his way from Poperinghe,' the CO is announcing, 'and Private Fuller will be laid to rest this afternoon at Lijssenthoek with full military honours.

'Patterson, Gilchrist!'

The two men stamp their feet. 'Sir!'

'You will proceed directly to the cemetery and dig the grave. The plot has already been marked out. MacIntyre?'

'Yes, sir?'

'You will lead the firing party. Select half-a-dozen men and report to Captain Harris for arms and ammunition. The rest of the company – Blake, Skerritt and the others – you will act as bearers.'

'Yes, sir.'

Lijssenthoek Military Cemetery is already marked out as the second-largest concentration of war dead after Tyne Cot. One more will hardly make a difference. The graves sprawl across the flat, featureless fields east of the railway sidings, creeping on towards the nearby village of Lijssenthoek itself.

Jack opens the tiny gate beneath the enormous brick arch that now separates the busy road to Poperinghe from the fields of wooden crosses. In the far corner of the cemetery someone is busy tending the ground. Jack calls over to him, but the man doesn't hear and carries on with whatever he is doing.

'Bloody 'ell.'

'Problem, Jacko?'

'Can't get the ol' boy's attention.'

'Want me to give him a shout?'

'No. Come on, we'll get cracking. Here, lift that wire will yer, we'll take a short-cut.'

'Hey!' The gardener has suddenly seen them and is striding over with surprising speed. 'Mind your bloody boots!' he shouts as the men wheel their barrows across the cemetery.

'What? Messing up the flamin' mud, are we?' Ocker shouts as he turns down the end of one of the rows of crosses.

'Look,' the gardener puffs, taking his pipe from his mouth and catching his breath.

'Hey, steady on, grandad,' Ocker laughs, putting down his wheelbarrow. 'Don't want to be digging two graves. They're not on special offer, y'know.'

'I'll address the organ grinder if it's all the same to you,' the man says, panting, 'rather than the flippin' monkey!'

'What's the problem, sir?' asks Jack, walking over to where the man is standing.

'These areas here, and here, and here.' The man points to freshly levelled patches of bare soil with the stem of his pipe. 'We've only just seeded them with grass this week. That's why they're cordoned off, you see. To give the seeds a chance to grow.'

'Sorry, mate,' Ocker says. 'Didn't see your dainty bits of string.'

'No, well . . .'

'Come on, Ocker,' Jack says. 'We can walk around the side instead. It's no further. Give t'grass a chance to grow.'

'Why don't you plant a few flowers for 'em while you're at it, mate?' Ocker shouts over his shoulder as he goes to collect his barrow.

'Oh we are,' the gardener calls after them. 'We've got some dwarf roses ready to plant this spring, and I've asked for some nasturtiums. That should nicely set off things like cornflowers and chamomile and charlock that grow here naturally – to say nothing of the poppies, of course.'

'Very pretty, mate, I'm sure.'

'Well, we like to do our best,' the man says. 'For the relatives, y'know.'

'Aye,' says Jack as he wheels the second barrow along the duckboard track to where the gardener is still standing. 'And we like to do our best for the dead. We've got a grave to dig, so if you'll excuse us . . .'

'Of course.' And the man removes his cap and stands aside. Too old to have fought. Jack wonders what has brought the old man out here to this windswept patch of bare earth to tend a thousand graves and to create a cottage garden round the crosses.

'Hey, Ocker!'

'What's up, Jacko?'

'Take yer time, will yer?' Jack nods towards the gardener, still standing bare-headed. 'Just . . . slow down a bit, will yer?' he whispers. 'We're not under fire.'

Ocker follows Jack's gaze to where the old gardener is standing, and both of the men are suddenly acutely aware of what they are doing. Ocker kicks some stray soil into one of the divots in an effort to tidy things up a bit.

'Hope we've not done too much damage to the grass,' Jack

says as they walk back to the cemetery entrance once the grave is dug.

'I'm sure it'll recover,' the man says.

'Want a Woodbine, cobber?'

The old man smiles and puts the pipe back to his lips.

'So what brings you out here then?' Jack says.

Puff after puff of blue-grey smoke billows from the bowl as the gardener gets the tobacco lit. He shakes the lucifer before tucking the matchstick into his top pocket and sucking on the lip of the pipe several times.

'Well . . .' He takes the pipe from his mouth. 'There's no work back in England, for a start.'

'Plenty o' work out here,' says Ocker.

'And I lost me wife four years ago, in 1916.'

'I'm sorry,' Jack says.

'That was the same year our lad was killed,' the man goes on. 'She never really got over it, didn't Hilda. Died of a broken heart, the doctor reckoned.'

'Christ, mate!'

The old man smiles. 'I'm not one to mope,' he says. 'Like to keep busy. And with all you lads coming back from France and taking your old jobs back, there wasn't much back home to keep me occupied.'

'So you came out here?'

'That's right. I thought it best. Thought I might, y'know, do my bit. For our kid; for the rest o' the poor blighters.'

'It's certainly looking a lot better since you fellas came and started taking care of things,' Jack says.

'Thank you,' the man says. 'I've always had green fingers, me. Mind you, you've got to be able to turn your hand to most things in this job.'

'Oh, aye?'

'Yes, next job is to take down all them crosses,' he tells them. 'They're putting proper headstones up this year.'

'That's not going to do the grass much good.'

'Aye, I know. That's why I've told 'em I'll take the crosses down myself. At least grass'll not be churned twice over.'

'I quite like it with the crosses, myself,' says Ocker.

'Didn't have you down as a holy Joe,' Jack laughs.

'I'm not. Had enough bloody religion down under. What are they gonna do with 'em, mate' – he turns to the gardener – 'once they're taken down?'

'Burn 'em,' the man replies.

'What?'

'That's what I've been told,' the old man explains. 'They're going to burn 'em and scatter the ashes on the ground. Be good for the soil, that will.'

'To say nothing of what the poor fellas underneath are doing for it.'

'Look out,' Jack says, throwing his cigarette to the ground. 'Here comes the next.'

'Another one for the trench?' The gardener shakes his head as the cortege approaches. The padre slowly leads the way to the open grave.

> *I am the resurrection and the life, saith the Lord: he*
> *that believeth in me, though he were dead, yet shall*
> *he live and whosoever liveth and believeth in me*
> *shall never die.*

Following behind the flag-draped coffin and at the head of the firing party, Mac gives the gardener a nod and then, as if the words have touched off some long-forgotten memory, breaks into a quiet, private recitation of his own:

Who's for the trench—
Are you, my laddie?
Who'll follow French—
Will you, my laddie?
Who's fretting to begin,
Who's going out to win?
And who wants to save his skin—
Do you, my laddie?

Jack and Ocker join the line behind the firing party, completing the procession. Once at the grave, the men remove their caps and wait. The chaplain coughs. Then the burial service begins, the words loud and clear in the afternoon air, the chaplain's voice unhurried, unchanged and unchanging. Somewhere nearby, a fluty-throated blackbird starts to sing.

The Lord giveth and the Lord taketh away; blessed
be the name of the Lord.

Did Fuller believe? Did any of the men believe? Jack isn't sure what he believes any more. Ocker? Who knows? Mac, though – Mac believes. For all his hard talk and Scottish oaths, Mac's Calvinist conviction never falters. No one sings the hymns more loudly at the church parade on Sunday. To have such faith, such certainty, never occurs to Jack. And he knows now it is probably too late.

Man that is born of a woman hath but a short time
to live, and is full of misery. He cometh up, and is
cut down, like a flower; he fleeth as it were a
shadow, and never continueth in one stay. In the
midst of life we are in death . . .

In the midst of death, in the midst of this expanding city of the dead, in the vast killing fields and among the twisted corpses, in the graves they dig but which aren't theirs, and in the tidy, newly levelled graves, in a dead man's tunic pockets, ripping identity discs from the relic of a neck or wrist, removing boots from rotten feet, examining mud-blackened teeth in an empty skull . . . in the midst of death there is the life of Jack and the rest of the men, the life of Katia and her father and the other locals. And there was the life – the brief life – of the boy, Fuller.

> *Forasmuch as it hath pleased Almighty God in His*
> *great mercy to take unto Himself the soul of our*
> *dear brother here departed: we therefore commit his*
> *body to the ground; earth to earth, ashes to ashes,*
> *dust to dust; in sure and certain hope of the*
> *Resurrection to eternal life, through our Lord Jesus*
> *Christ; who shall change our vile body, that it may*
> *be like unto His glorious body, according to the*
> *mighty working, whereby He is able to subdue all*
> *things to Himself.*

'Forasmuch as it hath pleased Almighty God'? Had it really pleased Almighty God to blow this boy's head open? Had it pleased Him to take unto himself the soul of Fuller, and leave the likes of Ingham here still standing, breathing, cap doffed, head bowed, mumbling the Lord's Prayer among the living?

> *Give us this day our daily bread;*
> *And forgive us our trespasses,*
> *As we forgive them that trespass against us . . .*

But some trespasses are too great to be forgiven. Some sins won't wait until the Day of Judgment for their reckoning. Some people standing here beside this boy's grave don't deserve to feel this sunlight on their cheek, or hear the blackbird singing from the stump of an old tree. Jack catches Ocker's eye, and they both take a sideways glance at Ingham. How easy would it be? How simple could they make it?

> *And lead us not into temptation . . .*
> *But deliver us from evil . . .*
> *Amen.*

> *Deliver us from evil.*
> *Deliver us from this evil.*
> *Deliver us from this evil man.*

Without a word, the two men exchange glances and are both instantly agreed. The details will need to be discussed; the plans drawn up and the arrangements made. But they are in agreement. Without a word, they know what now needs to be done.

But when?

No. 1 District
(This report cancels all previous reports)
Spring 1921

Report No. 1
Schedule No. 1210

PLACE OF BURIAL:
DUD CORNER BRITISH CEMETERY

COMMUNE: LOOS-EN-GOHELLE
Map Reference: Sheet 44a G.34 a6.6.

The following are buried here – PLOT 9. ROW D

Regiment	No.	Name	Rank and Initials
UNKNOWN BRITISH SOLDIER			
	ditto		ditto
	ditto		ditto
Royal Berks	33567	EDLINGTON Pte. W.	15.10.15
Gloucesters	46934	COWARD Cpl.	15.10.15
18th London	99766	WILLCOCK Pte. R.	15.10.15

23

'It's not as if we've not got enough to do here,' Mac is grumbling. 'What the devil does he want us to pack up and head across the border for?'

'They're getting rid of us, quick,' Jack says. 'Getting us away from here until things die down'

'Aye, and until Fuller is forgotten.'

The men are silent for a moment.

'It'll be Ingham's doing, no doubt about it,' Mac says. 'He wants us all as far away as possible, so there's no more gossip about what Fuller was doing in the middle of nowhere digging up an old ammunition dump.'

'Poor blighter!'

'There's unfinished business here, that's for sure,' says Ocker.

'Which is why he needs us to be as far away as he can send us.'

'Well, personally I'm just sorry that the trip ain't any longer. He could've sent me a hell of a lot further than bloody Loos, mate!' Ocker shrugs. 'One-way ticket back down under, that's all I'm after.'

'Is that all you can think about?' Jack turns on him. 'Young lad's been blown to bits and—'

'Look, Jacko, there's plenty more of 'em been blown to bits for the last four years. And blown to bits after doing a darn sight more than Fuller, too.'

'Aye – doing what an officer told 'em.'

'Maybe. But it makes a difference what the officer's telling 'em.'

'And why.'

'He's still dead, in't he?'

'Sure.' Ocker looks down at the floor. 'And I'm sorry, Jacko. The kid deserved better.'

'A lot better than to be caught up in Ingham's web,' Mac says, 'that's certain.'

'Well, 'appen you and I will soon be sweeping away t'cobwebs, eh, Ocker?'

'What's that supposed to mean?' Blake looks concerned.

'Nothing to trouble your conscience, Blakey.'

'I'm not sure what you men are on about,' Blake goes on, 'but I'm sure there must be a perfectly innocent explanation.'

'Innocent and Ingham aren't words you normally see together in t'same sentence.'

'Always looking on the flamin' bright side, Blakey, aren't you?'

'I don't know what you mean.'

'He means, lad, you believe whatever tale these tossers tell you.'

'Aye, you can tell the laddie was ne'er a soldier.'

Blake knows better than to answer. Mac grumbles to himself. Jack shakes his head. The mood is sombre. 'Well, we can be certain of one thing,' Ocker goes on. 'Whatever Ingham is up to, it won't involve doing favours for anyone else but himself.'

*

'Right, now gather round, men,' Ingham tells them, spreading out a large 1:10,000 trench map on the bonnet of the van half an hour later. 'The concentration cemetery is situated here at C:28 on the Loos Road, see it? It's right on the seventy-metre contour line just north of the Lens Road Redoubt. Tosh Cemetery here' – Ingham jabs his swagger stick at the map – 'together with Crucifix Cemetery, just to the west here, have already been cleared. We are to assist here' – the stick jabs at a point marked Le Rutoire Farm, east of the hamlet of Vermelles – 'which contains some eighty-two British graves—'

'Scottish, I'll be bound, sir.'

'—as well as a handful of French. We are to help clear this area and take the remains to the concentration cemetery.'

'And does this concentration cemetery have a name?' Mac asks.

'Probably just Loos Road I should imagine,' says Ingham. 'As that is where it is.'

'Welcome to Dud Corner,' the sergeant of the 10th Labour Company says when the men arrive later that afternoon. Originally tiny, containing just a handful of battlefield burials, Dud Corner cemetery is now greatly enlarged and beginning to resemble something of a building site. Foundations are being laid for the perimeter wall, as well as for an ornamental, arched entrance. At the back of the cemetery, the footings for walls to hold panels listing the names of the 20,000 men missing with no known grave are already being dug. An early attempt has been made to level the ground, and the graves have already been fenced off from the road and the surrounding fields.

The road is busy, and for miles around there are still rough, bare patches of churned earth. Wild flowers have begun to colonise the area, making small splashes of colour here and there – a few red poppies blow in the wind and the pale blue of cornflowers and the white of chamomile add to a thoroughly patriotic picture. But looming near on the horizon is the sinister black cone of Hill 70.

'Dud Corner?'

'That's right,' the Labour Corps man says cheerfully. 'So called in honour of some of the millions of shells you lot fired at each other but that failed to explode.'

'Not our fault if we were given blanks, laddie.'

'If they were,' the Labour man says, 'we'd not have had as much trouble clearing them. I've lost six men trying to get these fields safe so that French farmers can start ploughing again. That's why we need more hands. That's why you've been sent here, I suppose.'

'No,' Jack says. 'We're here because we've just lost one of our own lads, actually.'

The sergeant shakes his head, puzzled.

'Long story,' Ocker says. 'And it involves some very dodgy dealings by an officer.'

For the first half of the week the men are busy driving up and down the road from one cemetery to another, the back of the ambulance full of the rattling remains of recently exhumed corpses. But by Thursday, the lorry's fuel tank is empty. 'Nothing doing, I'm afraid,' the Labour Corps sergeant tells them. 'Can't get anything more until Saturday at the earliest. We've got some bicycles . . .'

'Oh yeah,' says Ocker. 'And how are we supposed to shift a body on a bike?'

'I'm sorry,' the man says.

'Haven't you got any horses?'

'You must be joking. They're demobbed quicker than we are!'

'Aye,' Jack says. 'We're lucky to have the Albion – even though it's not much use without a tank of petrol.'

'Not much better than a ton or more of scrap metal.'

'So what are we going to do now?' asks Ocker.

'Well, as Ingham isn't here . . .' The men all look at Jack. 'And Townend's off on leave . . . Looks like you're in charge, mate.'

'What do you suggest then, Jacko?'

'Well, there's not enough digging here for all of us,' he says. 'So how about this? I reckon you chaps have a cycle into Lens and take a look around. See what's happening. And I'll join you later.'

'What? Go into a Frenchie town minus our personal translator? Need you with us to speak the lingo, mate!'

'You'll be fine,' Jacks says. 'They probably all still know some English anyway.'

'Not if it was Jocks they learnt it from,' laughs Ocker. 'And even if they do, how the hell are we going to understand it? It's bad enough making sense of what Mac here has to say.'

'Ach, the Auld Alliance!' Mac smiles. 'We'll be fine lads, I tell ye. Come on, look sharp and do as the lance-corporal tells you. Joining us later, Jack?'

'Aye, Mac. I'll be along soon enough.'

'Some digging, eh?'

'Fine day for it, Mac.' Jack smiles. 'And it'll help me think, not having you lot pestering me. Go – get off and enjoy yer-selves.'

The men get on the bikes and race off down the hill to Lens and are soon out of sight. Jack takes out a cigarette and unfolds the cemetery plan. The large rectangle of ground is divided into nine plots laid out in ten rows with twenty graves in each row. The original roadside burials – just four officers of the 9th Battalion, Black Watch, and a private of the 8th Battalion Royal Dublin Fusiliers – are in Plot III and turned 90 degrees to the other graves. Plot IX is marked out on the plan and has been staked out on the ground but not yet dug. The soil here at the top of the ridge will be well drained, Jack thinks. He picks up his shovel.

Jack likes working alone. He likes the rhythm of the dig. It's what he does. And he does it well. Jack digs better than any of the men and better than many more besides. Always has done. Precisely where this ability comes from, he can't tell. He doesn't care much either. He just digs.

It's back-breaking work, of course, as well as arm-aching and stomach-churning. Jack's hands are hard and calloused: at first rubbed raw and then, later, cracked and blistered, scabbed over and, finally, scarred. But that's all well and good, because after sores have healed the skin will harden, and scar tissue is pretty good protection against most things that a shovel handle can inflict on anyone. But even in the coldest weather sweat runs down his neck, and the mid-April sun is warm enough to force Jack to take a break after the first three graves are dug.

So intent is he this fine spring afternoon on digging, on moving earth, on making holes and digging deeper, that at first he doesn't notice that the cemetery suddenly has a visitor. A man is walking up and down each row of the existing graves studying the tin inscriptions on the lines of wooden crosses. Jack watches as he wanders slowly back and forth along the graves several times, occasionally stopping to consult a thick bundle of paper. He sees the stranger's feet get nearer and nearer to the hole that he is digging.

'Hello down there!'

Smart boots, well polished; thick woollen stockings and the point of a stout stick.

'Don't let me stop you working,' the man says. 'I merely hollered so as not to startle you while you were below ground.'

The noise of the shovel stops. Jack hauls himself out of the hole.

The man smiles. 'Forgive me,' he says, and offers his hand.

Wiping the wet soil from his palm, Jack closes his calloused hand round the man's fingers. Their eyes meet – bold, brown eyes that maintain a steady gaze from behind small, round steel-rimmed spectacles; bushy, beetling eyebrows; a bristling brown moustache; a tired, careworn face. The blue of Jack's clear eyes hold the moment, and the two men stand in silence looking at each other for several seconds. The stranger's eyes are the first to glance away.

'A lovely afternoon,' he is saying. 'Fine weather, wouldn't you say?' His manner isn't hostile. Nor is it that of an officer – certainly not an officer who might have seen service here. The man is too old for a start.

'Aye,' says Jack. 'A perfect day for digging.'

The man closes his eyes and begins to recite:

A perfect day for digging, just
as sweet and dry was the ground as tobacco dust.

'Except that it's "sowing", of course, in the original. Cigarette?' he asks, opening a small silver cigarette case. His appearance is smart: belted Norfolk jacket, plus fours, stockings – quite the country gentleman, thinks Jack. He has removed the large flat cap that he was wearing and is holding it in both hands as if he were in church. The April breeze disturbs the few stray strands of hair combed across his otherwise bald head.

'Looking for someone?' Jack asks.

'In a manner of speaking,' the man says, and turns his gaze again over the untidy rows of crosses. Jack says nothing. 'I expect it won't be long before the headstones start arriving.'

'Oh aye?' says Jack. 'I wouldn't really know about that. I just—'

'Just imagine,' the man goes on, 'row upon row of bright, white Portland stones, all of uniform height and width, inscribed with the names of the men who lie here below, complete with regimental badge and rank – an eternal army battalion in parade-ground order. Magnificent!'

'Aye, well . . .' says Jack.

'Did you serve?' the man asks.

'Aye,' says Jack, 'I did.'

'Which regiment?'

'Tenth Battalion, West Yorkshire Regiment. Prince of Wales's Own.'

'Ah!' the man frowns. 'A noble history.'

Jack raises his eyebrows.

'Oh, yes. I know a little of your regiment's story. Who doesn't?

'Not many, I'm sure,' Jack frowns. 'Given what happened in 1916.'

'Quite,' the man nods. 'I'm researching a regimental history of my own at present, as it happens.'

'Oh aye?'

'Yes. I've been engaged to write the history of one of the Guards divisions.'

'Is that why you're here?'

The man doesn't answer. He points instead with his cane to

the small inscription on a nearby cross. 'It is so important, don't you think, that these regimental details should not be lost when carving a man's headstone?'

'Aye, I suppose . . .'

'My feeling is that whatever a man's civilian position, when he is once in the service of the King then it is for the Regiment he works, with the Regiment he dies, and in death he should be remembered as one of the Regiment.'

Silence. Jack stares across the rows of temporary wooden crosses. The cemetery suddenly feels exposed. The eyes of snipers or enemy observers could be on them, everywhere. 'You said you was looking for someone,' Jack says.

'Indeed,' the man goes on. 'Although I am unable to find his name in any of the cemetery lists. Look.' He holds out a thick wad of paper fastened in the top left-hand corner with a treasury tag. 'I've got the cemetery register right here for this very plot.'

'Oh, aye?'

'Yes,' the man holds up a thin, bundled section of the register. 'Look!' He points a triumphant finger and smiles. 'It includes the very graves that you are digging.'

Jack takes the neatly typed list of names and numbers, rows and plots, and starts to turn the pages.

'It's from the War Graves Commission. I do a little work for them, you see, in an advisory capacity.'

Names and names, rows and plots; ticks in blue, then red – marks against the graves whose details have been checked once, twice, three times. Handwritten notes in the margin; a few corrections; and a big, blue rubber stamp bearing the initials I.W.G.C.

'Anyway, as I was saying,' the man goes on, 'the soldier whose remains I seek served here in this very area.'

'Oh, aye?'

'Yes. And there are several men of his regiment listed in the burial register and, well, I wondered . . .'

'Wondered?'

'Well, I . . . I suppose I wondered if you or any of the chaps might have come across his remains. I understand you are clearing some of the smaller battlefield cemeteries. Here are his details.' The man hands Jack a handwritten card. 'Of course I know that according to the register he isn't here . . .'

Jack continues leafing through the pages of the burial roll, this neatly typed directory of the dead. Each of the graves he digs is numbered, referenced and recorded. Plots and dates are written down, along with ranks and regimental numbers. Even the bodies that he buries without a name are listed and their plots located with – of course – military precision.

'But I am also aware from the register that many of the men you are reburying were unidentified when first laid to rest.'

'That's right,' Jack says.

'Well, it's just a thought,' the man goes on. 'A hope; a slim chance.'

'A chance?'

'That something was, perhaps, overlooked when the man was first placed underground. I've no doubt some of these early burials were hastily conducted.'

'Oh aye,' Jack says. 'Under fire, at times.'

'Of course!' the man exclaims. 'That's why it would be so easy to have overlooked some . . . well, some vital clue, some small item, maybe personalised, a maker's name on a shirt, a brand of boots, a style of breeches.'

'We always check,' says Jack. 'If there's any means of identification left, sir, we'd find it.'

'I'm certain of it,' the man says. 'Yes, of course.' They glance down at the yawning, earth-brown hole beside them. 'So who is this plot for?' he asks.

'This is for . . .' Jack looks down at the burial returns. 'Plot 9, Row D . . . Unknown,' he says. 'Unknown British Soldier.'

'Unknown,' the man says quietly.

'I'm sorry,' Jack says.

'Oh no,' the man shakes his head. 'No, no. Not at all,' he smiles. 'Not unknown.'

'No?'

'No,' the man says. 'Not "unknown" at all. Never "unknown". Because' – he smiles – 'ultimately, all these men are known, aren't they?'

'Are they?'

'They are indeed,' the man frowns. 'All men are known personally to the One to whom they have returned in glory.'

'Well, I suppose . . .'

'Yes, Corporal,' he adds quietly. 'Known unto God.'

Birds sing, far off. Tiny birds, no bigger than a puff of feathers. Skylarks. Small, khaki, feathery forms holding steady in the breeze: facing enemy lines. The man looks down and prods the earth with his walking stick. 'Ah well,' he says at last, 'I shall continue my search. Having this' – he shakes the wad of paper in the air and smiles – 'having this makes the task so very much easier.'

'Aye,' Jack says. 'But if the name you want to find isn't on the list . . . Which regiment did you say this fella fought with?'

The man looks at him, but doesn't answer.

'I just thought, if you told me . . .'

'My son,' the man says quietly. 'Irish Guards . . . Forgive me,' he says. 'But it is so very hard, having no grave. His mother, you understand . . .'

'Aye, o' course,' says Jack.

'Well, you've been most helpful,' the man says, replacing his cap. 'May I ask your name?'

'Yes, sir. Patterson, sir,' Jack replies. 'Jack Patterson.'

The man smiles. 'Well, Jack, I shan't keep you from your digging any longer. *What shall I do? I cannot dig; to beg I am ashamed.*' And he turns on his heels and walks, head down, towards the cemetery gate.

Jack watches him, suddenly desperate to say something, anything, but equally unable to think of any suitable words. 'They're bringing men in all t'time,' he calls out eventually. The man keeps on walking. 'We're still finding them!' And they are. But only the birds now answer.

Jack plants his shovel in the ground and lights a cigarette. Far off, in the original corner of the cemetery, a small group of visitors place flowers on an old grave. Battlefield clearances are coming to an end. As farmers return to what were once their fields, as they plough and sow and husband the land once more, a bitter and dwindling crop will remain underground waiting to return in the years to come. But there are to be no more bodies buried here. All that remains for Dud Corner is for a permanent memorial to be built, for the wooden crosses to be replaced with bright, clean Portland headstones and for the grass to grow and regrow and for the flowers and shrubs, such as they are, to take a gentle hold on the landscape and soften it into a place of peace once again.

More people will come, and some will leave flowers of their own. In time, new roads will reach across the fields and take new visitors to this and other cemeteries. A small recess in a wall at the entrance will hold a printed copy of the book the man was carrying back on that windy afternoon in early 1921. But there will still be one name missing. There will always be one name missing.

24

'It makes a change to see a different pile o' rubble, I suppose,' says Ocker as the men freewheel down the hill into the town.

'Aye, laddie. And at least this one was destroyed by our guns!'

Like Ypres, Lens is basically a huge post-war construction site. Or more accurately, a reconstruction site. For although just a few miles behind the front lines, Lens was in German hands for much of the war. British shells seem to have done just as much damage to the French town as the German guns at Ypres.

It is dark by the time Jack finally arrives, but finding the men isn't going to be difficult, he thinks. He knows that all he has to do is to follow the noise and maybe ask the odd well-directed question of the locals. Yes, a party of Englishmen has been here earlier; no, they didn't say where they were going but the *estaminet* on Rue de Vermelles will still be open.

Jack has a pretty good idea of what he is likely to find too. With the exception of Blake, the men all cope with their nightmares and their grievances by getting drunk. They all have money, but few if any of them have any family responsibilities. There is food provided, too. After a day's searching for or burying bodies the unit cook will have boiled up something hot and tasty for them to eat. And there is always plenty of bread. So with meals provided and pay in their pockets, what the men earn is theirs to drink. And digging graves is thirsty work. To say nothing of the need to wash away the foul and lingering taste of death and decay.

Jack wheels his bicycle among the shadowy outlines of buildings. Unlike Ypres, the City of Fear, the shape of Lens at night is unfamiliar and holds few terrors. His footsteps echo on the sharp cobbles, but he doesn't hear the sound re-echo, doubled, trebled, multiplied tenfold, twenty even, as another ghost battalion is moved out through the Lille gate or sent along the Menin Road. No flashes of light on this horizon silhouette the known outline of shattered buildings; no remembered rumble of the guns suddenly sends a shiver up his spine. In Ypres, there is always something – a shape, a sound, even just a broken paving stone – ready to act as a reminder. Here there is just the ruin of an unknown town in the still darkness of the night and with the silver moonlight overhead.

Jack marches on smartly until he arrives at the brightly lit entrance of the *estaminet* on the Rue de Vermelles. Stepping up to the door of the bar, he knows that he has found the men at last. There is noise. Laughter. Singing. Someone is singing one of the old songs:

> *Pack up your troubles in your old kitbag*
> *And smile, smile, smile.*
> *While you've a lucifer to light your fag,*
> *Smile boys, that's the style.*
> *What's the use of worrying?*
> *It never was worthwhile,*
> *So pack up your troubles in your old kitbag*
> *And smile, smile, smile.*

Where had he last heard that song? And when? Suddenly there is applause. And then a crash. Someone falls down drunk from one of the benches.

'Jacko! Look, it's Jack,' someone shouts as they see the figure in the doorway. But Jack turns smartly on his heels and as the door of the *estaminet* shuts behind him the sudden stillness of the evening hits him like the shattering of breaking glass. Then, out of nowhere, Mac is at his side, slightly breathless, hurrying to keep up.

'Good God, man, where are you off to in such a hurry?'

'Sorry, Mac. It's just a bit too noisy for me in there tonight.'

'Slow down, laddie, look' – he coughs – 'I'm out o' puff.'

'Sorry.' Jack stops. 'I'm just not sure I'm in the mood for it this evening. I'll not be much company. I need to . . . I don't know. I need time to think.'

'You need a drink, man – spending all day digging holes for the dead is nae good for a fellow. Come back to the bar. It's a pretty lively place we've found.'

'I know. No, it's not what I need right now.'

'Suit yourself. But you're missing a good one!' Mac says.

We're here because we're here, because we're here
Because we're here, we're here because we're here
Because we're here, because we're here . . .

'Sounds like it. Have one for me, eh, will you? I'll go back t'billet and see you lads in t'morning.'

Mac's footsteps fade in the darkness. Jack finds himself alone, under fierce stars. He pulls up his collar and carries on walking, wheeling the heavy black bicycle along at his side. Above him stars move slowly in familiar patterns. The same moon shines on the road ahead as shone on Katia when they walked hand in hand along the ramparts. The same stars, same moon, and tomorrow the same sun will rise here just as it will back there. Will she be looking at this same knife-edge arc of a silver moon as she closes the curtains on her little room at the back of the bar?

Jack walks on. He doesn't notice the transformation as the sound of his footsteps changes from the hard scrape of boots sparking on cobbled streets to the softer shuffle of dusty grit on the country road. Only out in the fields, with his boots in the mud, under the constant stars and in the silence of the night, does he stop short and look at where is he is. No guns, no shells. No noise, no singing. Nothing. Just the blue-black night, closing in on all sides.

Back at the camp he lights the small stove in their hut and he waits. There'll be no point in trying to get to sleep, he thinks, until the rest of the men get back. But in spite of that he finds his eyes will not stay open. He drifts into a fitful, upright sleep until suddenly he's wide awake and bolt upright as the noise of shouting wakes him.

'Look sharp, old man,' says Mac. 'Did we scare you?'

'No, I was just, er . . .'

'Good, because we've got something to tell you,' Mac says.

'Oh aye?' Jack looks around. 'Where is he?'

'There was a spot of bother, I'm afraid,' Blake tells him.

'Gendarmes?'

'Yes, I'm afraid so.'

Jack groans. He starts to put his boots back on.

'Och, don't fiddle with your laces,' Mac says. 'You'll be fine until the morning. He's sobering up right now, as we speak, in the cells.'

'Oh God,' says Jack. 'How many of 'em did it take to get him there?'

'Och, just a couple . . . Well, maybe three or four. And we gave them a hand.'

'You gave them a hand?'

'Aye, man. We had to. It was for his own good. First Madame stopped serving him, then he picked an argument with a Frenchman – laid the fella out, too.'

'I'm sure,' says Jack. 'How did it happen?'

'Well,' Mac smiles to himself. 'This Frenchie starts pushing him about and, well, you know what Ocker's like.'

'I can guess.'

'He says to him, he says – Where was you when there was fighting to be done? At home in bed with your finger up a tart's . . .'

'Yes, thank you, Mac,' Blake interrupts. 'I think Jack can guess the rest.'

'And anyway' – Mac starts laughing to himself – 'Frenchie, he makes to hit him, but Ocker ducks pretty smart and then – wallop! He ups with his fist and the Frenchman's down on the floor, flat out cold.'

'Oh bloody hell,' Jacks sighs. 'Bloody hell.'

'I'm afraid that's not the end of it though,' says Blake.

'No?'

'No. Then he decides that if Madame won't serve him any more then he'll simply help himself.'

'He nicks it?'

'Oh no. He pays for it: leaves the money on the counter like the good honest Aussie that he tells us all he is. But takes the liquor all the same.'

'And that's when she sends for the gendarmes,' Mac says.

'Ingham'll be livid,' Jack sighs.

'If he ever finds out.'

'What d'you mean? Jack says. 'How will we keep it from him?'

'Well, turns out – we didn't know it at the time – but it turns out that he – the gendarme, that is – was working as a bobby in Villers-Bretonneux in 1918.'

'Really?'

'Yes,' Mac says. 'He was there when the Germans took it.'

'Oh, aye?'

'And there when the Aussies took it back,' Blake adds. 'Yes, and very impressed with them he was.'

'We're never going to hear the last of this are we?' Jack says.

'The bobby bought us all a brandy once we'd laid ol' Ocker out.'

'You laid him out?'

'Don't look at me!' Blake holds up his hands. 'You know how I abhor violence.'

'Jack, it wasn't difficult. The wee idiot was fleein'. He was no trouble.'

'Aye, but even so . . . he's a strong bugger, Mac. Hard, too. And Skerritt's not, well . . . is he?'

'The bigger they are, the harder they fall,' Mac is saying almost to himself, as he puts the kettle on the stove.

'Aye, well. We've that to be thankful for, I reckon. If it wasn't for a bunch of strong hard buggers like the Aussies giving old Fritz a fistful at Villers-Bretonneux, then we might've had a lot more argy-bargy with the redcaps, to say nothing of Ingham.' The kettle starts to whistle. 'Can't leave you fellas for a minute, can I?'

'He'll be as right as rain in the morning, once he's slept it off.' Mac hands Jack a tin mug of tea.

'Well, maybe,' Jack says. 'Let's hope so.'

'Got to see the funny side though, haven't you?'

'There's a funny side?'

'Of course,' Mac says.

'Anyway, if I may say so, sir, it was your fault for sending us on our own into that French town.'

Jack can't tell if Blake is being serious.

'Aye,' Mac nods. 'Blakey here reckons it's enough to lose you your stripe!'

'Why? After it yourself are you, yer cheeky bugger?'

'So.' Mac pulls up a chair beside Jack. 'Tell me what happened this afternoon. Get much work done, did you?'

'A little,' Jack says. 'Got most of row C dug and then . . .'

'Then?'

'Then this fellow comes along. Seemed like he wanted to talk.'

'And he chose you?' Blake raises his eyebrows.

'Here.' Jack picks up his empty mug and dangles it in the air. 'Go and make yourself useful for once and get your corporal another mug of tea.'

Blake puts the kettle back onto the stove.

'So anyway' – Mac turns to face Jack – 'was he looking for someone, this fellow o' yours?'

'Aye,' says Jack. And he tells them all about the strange, solitary figure in the cemetery. 'Works for the Commission too, apparently.'

'I knew it!' Mac shouts.

'What?'

'Must be the same chap we met in the town soon after we arrived. I'm afraid I might've been responsible, Jack.'

'Responsible?'

'Responsible for sending him over to you,' Mac says. 'I thought if anyone might know it'd be you.'

'Know what?'

'Know how to help him – where to find what he was looking for.'

'Or who.'

'I suppose so. There's no one digs more graves than you, Jack. As we all know.'

'Aye, well. This chap didn't need to ask me. Didn't need to ask anyone really. He had one o' them cemetery registers with him when I spoke to him. Showed me the great long lists all typed up neat, page after page but—'

'But no name?'

'Oh aye, Mac – hundreds of 'em.'

'Just not the one he wanted.'

'No,' says Jack.

'Sad,' Mac shakes his head.

'No sadder than the rest, the other thousands that we'll never find.'

'No I mean . . .'

'What?'

'Well, the man pulled strings, Jack. He's a bigwig, got his boy into the Irish Guards but he should never have been out here. Should never have been here at all.'

'None of us should ever have been out here,' Jack says quietly. 'Nobody should have seen what we've seen or gone through what we've gone through.'

'But the lad was hardly more than a boy, Jack.'

'I were only a boy myself,' says Jack quietly to himself.

'What?' Mac laughs, 'When you enlisted? What war was that, then Jacko – Waterloo?'

'He doesn't mean when he enlisted, do you, Jack?'

Jack shakes his head.

'What then, son?'

'We know there's something not quite right, Jack.' Blake's hand is hovering above Jack's shoulder.

'Aye, something's not right,' adds Mac. 'If you want to—'

'No.' Jack stands. 'No, Mac. It's not summat I can talk about. But thanks, anyhow.'

'Any time, son.'

'So this chap told you all about it, did he?' Jack adds, stoking the brazier and sending fresh gouts of smoke into the hut.

'It gets worse,' Mac says. Jack looks up. 'He was unfit, apparently. Short-sighted. Horribly short-sighted. Couldnae see a thing beyond the end of his nose without his spectacles.'

'Oh aye?'

'And the boy was killed just a couple of weeks after being posted to France . . .'

'Poor bugger.'

'And now his pa's looking for t'lad's grave.'

The kettle whistles, unattended, for a moment. 'So, anyone ever come across a "Lieutenant John Kipling" written on a cross anywhere?'

The men all shake their heads. Someone stokes the fire. Jack gets up and pours himself another mug of tea.

25

'Post,' says Ocker when they get back to Remy Sidings. 'Two weeks' worth, an' all. Blimey, Jacko, there's even one here for you!'

'You what?'

'A letter for Jacko' – he holds up the envelope – 'look!'

'What? Jacko never gets a letter!'

'Well that's because they know the poor fella can't read, ain't that right, mate?'

'Give that to me.' Jack snatches it from Ocker's hand and stares at the envelope, open-mouthed.

'Well, aren't you going to open it?'

'Maybe he's able to decipher it through the envelope using the power of his mind.'

'Perhaps he's working out which of his English girlfriends it's from?'

'Or which of their husbands has found out where he's hiding!'

Suddenly, without a word, Jack is screwing up the unopened letter and throwing it in the brazier.

'Bad news, then, I take it.'

But Jack doesn't answer.

Out in the sidings, a long train slows to a halt. Steam hisses and the wagons clank as the brakes take hold. A man walks along banging a stick on the carriages and shouting, 'Remy! Remy Farm! Remy!' Carriage doors slide open as passengers begin to disembark – older ones being helped down, others ignoring the steps and throwing their bags from the train before jumping down onto the adjacent track. Crates of tools – hoes, rakes, barrows – are unloaded from the open freight wagons. The new arrivals look around, a few recognising their surroundings, and some seeing familiar faces in the small crowd that has gathered by the train to help unload the horticultural supplies.

'Well, well,' a voice calls as a man picks up a small bundle of his belongings. 'Who'd have thought it? You're back in a bleedin' hurry,' the soldier says, grinning at his friend.

'Yeah, but not in the Army no more,' the new arrival tells him. 'War Graves Regiment now – gardener, first class.' He brings a hand smartly up to his large, flat woollen cap in mock salute.

'Gardener?' the man shouts. 'You? You wouldn't know a calendula from a linaria.'

The other man laughs. 'No, but as long as someone else does I'll dig the holes for him to plant 'em in.'

'Anyone else here from the old battalion?'

'If there is I've yet to meet them!'

The men slap each other on the back and wander off to find some breakfast. Billets are allocated for the new arrivals in Nissen huts recently vacated by the latest batch of demobbed soldiers. The few men still in uniform know now that it won't be long before their own turn comes. For most, it can't come soon enough. But for a few, the dreaded day is something they would happily see delayed indefinitely.

*

273

'Are we wanted then today?' asks Ocker, as the men return from breakfast. 'Or are we officially off duty?' Ingham is nowhere to be seen.

'Didn't bump him off did they, while we was in Loos?'

'What, Jacko – and deprive us of the pleasure?'

'And what pleasure might that be, then?'

'Oh, there you are, Sarge. We were just saying how much we'd missed you, while we've been away.'

''SHUN!' Townend bawls suddenly, and the men are springing to their feet. Except for Ocker, who slowly rises, throws his cigarette butt to the floor and casually brings a hand up to his head.

'Sir!'

'Why aren't you lot on fatigues?'

'Just got back from a month's work at Loos, sir.'

'Oh yeah?' says Townend, puzzled. 'On whose authority?'

'Lieutenant Ingham's orders, sir. Fixed it while you was away on leave. That's obviously why you don't know owt about it.'

'Although there might be another reason,' Ocker mutters.

'And who was in command at Loos?'

'Lieutenant Franks, sir. Their company was a bit below strength, apparently. We was sent out there to help.'

'To help? God Almighty, then they must have been bloody desperate.'

'That's a bit unfair, sir.'

'Well,' Townend says, 'we can't have you sitting around here sunbathing all day, can we?' He looks down at his clipboard and smiles. 'Here's a nice one for you lot.'

'Boat trip back home is it, Sarge?'

'Get yourselves over to Tyne Cot,' Townend says, ignoring Ocker's interruption, 'and report to Captain Harris. While you've been off on yer bleedin' holidays, the exhumation teams here have been working overtime clearing the last of the battle-field cemeteries.' He looks back down at his clipboard, tilts back his head and starts to read aloud: 'Iberian Trench; Kink Corner; Levi Cottage; Waterloo Farm – they've all been done.'

'Blimey, Sarge, those names take us back a bit.'

'Sounds like a roll-call of some of our finest battles and advances, does that, Sarge.'

'As well as some of our most miserable failures,' adds Mac.

'OK, OK, once you lot have finished your fuckin' trip down memory lane—'

'Sorry, Sarge.'

'—there's a pretty smelly backlog of bodies in the morgue at Tyne Cottage waiting for a bunch of men like you to dig 'em a nice, deep trench and put 'em all to bed.'

'Oh, bloody great!'

'Jeez, that place has got bigger, hasn't it?' Ocker says as the truck begins the gentle climb from Zonnebeke.

'Aye, and we're about to make it even bigger,' Jack says, as Blake hauls round the steering wheel and heads along Roes-elarestraat. The men sit in silence for a while. From the back of the truck, the only sounds are Mac's snoring and Skerritt's mumbling. Ahead of them on the bare hillside, a seemingly endless army of wooden crosses marches up towards the smudge where the village of Passchendaele once stood. The fields on either side of the road are churned, not ploughed. And the only crops being tended for miles are these neat rows of wooden crosses.

'Remember that old cove we almost ran over last time we was here?'

'What about him?'

'Wonder if he ever found what he was looking for.'

'Must've done,' says Jack as they approach the cemetery. 'Look – they've started rebuilding his farm.'

'Well,' Ocker sighs. 'Good luck to 'em, I say.'

'At least sound like you mean it!'

'Why wouldn't I, Jacko? No – bloody good on 'em. Just wish I was getting on with my own life, too, instead of dealing with death day in, day out.'

'Someone's got to do it,' Jack says.

'True enough, Jacko.' Ocker jumps down from the cab. 'But does that someone have to be me? Come to that, does it have to be you? Does it have to be any one of us? We fought here, Jacko, you and me.'

'Aye, and Mac's been fighting here longer than the rest of us, the old sweat.'

'Yeah, and meanwhile there are some fellas' – Ocker aims a kick at Blake's backside as he lowers himself down from the cab – 'there's some fellas here who either couldn't fight or wouldn't. And I reckon it's about time they took a turn.'

'Leave Blakey out of it, Ocker. At least he came here to do what his conscience would allow him to.'

'Unlike them buggers who wouldn't even wear the uniform. Why did they stand on their flamin' dignity like that, eh, Blakey?' Blake simply smiles, as inscrutable as ever.

'There was plenty o' civilians on that train this morning,' Jack says. 'Won't be long now, lad, you'll see.' They leave Mac sleeping as they wheel barrows loaded with shovels, picks and wooden planks to the designated plot. Marked with chalk on the muddy earth, the trench measures 30 feet by 6, and is to be dug to a depth of 6 feet.

'It's going to take us all day.' Jack shakes his head. 'If Townend thinks we can get those fellas buried in one afternoon, he's dafter than I thought.'

'Not so fast, Jacko.' Ocker points. 'Reckon the cavalry's arrived. Reinforcements, look! And in time, too, for once.'

'How do!' Jack calls out. 'Didn't know we'd sent for backup.'

'Johnson, sir.' The youngest member of the works team replies. The others put down their wheelbarrows, take out cigarettes and matches and light up. 'We're from the War Graves Commission. Once they realised that you'd been given the fatigue alone, someone reckoned that we'd better come and lend a hand.'

'Thank goodness someone round here's got a bit o' common sense. Come on then.' Jack picks up his shovel. 'Let's get cracking.'

The combined forces of the two teams excavate the trench in double-quick time. Tools are tidied away before the men trudge up the gentle slope to the morgue to collect the bodies.

None of the bundles is heavy. These days they seldom are. Once any remaining Belgian soil has been scraped from the bones, and once pockets (if they exist) have been emptied, once guns and ammunition, rusted, twisted water bottles and personal possessions necessary for identification purposes – but useless in the long wait for Judgment Day – have been removed, then the weight of the neatly sewn cresol-soaked canvas sacks barely even registers as they are lifted on the stretchers. The dry bones of what were once men, men who were once soldiers, men who were husbands, sons, fathers, lovers, living, breathing human beings, shift and creak on the bumpy journey to their final resting place.

The chaplain arrives soon after each of the bundles has been laid – six inches apart – side by side in the long trench. But the committal is brief in what is already consecrated ground. The men stand around waiting to back-fill the hole. 'And when you've finished you can dig up those damned heathen poppies, too,' the padre shouts as he strides off, cassock flapping in the breeze.

'Right then, lads,' Jack says once they've packed the wagons. 'We drive back via Wipers, and it's traditional for Number One section to break the journey at a little local hostelry we know. Fancy joining us?'

Johnson, the young IWGC foreman, looks down. 'I don't drink, sir. Teetotal, me. Took the pledge five years ago. But—'

The others smile to themselves. 'We'll leave him minding the vans,' one of them says. 'He can keep your Blakey company.'

'Aye,' another laughs. 'They can read the Bible to each other.'

It's already getting dark by the time they set off down the hill from Tyne Cot, and by the time they reach Ypres the ruins, the scaffolding and the building works are all no more than shadows. The pale yellow lamps on the lorries light up the immediate road ahead, throwing a beam just far enough for the drivers to avoid the few remaining potholes, but little more.

'Right, lads, I reckon we owe you one,' Jack says as they reach the bar. 'This round's on me. Saved us a lot o' sweat back there this afternoon.' The men push a couple of tables together while Jack orders the drinks.

'Hello, stranger!' The woman starts decanting a jug of Leroy pils into a line of empty tankards.

'You seem pleased to see us for once, Margreet.'

'I am always pleased to see you, Jacques, you know that.' She puts the jug down on the bar and runs a finger along Jack's chin. 'And anyway' – she starts to put the tankards on a tray – 'I have some news for you.'

'Oh, aye?'

'Yes – there has been somebody here looking for you, Jacques.'

'Looking for me?'

'Yes.' She looks at him and nods slowly. 'While you were away.'

Jack closes his eyes. 'Why is it you always seem to enjoy it when you've got bad news, Margreet?'

The woman laughs. 'Oh yes, Jacques,' she goes on airily. 'She has been in a couple of times, actually. Katia . . .'

'What did she say to Katia?'

The woman suddenly stops pouring. 'Oh Jacques,' she soothes, 'you are angry? You think she told Katia something . . . something you would rather she had not said? Something you would rather Katia did not know?'

'What did she say?' Jack leans across the bar close into Margreet's face.

'Oh Jacques!' the woman shakes her head, stepping back. 'How am I to know? It was you that she was looking for. It was Katia that she spoke to.'

'Where is she? Where is Katia?'

'In Poperinghe. With her papa.'

'Damn!'

'And maybe the woman is there too, no? Maybe she is still looking for you?'

'Did she . . .' Jack pauses. 'Did she say, precisely, who it was she was looking for? I mean, did she mention me by name?'

The woman shrugs. *'Je ne sais pas!'*

'Aye, well . . .' Jack takes the tray of beers. 'If she comes here agin, tell her, right?'

'Tell her what, Jacques?'

'Just tell her,' Jack shouts over his shoulder.

'Trouble, Jacko?'

'It's nowt. Here – sup up and shut up. Yer beer's getting cold.'

'Oh, pardon me, Lance-Corporal, sir!'

'Sorry, Ocker lad.'

'Do you want to talk about it, son?'

'No thanks, Mac.'

'Ah, well.' Ocker smacks his lips. 'Your secret's safe with us, Jacko. Ain't that right, Mac?'

'And what bloody secret's that then, eh?'

'*Thou knowest Lord, the secrets of our hearts . . .*' Mac says, draining his beer. 'But in my case it's no secret that I'm starving. It's been a pleasure working with you boys.' He nods to the War Graves men. 'But I hear the call of the cookhouse. Anyone else ready to hit the road?'

'Come on lads, drink up!' says Jack.

'Right! Early start tomorrow, eh?'

26

The lamps are all already lit when they arrive back at camp. The others go straight to the canteen but Jack isn't feeling hungry. He lies on his bunk and listens as trains clank, trucks drive past the hut, men return to billets and – eventually – as the Last Post is sounded. The night is long. Daybreak comes, but Jack has been awake for hours.

'What's this?' the doctor asks, listening through the stethoscope. 'A case of *Timor mortis conturbat me*?' Jack stands holding up his shirt, the only patient present at the sick parade that morning. 'The fear of death doth trouble me,' the MO translates. 'Putting you out, is it?' he asks. 'Because there's nothing physically wrong with you. There's something rattling in your lungs a bit – you were gassed, weren't you?'

'Aye, sir.'

'Still smoking, though?'

'Aye, sir.'

'Good. That'll keep the tubes clear.'

Jack tucks his shirt back in and pulls up the braces of his trousers.

'I'm going to give you a chitty for twenty-four hours, Patterson.'

'Aye, sir.'

'Report here again tomorrow morning, six-thirty.'

'Aye, sir.'

With that, Jack returns to the hut. The others are already busy getting ready for another day's digging. Only when they're just about the leave do they realise that Jack, without a word, has climbed back into his bunk and pulled the blanket up over his face.

'Jacko?'

'We're on the road in five minutes, man. What are you—?'

Jack slowly waves the sick note in the air like a white flag; his eyes are closed, his head is spinning.

'He's bloody surrendering!'

'OK, son,' Mac says at last. 'We'll see you later, then.'

Without another word, the men leave and Ocker quietly closes the door of the hut behind them. Jack hears the engine splutter as the truck is cranked. A few shouts follow as the men embark. A crunch as first gear is engaged, then a growl as the truck finally drives away. The sudden silence is punctuated by parade-ground shouts. Far off, a whistle blows; steam hisses and a train puffs and wheezes into life in the siding. Then, nothing.

'Is it a girl?' the woman pants, her hair a mess of blood and sweat. 'A girl?'

Jack already knows the answer. It is right there in his arms.

The woman's breathing slows, her grimace gradually transforms into a thin, tired smile. Then nothing . . .

'You never told me about her, Jack.' Katia's voice now. 'You didn't say her name.'

'Aye, well . . .' Jack's eyelids press down on his eyes. 'It were a long time ago,' he says.

But Katia hasn't heard him. Or if she has, she isn't listening. 'So why do you not go back to her?' she asks. 'Back home?'

He sits up in bed and looks at her as if seeing her for the first time. Her bare breasts are white and soft to the touch as his finger delicately traces a small circle round each nipple.

She closes her eyes. 'Not saying something,' she is murmuring, 'is saying something too, you know.' He looks up, but her face is now a blur. Only her voice, in his ear. 'Tell me about her, Jacques. Tell me all about her . . .'

Tell her? How can he tell her? What is there to tell? Where can he begin?

'You loved her, Jacques.'

Jack shuts his eyes, tight. 'Aye,' he says. 'I did. I do. I wished, I wish . . .'

'Be careful what you wish for, Jacques . . .'

The voice trails off. Jack's head is pounding, heavy artillery thudding through his skull. He feels sick. Hours pass. And then the guns stop. Silence. A breath, held. Then suddenly a rattling of gassed lungs, coughing you could see but couldn't hear; a shining whistle pinched between the subaltern's cracked lips flares briefly as it catches the sun; the officer's startled, hare-eyed gaze is fixed upon the second hand of his pocket watch.

The ground beneath Jack's feet is still. Everything is still. Above his head, the air is blue, the sky clear. And up there, high then higher in the clear air, a bird – a lark, skylark – rising, singing, piping, flapping, fluttering, fluting, climbing higher, clawing and singing its way to heaven, rising almost vertically above the trench. Facing the enemy.

Suddenly a heavy hand is slapping him. He holds the ladder. Then he is following the boots in front, one rung at a time, hands and feet rising as if pulled by a puppeteer's strings. And then he's up, head above the parapet. There's a shock of crimson running down the chalk in front of him. He grabs the foliage at the edge of the trench for extra leverage. A handful of poppies come off in his grasp. He looks down. Is still. Then a bump as the man behind, head down, reaches the top of the ladder.

Move! Jack throws the flowers down. Petals sticking to his palm, he holds his rifle and moves forward. Smoke. Zzzpp, zzzpp! Bullets seem to brush his ears. He flicks his head from side to side as if avoiding flies. A sudden shower of mud and chalk sprays over him and he is spitting soil, wiping his mouth on the back of his hand. Still that bloody poppy! He stops, and wipes his hands down his tunic. Move forward! A body. Someone's body. Dead. Red. More poppies. Had he grabbed a handful too? No. Blood.

Forward. The smoke is choking now. His lungs are burning, eyes stinging. Jack is hot, too hot, under the heavy pack, stumbling across the hard ground. The dust, the smoke. Zzzpp! Zzzpp! Zzzpp! Flecks of dust in his eye. The fog clears. He is stepping over more bodies, mouths move, cries, shouts. Jack looks at them. And carries on.

Suddenly he's spinning, airborne, flying, puzzling before thudding into the ground, his eventual fall broken by the bodies of men already in the shell-hole. A desperate, unbearable ringing in his ears. Then nothing.

At last, when he can open his eyes it's quieter. Someone's mouth is moving, eyes are looking at him. But he can't hear what they're saying. He stares back. They shake their head. His eyes close. He feels the rough lifting and the bumping journey on a stretcher, feels it jolt as the bearers lower him to the ground. The sky above is blue, still. Small puffs of light brown smoke burst like birds appearing out of thin air. Soft summer clouds drift across a clear blue sky. His eyes close. And when he opens them again the sky is black and pocked with fierce stars.

'Your wound is healing nicely, Jack.' The young nurse smiles at him. One of the few that will. The younger they are, the more briskly efficient the nurses seem to be. 'Roll over please, Mr Patterson. This won't hurt.' They knew it would. 'There, that wasn't too bad now, was it?' But they knew it was.

But this particular nurse . . . What was her name? Where has she gone? He can't see her any more. But he can feel her in the darkness of his throbbing head.

'Hold me, Jack.' The girl is warm, but her warmth won't last till dawn. 'You won't forget me, will you, Jack? Promise me you won't forget.'

'I promise . . .' Jack says. I promise, he thinks. It won't be hard. He has done it before. But still there is something, someone that he can't forget, no matter how hard he tries, no matter what. You don't forget something like that. You can't. Because the hole where she used to be can never be filled. And the hole aches. The hole is cold. As cold as the grave . . .

'You are going, Jacques,' Katia whispers, her head beside his on the pillow. 'Home. I know you are . . . to see her.'

'No.' He clenches his teeth hard. 'No,' he says as his jaw slowly relaxes. 'I came here to get killed,' he calls out. 'I can't go back.'

Somewhere in the darkness, a whistle blows. The line of men begins to move forwards. A strange-looking crowd, each man in a long wet greatcoat, pockets stuffed with useful bits and pieces and carrying, not rifles now, but large, pointed shovels, pickaxes and a sheaf of empty sandbags. Watching is their occupation; watching and walking. That is what they are paid an extra half a crown a day for doing – watching mud, watching their own wet footsteps, watching the ruined ground and straining their eyes for the slightest signs of life. Or rather, death.

Suddenly, something glistens in the wet ground. Jack stoops to look, but the uniform is wrong. French? It's red, even after so long underground; the red of the uniform is clear, as is the blue. And suddenly the bleak landscape rolls back time as army after army marches on to the beat of the drum, following the flag, with muskets shouldered, fifes whistling like raucous canaries and with horses trotting and snorting and stamping their hooves.

She allows him to undress her, sitting with her head bowed on the corner of the bunk as he gently unwraps her layer by layer, laces, ribbons, buttons, buckles and bows. Her small breasts pucker at the nipple in the cold air. He puts his arm around her and she hitches her bare bottom farther up the bed and lies down beside him. Her eyes close.

Timor mortis conturbat me . . .

The priest gently brushes the young girl's eyelids with his thumb. The family says, 'Amen!'

27

'Sir! Sir! Lieutenant Ingham, sir!'

'What is it, man?' Ingham fumbles in the darkness for his spectacles. 'What time is it?'

'Sorry, sir. Spot o' trouble, sir. Private Gilchrist's been out looking for that fella you was telling us about . . .'

'Fellow? What fellow?'

'Chap buried at Tyne Cottage, sir. You know. The one . . .' Jack looks left and right and checks he won't be overheard. Captain Harris's snores echoing from the opposite end of the otherwise empty barrack block confirm that he is fast asleep, and Ingham's batman has long since been dispensed with. 'Have to make me own tea now, what?'

'The, er . . . fella you was suggesting we might want to dig up,' Jack says in a hoarse whisper. By now Ingham is wide awake, swinging his legs out of his bunk and hurriedly pulling on his breeches.

'Good Lord, what kind of bother? What in the name of God was Gilchrist doing anyway? I thought I had issued strict instructions—'

'He thinks you wanted one o' us to dig the fella up so he could be sent home. Dead fella, that is, not Gilchrist. Anyway, he's gone out there to do the honours on his own.'

'Good God!'

'He seems to think there'll be some money in it, sir. And what with his demob coming up and all that, I suppose . . .'

'Money? Well, I . . . I mean I . . .'

'I know, sir, daft idea. Bloody stupid.'

'But what kind of bother is he in, Patterson? Not drunk, is he?'

'No, sir. Got lost. Reckoned you wanted the body left at Shrapnel Corner and he was reburying it there for you to collect later when he hit an unexploded shell.'

'My God! Is he badly hurt?'

'Don't rightly know, sir.'

'Corporal?'

'Yessir?'

'How do you know any of this? I mean, if Gilchrist was acting alone as you suggest . . .' Ingham rubs his eyes, then frowns. Jack suddenly sees the whites of his eyes in the darkness.

'Followed him, sir. Didn't trust him, sir.'

'Well no, quite. Always been somewhat unpredictable, that man. Typical damned Aussie. I told the CO not to accept him when he was transferred. British mother, apparently. No wonder they got rid of him.'

'Well, I wouldn't know about that, sir.'

Ingham is now pulling on his boots. 'So, you followed him. Capital, man, capital! Shows initiative, that does. Well done!'

'Thank you, sir.'

'Yes, have to see if we can add another stripe to that arm of yours, Corporal.'

Jack looks away as Ingham buttons up his flies. 'Followed on that motorbike you keep, sir. Hope you don't mind.'

'No, no, of course—'

'And I came across him digging this temporary 'ole in the middle o' nowhere, like I said. Or rather, I came across him just afterwards. Sir, he in't in no fit shape for digging now.'

'Oh, my God.' Ingham grimaces, pulling up his braces. 'Patterson – no one else must hear of this, d'you understand? If Gilchrist blabs I'll have him certified insane or else court-martialled. This incident . . . well, it never happened – understood?'

'Don't worry, sir. Private Gilchrist won't blab.'

'Yes, well . . . This nocturnal escapade of his is an aberration and we – you and I – are now merely going in search of an absent soldier, someone we believe might be in danger.'

'Yessir.'

'And, of course,' Ingham's buck-toothed grin flashes in the darkness as he ties his tie, 'of course you'll be, well . . . I'll see to it that you are amply rewarded for your service.'

'Very good, sir.'

The two men climb into the RAMC ambulance. No one had noticed the noise of the old Albion lorry leaving camp an hour earlier amid the noise and clatter of the last train from St Omer. In the darkness, amid the routine noise and movement, no one took much notice of the space where the truck had been parked. And no one noticed the 'souvenirs' Ocker appropriated from the quartermaster either. No one, that is, except for Jack.

The journey from Poperinghe to Ypres is largely silent. The night is dark and the dim yellow beam of the gig lamps offers little assistance in avoiding the potholes, but in the distance the silhouette of the ruined Cloth Hall campanile looms black on the horizon against the slowly lightening eastern sky. Half an hour later they are in Ypres, crossing the river and heading straight down Elverdingestraat towards the ruins of the cathedral. Turning east once more, the truck bounces across the smooth cobbles of the Grote Markt, shining in the pre-dawn darkness like the tops of a thousand skulls, worn clean by the march of a million pairs of boots. Heading out through the ramparts and along the Menin Road, Jack takes a sideways glance at Ingham and notices him biting at his bottom lip.

'I thought you said that Gilchrist was at Shrapnel Corner?' Ingham says as Jack turns left and the truck bounces off along the old corduroy road by the railway cutting. Jack says nothing. A short time later he is pulling the truck over to the side of the road and turning off the engine.

'This'll do,' he says at last.

The engine ticks down, slowly cooling. A slight breeze wafts the scent of wet mud into the cab. A sudden, slow flapping of wingbeats like the sheets outside the laundry room breaks the silence as a skein of geese slants low overhead. The two men sit in silence. Slowly, through the canvas screen separating the cab from the back of the truck, the cold nose of a service revolver pokes blindly towards a pulsing vein in Ingham's neck. The steel muzzle meets flesh a fraction of a second before Ingham realises what is happening, but as he tries to turn his head the metal jabs hard into his trapezius.

'What the—'

'Shuush now, Lieutenant Ingham, sir,' a voice from behind is saying. Jack is staring straight ahead. Ingham tries to turn again, but the voice urges him to keep his head still or else risk getting it blown off.

'Gilchrist! But I thought . . . ? Patterson, you told me . . .' Ingham takes a sideways glance at Jack without daring to turn his head.

'Dig the hole, did you, mate?' Ocker asks Jack, pulling back the canvas curtain with his free hand.

Jack sighs, nods briefly, staring straight ahead, then turns to Ocker. 'It's all ready for thee, lad.'

'Right-o, Jacko. Let's just hope we don't actually need it, eh?'

'Look! I don't know what the devil is going on here,' Ingham hisses through clenched teeth, staring straight ahead into the darkness. 'But mark my words I'll have the both of you shot for this! This is an outrage!'

'No, sir,' Ocker interrupts. 'If there's any shooting to be done it'll be done by me,' he goes on. 'Now be a good chap and shut yer clacker.' An owl hoots somewhere in the darkness.

'Everything's planned,' says Gilchrist, clicking off the safety catch of the Webley revolver he has managed to acquire. 'And Jacko here' – he nods his head towards the driver's seat – 'Jack'll do the burying. Proper expert Jack is, y'know, at burying. Digging, burying, covering over . . . Why, he'll have you six foot beneath this filthy Belgian shit in no time, "sir", if you don't play the game.' He pauses.

Ingham isn't sure whether to answer or not, or even if it's safe to try and shake his head. His mind is racing. He is staring straight out of the truck into the darkness. The stumps of shell-shattered trees punctuate the near horizon. They are facing north, Ingham calculates, with the faintest lightening of the eastern sky out to the extreme right in his peripheral field of vision. There is no moon; even the few stars visible on the journey seem to have slowly gone out, one by one, like blown-out candles. Ingham feels with his left hand for the latch of the door. His mind, working feverishly, calculates that he could dive over the top of the door if necessary, but opening it would make a quick getaway more likely to succeed. And these two clowns have let him keep his hands down. What the devil are they playing at?

'If it's money you want . . .' Ingham reasons that the longer he can keep them talking, the more chance he has of reaching the door handle without them noticing.

'Money? You hear that, Jacko?'

'Aye!'

'No need, mate . . .' says Ocker. Ingham bristles, even with a gun at his neck. 'We don't want money, although if we did, I'll wager you could supply us with a tidy sum given all the back-handers you've been getting from some o' the locals.'

'What?'

'Keep yer voice down, sir. D'you want to wake the dead?'

'No, mate, he wants to dig 'em up and send 'em home – pro-vided someone's paying him, that is.'

'You chaps have got this all wrong,' Ingham is saying. The thought of them knowing quite as much as they seem to know has set his mind racing. 'I couldn't possibly sanction such behaviour. Why, it's—'

'Pretty lucrative, I'd say, judging from the size of them brown envelopes de Wulf keeps giving you.'

'Ah.' Ingham laughs nervously. 'No, no, no. Those are merely payments for supplies – Monsieur de Wulf pays a good price for, er . . . scrap. You know how useful scrap is to the Belgians, after all.'

'And guns. They useful to the Belgies too, are they, cobber?'

'Decommissioned weapons, naturally.'

'Still government property though,' says Ocker, whistling through his teeth.

'I think you'll find—' Ingham is struggling to contain his indignation.

'I think you'll find, sir,' Jack says calmly, 'that we've got all t'details written down right here.' He turns on a torch, then holds up an envelope for Ingham to see. 'De Wulf has told us the whole story,' Jack continues. 'Mind you, Ocker did 'ave to persuade him a little bit, didn't you, lad?'

'No trouble! In fact, it was a pleasure rearranging his fat face.'

The bulging envelope is sealed, and even in the dim beam of the torch Ingham can see that it is addressed to Army HQ.

'We do' – Jack puts the envelope back in his tunic pocket – 'we do have another letter.'

'As well as several signed copies of that one, Lieutenant Ingham, sir, should you be thinking . . .'

'Oh no. No, not at all . . .'

'Good! 'Cos we're one step ahead of you, yer snake.'

'Now l-l-l-look here, chaps . . .'

'This other letter, on the other hand—' Jack brings out a thinner envelope, and Ingham notices a label in his own handwriting addressed to his mother in England.

'You bounders! You've been through my . . . how dare you?'

'Very organised, sir, I must say. Little white gummed labels with yer ma's address on.'

'Yeah, that was certainly a bonus, eh, Jacko?'

'Aye, lad. Mind you, I bet you don't send yer mam a typed letter normally, do you? Isn't good form, is it, sir?'

'Not that you'd know about form.'

'Typed letter? What are you talking about?' Ingham's hand has crept along the door unnoticed. He has managed to shift position imperceptibly and his fingers are now tightly wrapped around the door handle, feet braced on the floor of the truck and upper body turned very slightly – tensed, like a spring.

'Well, sending yer mam a goodbye letter and not writing it yourself . . . bad form, I suppose. But can't be helped under t'circumstances. She'll understand, I'll be bound. Given the circumstances.'

'Circumstances? What "circumstances"? What in God's name—'

'Don't take that tone with us, sir. We're doing you a favour, really. I mean . . . we could send a copy of this letter to the colonel.'

'What bloody letter?'

'Better read it to him, Jacko.'

'Aye, right . . . *Dear Mother*—'

'Couldn't be quite sure about "mother", could we, Jacko? Some of the others reckoned "mama". I thought "Dearest Mother", personally. What d'you reckon, sir?'

'Others? Others? How many of you are in on this . . . this . . ?'

'Anyhow, we did a couple o' versions just in case. Mama, sir, or mother?'

'Oh, do get on with it, man!'

'Come on, Jacko. The suspense is killing him.'

'It's not suspense that'll do for him in t'end though, is it?'

'No, mate. It'll be the shock!'

Jack starts again to read the letter. In the torchlight Lieutenant Ingham can see that it appears to be well typed – a professional job. He can't help wondering whose work it is. But not for long – after the opening salutation, the letter gets straight to the point.

'The fact that you are reading this letter, mother, will, as I am sure you are aware, confirm your worst fears.'

'Worst fears?' Ingham splutters. 'What the devil—'

'D'you want to hear the rest of t'letter or don't you?'

Ingham nods, clenching his jaw tight to stop his teeth from chattering.

'Please do not grieve for me, dearest mother . . .' Jack squints and moves both the torch and his eyes closer to the paper, '. . . *for I know I have given my life in a good and right-eous cause – the cause of*—'

'Fillin' his fuckin' boots with blood money from the folks who fancy buying a return passage for the WCs we've spent the last three years transferring to the rest camp.'

'Can you not keep yer gob shut, Ocker? Even while I read his bleedin' final letter?'

'Sorry, Jacko. Carry on.'

'Aye, right.' Jack holds the letter closer and continues. 'I have disobeyed orders—'

'Done WHAT?' screams Ingham.

'Hold yer horses. I have disobeyed orders only because I felt it was my duty to a high and noble cause . . .'

'My God!'

'That's reet, isn't it, Ocker lad?'

'That's what they said. *The cause of returning a fallen comrade to his native soil – back to the dust that bore him.*'

'That's what *who* said?'

'I don't know – Rupert Brooke wasn't it, sir? I'd have thought you'd have known that, sir. Being an officer.'

'No, don't be stupid. I mean—'

'Who told us about yon goings on?'

'About your little deals?'

'About the empty graves?'

'And missing bodies?'

Ingham nods slowly.

'Well, sir, little Fuller told us quite a lot, before he went west.'

'Always wondered why he suddenly had that "accident" when he did, sir.'

Ingham's hand begins to tremble as it stiffens round the handle of the door. The tense muscles in his left arm twitch and his thighs, too, braced with his feet pressed hard against the floor, begin to shake uncontrollably.

'But what you didn't know, sir,' Jack says, 'is that he told us first.'

'Yeah,' Ocker continues. 'Doesn't paint a pretty picture does it, sir? Which brings us back to the letter.'

'Ah yes,' Ingham grits his teeth, 'the letter.'

'We knew you were t'kind o' chap to write one,' Jack says.

'After all, very handy with the little brown envelopes.' Ocker nudges him. 'Aren't you, cobber?'

'Still, we know how busy you've been just lately, sir.'

'Can't be easy, secretly shipping the odd body back to Blighty.'

'Aye, an' making sure the locals get a good deal on ex-Army scrap.'

'I'm not the only one, you know, who—'

'No, sir.'

'Course not, sir.'

'So anyway, we thought we'd save you the bother.'

'Bother?'

'We've written t'letter for you.'

Ingham suddenly releases his grip on the door and holds his hands to his face. 'It was never meant to . . .'

'Meant to 'appen? I'm sure it wasn't, sir.'

'But it did, didn't it?'

'And now it's only right that you should make amends.'

'Yeah, sir. Put things right.'

'Which is why we've concocted this little letter to your mother—'

'In case anything should happen.'

'Happen?'

'Yes, sir. Happen. To anyone else.'

'Like us, for instance.'

'Aye, we thought a signed confession – to be opened only in the event of my death – would do the trick.'

'That's enough!' Ingham says. 'I've had enough.'

'There is,' Jack says at last, 'another option . . .'

Ingham's shoulders gently heave with the sobs he is trying to hide. 'Give me the gun,' he whispers at last.

'I think you mean the pen, sir.'

Ingham takes the papers passed to him by Jack and reads, hurriedly. He scribbles what he hopes the men think is his signature as tears begin to smear the ink, then hands the letters back.

'Thank you, sir. Do you want to keep a copy for yourself or shall we . . . ?'

Ingham shakes his head, calm now in the face of the inevitable. But Ocker seems to have relaxed his aim and moved the gun slightly to give Ingham room to sign the letter. He can't see the pistol in the darkness; he knows the muzzle is only a matter of an inch or two away from his head. But he calculates that the distance might be just enough to give him one final, mad chance. Whatever he does, he's doing it head-first.

'Thank you, sir.' Jack takes the letter and places it carefully back in the envelope. 'There really wasn't any alternative, sir. I'm sure you understand.'

'And no one – not the colonel, not your dear ol' mum – need ever be any the wiser.'

'Provided this repatriation nonsense stops.'

'Remember, sir. We've got a signed confession.'

'And you, sir, you've got an honourable way out, should you ever need to take it.'

'Just couldn't stand it any more, could you, sir? The strain, the bodies, the memories. At least this way we'll be the only ones who know the real reason.'

'Glad you saw it our way in the end, sir,' he adds. 'There really is no alternative.'

'Oh yes, there bloody well is!' Ingham is suddenly swinging open the door, diving from the truck with the aim of rolling in the darkness down the railway embankment. A fraction of a second later Ocker's brain registers the movement and he fires, putting a neat bullet hole through the cab door as it swings back.

'Oh dear,' Jack smiles. 'Taken a tumble, sir? Let me help you back up into the wagon.' Only then does Ocker see the spur glinting in the torchlight and Ingham's boot caught on the running board of the truck.

'Blimey, Jacko, you were the coolest thing unhung back there I reckon,' Ocker says as they hand Ingham's stretcher over to the medical orderlies back at Remy Farm a little while later.

'Didn't feel much like it at the time,' Jack frowns. 'In fact, when Ingham tried to do a runner and you fired I was shit-scared that we'd be t'ones who'd end up getting hung,' he says.

'Scared?' Ocker rubs the palms of his hands. 'You, Jacko? Reckon they'll be bottling your blood, mate, before long.'

'Aye, well,' Jack shakes his head and smiles. 'Thank Christ you're such a bloody bad shot!'

War Diary or Intelligence Summary: Army form C. 2118
1921

DIVISION MAIN DRESSING STATION—Remy Siding
Map Sheet 28; Grid reference: L.22 d.6.3

July 19th – Lt. G.R. Ingham admitted to hospital with
accidental gunshot wounds. Parades held under Coy
Commanders.

July 21st – Lt. G.R. Ingham transferred to hospital in England.
Band of 8th Battalion, West Yorkshire Regt. gave concert in
the afternoon. Baths parade, Poperinghe.

July 23rd – Three Officers and 23 O.R.s (CADRE 'A') to
Concentration Camp for dispersal. Of the party for dispersal
on this date, one Officer and five Other Ranks detailed as
Colour Guard and charged with handing over King's Colour
to the authorities at Catterick Garrison.

July 25th – Lt. G.R. Ingham retained at hospital in England for
medical board and struck off strength of Battalion.

July 27th – Battn now reduced to CADRE 'B' plus one officer
and 6 O.R.s of No.1 Labour Company. Equipment guard of
Battalion proceeded to Dunkirk. Colour Party to England
via Calais leave boat. Remaining personnel henceforth to
come under the command of 34th Battn Royal Bucks
Fusiliers while awaiting further instructions for departure.

28

'So the British Army has at last decided that the war is over, has it?'

'Reckon so, mate. Only three bloody years late – typical of your flamin' artillery!'

'Come on, chaps,' says Blake, putting his arm round Ocker's shoulder. 'No fighting. Not today. This is our Armistice Day. Our, er . . .'

'Victory parade?'

'Yes, I suppose so,' Blake nods. 'Although I don't really approve of "victory" as a concept.'

'You wouldn't, would you!'

'There are no winners, are there,' Blake says, 'in a war like this?'

'Aye, laddie, especially for those like you who wasnae fighting the darned thing in the first place!'

'Just a shame ol' Ingham couldn't stick around long enough join t'party, eh?'

'Don't feel sorry for him, do you, Jacko?'

'For Ingham? Christ, no!'

'Good. 'Cos if anything, I reckon we was too soft on him.'

'Aye, well . . .' Jack pats his tunic pocket. 'We've still got that signed letter, though, 'aven't we?'

'Quiet in the ranks!' The men on the parade ground gradually fall silent.

'I have called you here today,' the CO begins, shuffling papers in his hands, 'because I have what I am certain will be very welcome news for you all.' The men stare impassively. The CO's idea of good news isn't usually what they want to hear. 'You have served your King and Country with diligence and patience for three long years following our glorious victory over the enemy. Many of you have nobly assisted with some of the least welcome but nevertheless essential tasks facing our victorious army, and it is thanks to you men in particular that our brave fallen comrades have in so many cases been found and laid to rest.'

Cheers ring out across the parade ground.

'Our orders today are to begin immediately with arrangements for the dispersal of what little remains of the Battalion. Those men who have already indicated a desire to remain in the King's service have, as you know, been transferred already to other units. The rest of you will shortly be returning home – home to families, to loved ones, and home, of course, to a grateful nation.'

'Home! D'you hear that, Jacko?'

'Aye, lad, I do. Just a pity I don't know where the bloody hell it is any more.'

Ocker tries not to laugh as the CO finishes his speech. Eventually, the men let out a cheer. Caps are thrown in the air. Even the sergeant major manages a smile as the men line up to sign their discharge papers and to collect travel warrants and other documents.

'Patterson, Gilchrist, MacIntyre?'

'Yes, sir?'

'Not so fast. Look at the dates on those travel warrants o' yours.'

'Oh, sir!' Ocker says. 'Three more days in camp? You shouldn't have!'

'All heart, the Army,' Jack says.

'That's right, Patterson. And while you're waiting you can report to Captain Harris. If you look sharp there's just time for a bit more digging.'

'Oh great!' says Ocker. 'Flamin' marvellous.'

'Come on, lad.' Jack puts a hand on his shoulder. 'At least you know now when you get to go back down under.'

'Suppose so,' he mutters, looking at his discharge papers. 'Should be back in time for summer.'

'Nice.'

'Maybe.'

All over the parade ground men are shaking hands, slapping backs, saluting, smiling. Jack and the others stand huddled in a corner, talking.

'You don't seem very keen, lad' – Jack puts a hand on Ocker's shoulder – 'now that the big day's finally arrived.'

'Truth is, mate,' says Ocker, chewing his lip. 'I'm not so sure I am any longer.'

Jack takes two cigarettes from his tunic pocket, offers one to Ocker and lights the other.

'Cheers, mate.'

'So, what's the problem?'

'Look, mate' – Ocker closes his eyes and slowly exhales a lungful of tobacco smoke. 'I know I've been bangin' on about getting home for years.'

'I'd never have noticed.'

'But I could've caught a bloody banana boat back before

now if I'd wanted to,' he says. 'With or without this bit of paper. The bloody British Army wouldn't have stopped me.'

'I'm certain of that,' Jack laughs.

'And they'd never be able to find me once I got back home, neither.'

'No?'

'No, mate. Big country, Australia. Plenty of room for a fella to go missing. Plenty of folks who aren't going to ask any bloody silly questions.'

'So . . . what's the problem then?'

'Dunno, mate.'

Jack smiles. 'I do,' he says. 'I know.'

'Do you? Do you really, mate?'

'Aye, lad. Why d'you think I'm still here?'

Ocker laughs, takes a long drag on his Woodbine, then sits on his haunches and draws patterns in the gravel with a stick. 'Truth is,' he says, pausing once more to exhale. 'Truth is, mate' – he shuts his eyes – 'truth is, I'm not sure what I am any more – without a war. I mean, well . . . That's the only reason that I've stayed on here, I suppose . . . I dunno. I am someone. For the first time in my life I know who I am, why I'm here.'

'Aye,' Jack nods.

'It's like this is, well . . . like it's the only life I've led. There is no family down under . . .'

'No?'

'Nah. No one. Brought up by a bunch o' bastard priests in Wagga Wagga once me mother died.'

'You actually went to school, did yer?' Jack raises his eyebrows.

'If you can call it that. Flamin' prison camp, more like. Orphanage, to be precise, where the fuckin' holy Joes could play at dispensing Christian charity – which in their case seemed to consist of beating the living daylights out of anything that spoke—'

'Not that you do much o' that, eh, lad!'

'—and buggering everything that moved. Anyway,' he goes on, 'I didn't stay there long.'

'No?'

'Nah! Legged it as soon as these' – he pats his thighs – 'was long enough to sprint faster than the flamin' Holy Fathers.' Ocker looks down at the floor, then smiles. 'But not before I'd given the worst of 'em a damn good walloping.'

'What? You hit a priest?'

'Didn't just hit him, mate. Near as dammit killed him.'

'Bloody 'ell.'

'Oh, mate, he deserved it. You . . . well, you don't want to know what he did.'

Jack stares across the camp. Steam hisses and spits as a train departs with one of the last batch of men to be demobbed. Carriage couplings clang and the iron wheels screech on rusting rails.

'So, then, well – I'm living rough, doing odd jobs on the ranches, bit of this, bit of that, in return for a place to sling a hammock and a crust of bread, y'know?'

'Aye, I do. Did pretty much the same myself back in Yorkshire. Well, wi'out t'hammock, obviously. Bit cold for an 'ammock up on the moors.' They laugh.

'And then along comes the war and, well, to be honest, Jacko, it was such a bleeding brilliant opportunity.'

'Aye,' Jack says. 'I know.'

'I enlisted as soon as I could get to the nearest town, travel warrant to Liverpool for training, then eventually a troopship, bloody great thing – the *Wiltshire* – setting sail from Sydney harbour on the greatest adventure ever.'

'And now it's over.'

'D'you know, we had the time of our bloomin' lives on that voyage? Didn't know what a bloodbath our fellas were going through at Pozières, of course.'

'If you had have done, you might have jumped ship.'

Ocker stares into the distance for a while. The sidings are empty now and the rest of the camp is silent. 'All the time our chaps are going through hell here while we're marching through bloody bunting and streamers and behind the bands and being kissed by all the sheilas and with the old blokes chucking coins at us. Didn't even stop once we was aboard, when the gangplanks were lifted and when we were nosing our way out of Sydney harbour.'

'What – all swim after you, did they?'

'Wouldn't have put it past a few of 'em,' Ocker laughs. 'Nah, great load of porpoises swam alongside the ship, though. And then all the little boats, filled to the brim with folks waving and cheering and all the rest until the boats stop, passengers still waving their bloody arms off, and we sail on to Melbourne, Adelaide, Fremantle, picking up a few hundred more coves at every port.'

'Did they say where you was heading?'

'We thought we were heading up to Suez until the bloody ship goes and takes a left turn and we're off instead to Durban, so they say.'

'Why was that then? Enemy action?'

'Dunno, mate. No one told us. Jerry warships, someone says, another says we're off to Africa to kick the arse of Fritz there.'

'Most likely U-boats,' Mac says, joining them. 'They were probably just trying to stop you having to swim here.'

'So, what did you get up to in Durban then, lad?'

'Nothing much. Ship took on coal, that was about all.' Ocker shakes his head slowly, then suddenly lights up in an enormous grin. 'And if you believe that, mate, you'll believe anything!'

The men laugh.

'Giving Australia a bad name, eh?'

'Not half,' Ocker smiles. 'Although we can't have been that bad,' he goes on. 'After all, they let us go ashore again when the boat docked in Cape Town.'

'They must've been mad.'

'Oh, mate, we sure as hell gave Australia a bad name there,' he laughs.

'I'll bet,' says Jack. 'Then on to Blighty I suppose?'

'Yeah,' says Ocker. 'But you know what?' He shakes his head. 'Could never quite understand why if you lot was so desperate for us to join the party here, you put us down at bloody Plymouth, rather than dropping us straight off in France. Jeez, we was all ready for a bit of a fight by then, I can tell you.'

'I'll bet you didn't have to wait long,' says Mac.

'Not exactly. Just a pity first real scrap we got into was against a bloody Pommie canary at the Bull Ring. Wouldn't have minded,' he goes on, 'but they'd sent us to Boulogne in a bloody rowing boat.'

'Get away!'

'Felt like it,' says Ocker. 'We'd done twelve thousand flamin' miles across the sea without a murmur and suddenly we're all having a perk over the rails and the bloody cattle boat stinks of sick.'

Blake appears carrying mugs of tea. 'That's the Channel for you. Gets to everyone, even those with the strongest sea legs.'

'Cheers, lad.' Jack wraps both hands round the mug.

'So, what are we discussing?'

'We was just reminiscing, actually – well, Ocker was – about enlisting.'

'Not something you'll have a tale of your own to share, eh, laddie?' Mac begins to fill his pipe.

Ocker sucks on his tiny remnant of a cigarette before resuming his story. 'There was this one cove in charge of bayonet drill,' he says.

'At Eat Apples?'

'Yeah. Keeps telling us to go at it harder, run faster, stick the bloody knife in deeper.'

'They was all like that,' Jack says.

'Anyway this bloody big bugger in our unit – a farmer he was back home, not the strongest, not the smartest or the quickest, but by God, he was the hardest. And this Pommie corporal starts giving him a hard time, telling him he's mincing about and saying that he couldn't stick his todger in a fat whore's fanny – really riles him, he does. Really gets to him.'

The men laugh.

'And then he says to him, come on then, have a go at me, don't stick it in the bloody sack, come and have a go at me, come on, and he's roaring at him and winking at us and Farmer Boy sees red like a bloody big bull and runs at him faster than he's ever run and before the corporal knows it, he's flat out on the ground and Farmer Boy's about to bring down his bloody great bayonet in his throat!'

The men roar with laughter.

'And then what happened?'

'Well then, we dashes over and gets him off, pretty smartish. Corporal dusts himself down and stalks off in a huff and that's the last we hear of bayonet practice for the day.'

'So you missed the Dardanelles then?' Mac asks.

'Yeah, mate. I was out on the second boat out of Ozzie. Came straight here.'

'But you enlisted straight away?' says Jack.

'Ye-es,' he hesitates.

'But?'

'But the bastards kept me back on account of . . . well, shall we say I didn't take to saluting the Ruperts very easily!'

'That'll do,' Jack says, and exchanges a knowing look with Mac.

'Anyway, that's me then,' Ocker says after a while. 'That's my lot. Pretty standard stuff for us. We were all just a bit too eager for a bloody great adventure.'

'And now it's over.'

'Back to normal life, whatever that is.'

'What I don't get,' Ocker says eventually, 'what I really can't understand is why you lot take it like you do. You're all so flamin'—'

'Subservient?' Blake offers.

'Sub— what?'

'He means we do as we're told, we don't kick up a fuss.'

'Not like some we could name,' Mac says with a wink.

'Yeah, right. You bloody did as you were told all right. You did what the Ruperts told you, respecting them just 'cos they talk like someone's slipped 'em a gobstopper. Didn't kick up a fuss on the Somme, did you, fellas? Oh no! Did as you were flamin' told there, and if you was told to die, you had to do it their way – Come on, chaps,' Ocker says, mimicking a British accent, 'hold the line, don't run, steady orn.'

'It's called obeying orders, laddie.'

'What we're here for,' adds Jack sardonically. 'Do as we's told, mind us P's and Q's and know us place. Doesn't end with the war, either. It'll be just the same, back home.'

'Not for me, mate.'

Jack takes a long draw on his cigarette, saying nothing.

'Well, I'm ready,' Mac says at last. 'No work, mind. No missus any more, either. But – ach! something'll turn up. It always does.'

'You're not tempted to stay on then – in t'Army?'

'Och, no! I joined – make that rejoined – for the duration of the war,' says Mac. 'I've done my service, kept my promise and a whole lot more besides. It's time for them to keep their part of the bargain – not least by giving me my Army pension.'

'Aye, well,' Jack says at last. 'For the present, we're all still all in t'Army—'

'Not for much longer.'

'And while we are we've got some work to do. Come on.' Jack stands up and stretches. 'Let's go and do our duty by them poor sods as isn't ever going home.'

29

'One last job then, fellas,' Ocker shouts jumping down from the truck at the side of a muddy field near Vlamertinghe. 'Let's make it a good 'un, eh?'

'Right,' says Jack. 'I'll take the far corner. Skerritt, you come wi' me. Mac, Ocker – you work up from this side and we'll meet in t'middle. Remember what we're looking for?'

'Another anonymous landowner,' says Ocker.

'It's been a while,' says Mac.

'Certainly has.'

'Reckon there's something a bit odd about this one, if you ask me.'

'Odd?'

'Mysterious soldier. Kind o' thing Ingham would've had us doing.'

'If he was still here.'

'He's probably still tucked up in bed in Blighty getting over his little accident,' Jack laughs.

'Ashamed to show his head,' says Ocker, 'given—'

'Steady!' Jack nods towards Mac and Skerritt.

'Given – as I was about to say, Jacko,' Ocker winks, 'that he couldn't even hit it with his own revolver!'

Jack smiles. 'Right, well, as long as everyone knows what we're looking for this shouldn't take us too long.'

'What are we looking for, Jacko?'

'Well, t'ground, obviously,' Jack says. 'Look at the grass. It'll be greener than round and about.'

'Nourished by the blood and bonemeal, no doubt.'

'You putting yourself forward for a gardening job, eh, Mac?'

'Just interested, son, just interested. It's fascinating what you can learn from those horticultural chaps back at Remy of an evening.'

'So what have they got to say about the rat holes then, Mac? The digging and scraping done for us by our four-legged friends?'

'They'd probably say it aerates the soil, or some such.'

'Well, well. They'll have you staying on at this rate. Right' – Jack starts to move – 'let's get cracking. Sooner we're finished here the sooner we can get packed up ready for home.'

Clouds of small white butterflies flit from one small patch of wild flowers to another as the men pace slowly across the field. Young swallows gather and chatter overhead. Working outwards from the spot where the Belgian farmer first reported having found a body, Jack soon spots the telltale signs that something else is buried underground. He scrapes back the topsoil, digs a little further, then a little deeper. 'Right, Skerritt lad, get the stretcher ready.'

At first what Jack uncovers looks like no more than a discarded pile of old uniform. Only as he gently presses sleeves and lifts trouser legs does he discover bone sticking with the remnants of rotten flesh to the inside of the clothing. Sunlight flashes on the shovel blade as he carefully digs round the corpse.

And then, suddenly, he has hit the head – naked bone, skin

shrunk back like rotten leaves, a tin hat framing the skull like a black poke bonnet. The soil all around is stained and dark with what must be the maggoty remains of brain. Jack is scraping with the sharpened shovel, then he's kneeling, examining bits of soil in his hands. Where do you stop digging? How much of a soldier does a grave need?

In sure and certain hope . . . In sure and certain hope of what? Could you scrape the thoughts, hopes, loves, fears, ambitions, the memories, the secrets, the glories and the shame of what was once a man as quickly, Jack wonders, as his shovel now scrapes the stinking, rotting, liquefying mash of what is left by what the man once was? Suddenly Jack realises he is, quite literally, trampling on another's dreams. The grip of his Army boots cakes with what he can't scrape into the sandbag Skerritt is shaking open at the side of the hole.

'Right, lad.' Jack turns away. 'You can have a rummage for his ID, the poor sod. I need a fag.' The match cracks like a rifle shot. Jack sucks the cigarette to life, lips hissing like gas. Skerritt is mumbling something. Jack's mind is wandering.

In sure and certain hope of the resurrection of the body. At least this man *had* a body. What about the men who had nothing, the men who ceased to exist the moment a shell destroyed what they had once been or when a mine atomised their bodies so completely there was never going to be anything left for anyone to find – nothing more than flotsam, floating on the breeze? What difference would it make *not* moving him? What difference did it make moving any of them? Not that all of this one could be moved anyway. There'd always be something of him here, soaked into the soil, leaked into the land, impossible to scrape up. Neater, of course, to have a grave. Is that what this is all about – neatness? A great tidying-up operation?

They said that Fritz used the corpses of dead soldiers for making candles. Kadaververwertungsanstalt – the corpse factory. Another atrocity story? What would it matter if they did? What difference would it make? Jack takes a long, last look at the man lying at his feet, old blood blackening the earth, heart and lungs shrivelled like rotten apples in a basket of broken ribs. Ashes to ashes? Dust to dust? Was 'he' – the man, the soldier, corpse – now no more than the ground, the earth, the black water in the bottom of the shallow hole, the worms and maggots crawling through the empty eyes and out across the open canvas shroud?

Mac and Ocker appear from the other side of the field, empty-handed. 'There's nothing, Jack,' they say. 'We've looked. Believe me, we've looked.'

'Just this 'un then,' Jack shrugs. 'Might as well bury him, I reckon. Fancy digging one last grave, anyone? Where's he for?'

The others stand and look at Jack. 'All yours, mate,' says Ocker. 'We've got packing to do.'

'Just leave me my bike, then,' Jack says when they unload the corpse at Vlamertinghe cemetery. 'I won't be long.'

'What about your shovel?'

'I'll leave it here. Won't be needing it any longer, will I?'

'Watch they don't dock your pay for it, Jacko.'

Once the noise of the wagon has faded into the afternoon air, once another cigarette is smoked, Jack removes his tunic and gets down to work. Flies are already buzzing round the stitched bundle lying by the marked grave. Another hour and they'll be unbearable.

Jack picks up the shovel and begins to dig. The first sod, the first clean cut of the shovel into turf – the easy loosening and lifting and then the gentle laying – is just a prelude to the serious digging. After this comes the hard work – the regular, fast mechanical action: the cut of the spade; the loosening sod; the lift; deposit. Jack's shoulders and arms, his legs braced keeping his body in position, seem after a while to become the very forces necessary to move the growing mound of soil. His large, calloused hands that now no longer blister close loosely at first, then tighten into fists around the handle of the spade. His long, lean arms are perfectly proportioned for the job of cutting great thick slabs of earth then lifting them high over the deepening sides of the grave. Is it years of pitching hay and straw high onto farm carts stacked with sheaves under the hammer of a summer sun that did it? Is that what forged such skill? Or is it the winters digging drainage ditches in the lowest-lying fields? His body has been made for this. And more than just his body. A memory of watching someone digging, a shadowy figure shovelling, working the ground just the way Jack is doing, flits across his mind like the fleeting glimpse of a swallow swooping low to catch one of the flies buzzing round the bundled corpse. The man stops, straightens up and is now laughing as the little boy begins mimicking what he's just seen the older man doing. Bend, dig, lift, turn and throw; bend, dig, lift, turn and throw. Jack can see the man's teeth as he throws back his head and opens his mouth; he can smell the man's sweat beneath the stained shirt, see his eyes wrinkle as he smiles and laughs. But that is all. No face. No place or name. Unknown.

The CO, Major Dundridge of the Royal Buckinghamshire Fusiliers, is turning down the row of graves, picking his way across the duckboards, avoiding the newly excavated holes while taking special care not to walk across the old ones. Behind him, a well-dressed young woman tries her best to keep up. The heels on her shoes aren't helping. Jack sees them both, then turns back to the grave, gets his head down, slices the shovel into the ground at his feet, loosens another load of soil and throws it neatly out of the hole. He repeats the action, faster. Then again, and faster still. Big, furious shovelfuls of Belgian earth are flying up over his left shoulder and the hole is rapidly getting deeper. First his shoulders disappear and pretty soon his head is below ground, and all that can be seen is the top of his shovel, flashing in the sun as it lifts out yet more earth.

'Patterson, you can stop digging now,' the CO is calling, more mindful of the soil peppering his uniform than anything else. 'I said, STOP DIGGING, DAMN YOU!'

Major Dundridge turns to the woman. 'I do beg your pardon, miss.'

'Not at all, Major.'

'Sorry, sir,' Jack calls out of the hole without turning round or looking up. 'Didn't hear you just then.'

'Well, now you have heard get out of the damned hole, will you? There's someone here who wants to see you.'

Jack stops. He puts down his shovel, wipes his muddy hands on his shirt and steps up onto the first rung of the ladder.

'Right, I'll leave you, miss, to have your, er . . . to discuss your private matter here with Corporal Patterson.'

'Hello,' the girl is saying, reaching her gloved hand into the hole as if to haul Jack back into the land of the living. He looks up at her, but doesn't take the hand she's offering. Not that it'd be much use if he did. The slip of a girl'd be down here at the bottom of the hole as soon as he touched her, he is thinking.

'I'm sorry,' he says. 'But this is no place for a young lass like thee. The CO would've known that if he'd ever been out on a search himself.'

315

'No, no. I can see that you're busy. What is it that you're doing?'

Jack continues climbing up the ladder, rising slowly from the grave, sucking and squelching as the wet mud from the bottom of the hole is squeezed between the soles of his boots and the rungs of the ladder.

'I really am most grateful to you for breaking off like this to see me. I wouldn't mind, but I've already been here once before, looking for you. Only, you weren't here.'

'If it's urgent,' Jack says, 'then we'll have to go somewhere else. We can't talk here.'

The girl turns away as Jack buttons his shirt and pulls up his braces. 'Swallows,' she says, pointing across the cemetery. 'They're getting ready to leave.'

Jack pulls on his tunic and follows her gaze. 'Parent birds'll be off home soon, I reckon. But this year's brood'll be around another month or so. Know much about 'em, do you – swallows?' He studies her carefully: neat hat, gold pin, expensive clothes, a young face. She can't be much more than eighteen, he thinks, all the time wondering what it is that seems so familiar, and what on earth she's doing wandering alone round a Flanders cemetery.

'I was brought up in the country,' she says. 'And my mother was so very fond of birds.'

Ah, he thinks. Of course. 'There's a tiny place over there in t'village.' He nods towards the group of recently rebuilt houses clustered round the church. 'Don't know about you, but I could murder a cup o' tea.'

'That would be . . . nice,' says the girl, nodding.

'Jack, by the way.' He offers her his hand. 'Jack Patterson.'

'Yes,' the girl replies. 'I know.'

'Oh, aye?' He turns his head. 'Of course.'

The little village café behind the remains of the church is quiet. Locals only. And Jack can tell if anyone is talking about them. He pulls a chair out for the girl, removes his cap then sits down opposite. 'I'm sorry, miss. Back there, I must have seemed a bit . . .'

'I know,' she looks at him. 'I understand. You were miles away.'

'Aye,' said Jack. 'I were.'

'My name is Anna.' She removes her hat and gloves, placing them beside her on the table. 'Anna Bowker.'

'Aye,' Jack nods. 'I know.'

'You do?' The girl looks puzzled. 'I'm somewhat surprised.'

'Aye, well,' he sighs, looking down at the red-and-white pattern of the tablecloth. 'I reckon that's not going to be for the last time this afternoon, neither.'

'Go on,' she says.

'Nay, lass. You've come all this way. Ladies first.'

'Well,' she begins. 'This is actually a little awkward. But my mother—'

'Your ma,' Jack interrupts. 'Was it she that sent you?'

'Ye-es,' the girl looks down at the floor. 'Yes,' she says. 'I mean, she did. It was her idea. But that was before—'

'Thought so.' Jack picks at soil from beneath his fingernails. 'Aye, well. Go on, lass.'

'Oh. Oh, I see. Well . . .' The girl is expecting this to be a little awkward. But she isn't really anticipating it being such hard work. 'Well, as I was saying. My mother . . .' The girl pauses. 'Well, before she died Mama was very active in the committee establishing a war memorial for the village, and—'

'Edgham?' Jack says. 'The village, that is.'

'Yes,' she nods. 'That's right.'

'O' course,' Jack smiles. 'She would have been.'

'Would have been what?'

'She would have been active, I mean, love. On t'committee, that is, before she, er . . .' He pauses for a moment. 'I was sorry to hear that she'd passed away,' he says at last.

'But how . . .' The girl's mouth carries on moving, silently.

'How do I know? Why wouldn't I know?' Jack says.

'I'm sorry, Patt – er, Mr Patterson.'

'Jack.'

'Jack. Oh yes. Oh dear,' the girl flusters. 'You see? I really don't know what to call you.'

'I can think o' summat.'

'Well . . . Jack, as I was saying. My mother,' the girl looks down, briefly, 'she was instrumental in establishing a memorial to the men of Edgham who had fought in the war. For a small village there was quite a sizeable contingent . . . But then, you know that don't you? Yes, of course you do. Excuse me.' The girl leans forward. 'Excuse me, Jack? May I have a drink?'

'Aye, of course, lass. Sorry.'

Jack orders tea. Once the waitress has returned to the kitchen, the girl takes out a folded piece of paper from deep in her handbag. Without a word, she pushes the printed form across the table. Jack opens the letter.

ARMY FORM B.104-82 is stamped in bold at the head of the paper, as is the terse instruction to quote 'reference number K146 if replying to this letter'.

What would you say by way of reply to a letter like this? Jack wonders.

'Dear Madam,' the note begins. The remainder of the letter is a mix of pre-printed words and handwritten phrases filling in the blanks.

It is my painful duty to inform you that a report has been received from the War Office notifying the death of:-

```
No. 24910
Rank: Cpl.
Name: Patterson, J.
Regiment: West Yorks.
Which occurred: in the field in France
On the: 1st July 1916
The report is to the effect that he was:
```

KILLED IN ACTION

The last phrase is stamped in bold across the middle of the page. What else did they have ready to rubber-stamp across that line, Jack wonders – SHOT AT DAWN maybe? Or LOST IN MUD, perhaps?'

He reads on:

By His Majesty's command I am to forward the enclosed message of sympathy from Their Gracious Majesties the King and Queen. I am at the same time to express the regret of the Army Council at the soldier's death in his Country's service.

I am to add that any information that may be received as to the soldier's burial will be communicated to you in due course. A separate leaflet dealing more fully with this subject is enclosed.

Jack wonders what was in the leaflet.

'Please forgive the, er . . . Well, I don't know. The intrusion,' the girl stammers. Jack is shaking his head and looking at the letter.

'Can I hang on to this?' he asks.

'I suppose . . . yes, of course. It only seems only right, after all.'

'Aye,' he says. Then he smiles. Then suddenly, Jack is laughing. He is laughing loudly without quite realising what it is that he is laughing at. And then, once he does, he starts laughing even louder, and for longer.

'Well you see,' the girl goes on hesitantly, unsure what it is that Jack finds quite so funny. 'I mean . . . Well, apparently no one ever did receive notification from the War Graves Commission telling us about your burial.'

'Aye, well,' Jack is dabbing his eyes. 'For a start, there'd be no one to tell.'

'No one?'

'Well, that's not quite true.' He looks at her.

'My mother,' the girl goes on. 'She took a personal interest, of course.'

'Aye,' says Jack, folding his handkerchief. 'She would.'

'I do understand' – the girl is slightly irritated now – 'I was informed that you had no living relatives in the village.'

'Were you?' Jack narrows his eyes. 'Well, that's not quite t'whole truth, is it?'

'Isn't it?'

'But even if it was' – Jack turns away – 'no one would've received any letter from t'Commission about my burial, would they? How could they?' He smiles and spreads his arms. 'I'm here!'

Silence.

'Why . . .' she hesitates. A kettle whistles in the café kitchen. 'Why did you never . . . ?'

'Why did I never come home?' he says.

'Even on leave?' she adds.

He looks at her. 'It's a long story,' he sighs. 'Let's just say there was plenty o' folk quite happy never to see my face in t'village agin.'

'I can't believe that,' the girl widens her eyes. 'A war hero. Our own war hero. My mother for one was very keen that I should—'

'Yer mam . . .' Jack interrupts, then stops. 'Yer mam was a good woman,' he says softly. 'But she were in a difficult position.'

'I don't understand?' The girls frowns. 'Are you saying that you knew my mother?'

'Oh aye,' Jack smiles broadly, 'I knew yer mother all right!'

They sit in silence for a while, sipping tea. 'More?' Jack asks, once the mugs are empty.

'No, thank you. Would you mind . . . ?' the girl begins. 'I mean, it's getting late. I have a train to catch. Either that or else find somewhere nearby to stay. I signed out of my hotel this morning.'

Silence. 'What is it that you want, miss?' Jack asks eventually.

She looks at him for a long time. 'Well,' she says. 'As I was saying, my mother—'

'Aye, your mother.'

'You know her.' She tilts her head and narrows her eyes. 'You know her, don't you?'

'I don't know anyone.' Jack looks out of the window at the ruined church tower. 'I'm a dead man, remember?'

'Oh dear, I'm so sorry, I had no wish to—'

'Look, miss.' Jack waves the piece of paper in the air. 'There were mix-ups like this all the time.'

'Yes,' she says. 'That's what Major Dundridge told me. But—'

'But?'

'My mother . . . before she passed away. Well, she did a little digging.'

'Digging, eh?' Jack shakes his head. 'Well, we've that much in common, then.'

'Yes,' the girl nods. 'Yes, I suppose so. And she did think it was a little strange that there seemed not to be a letter.'

'Letter?'

'From your commanding officer. Not even a brief note from an NCO.'

'No,' Jack says. 'Well, there wouldn't be. Not after the battle we was in.'

'Really?'

'There was no officer and no NCO,' Jack pauses. 'There was nobody left that day but me.'

'Oh dear,' she says. 'That must have been . . .'

'Aye,' Jack says. 'It was.' Don't ask no more, he is thinking. Leave it there.

'Anyway, as I was saying, my mother did a little digging and she managed to establish that your Army pay seemed to have been resumed. Only the details . . .' She hesitates. 'Well, she couldn't be sure it was the same man.'

How could you? How could anyone? And what did it matter, after all?

'Which is why she was so keen for me to come here person-ally.'

Aye, Jack is thinking, an' I'll bet that wasn't t'only reason.

'Yes.' The girl looks down at her hands. 'Mama really was most adamant that I should come out here and find out for myself . . .'

The bell rings as the door of the café opens. Suddenly the girl starts laughing. 'It's ironic,' she is saying as the laughter turns to tears.

Jack passes her his handkerchief. 'Ironic?'

'Well, if it turns out that it *was* you after all, then . . . Well, that would make a difference to the memorial.'

'Memorial?'

'Yes,' the girls dabs her eyes. 'You see, Mama was fundraising, before her final illness, for a memorial to the men from the village who went to war and who never—'

'Oh aye – *The Glorious Dead.* Those who never returned. Of course.'

'Well, yes . . .' the girl's voice trails off. Jack can't take his eyes off her, even though he realises that what she is about to say is going to alter everything, for ever. 'That was the intention, certainly. Back in 1918.' The girl smiles. So like her mother, Jack thinks. So incredibly, unbelievably like her late mother.

'It seems so long ago.' Jack shakes his head, still looking at the girl.

'It does. And back then, of course, before the war was over, well, we hardly dared imagine—'

'Imagine?'

'That the village would be spared,' she says.

Jack frowns.

'Mm,' the girl nods. 'All the brave men of the parish who enlisted and who went to war survived. They all came home.'

'Oh, aye?' Jack looks away. The old couple at the next-door table rise and leave. 'Well there's one of 'em here that didn't, isn't there?' he mutters quietly.

'I beg your—'

'I'm still here, lass, aren't I?'

'Well yes, yes of course,' the girl is flustered, 'I mean, at the moment.' She puts a hand up to her cheek. 'But not for very much longer, surely?'

'No?' Jack says, much more loudly than he had intended. 'Why not, then, eh?'

'Well, I—'

'Why shouldn't I stay out here for ever?' Silence. Outside the café swallows swoop and twist past the large, sunlit window – a brief blur of movement like a rifle bullet. Beyond the church, the graves in the military cemetery are just visible, shimmering in the heat. 'There's thousands of 'em that will. At least I have the choice.' Jack jerks his thumb in the direction of the cemetery. 'Unlike them poor buggers.'

'Of course,' the girl leans forward. 'But I understood . . . Major Dundridge said you were about to be demobilised.'

'Aye, I am,' Jack says. 'We all are.'

'Well then?'

'But that doesn't mean I'm going home. Wherever "home" is!'

'You mean, you're staying here?'

'Aye, well. There's certain arrangements to be made, yet. But, yes. That's the plan.'

'Of course,' she sits back. 'That's understandable. You've been out here for so long. Of course I understand. But—'

'But what?'

'At least, if we can confirm that you're, well . . .'

Jack raises his eyebrows. 'Alive?'

The girl nods. 'The point is that your name, well . . . your name won't need to be included on the war memorial as the only one from the parish who fell. And the village—'

'Edgham?'

'Yes, Edgham can now officially be recognised as a Thankful Village.'

'A . . . what?'

'A Thankful Village,' Anna says. 'There aren't very many, you know.'

'Aye, well . . . I can certainly believe that.'

'No. But with you alive we can at last erect a memorial to the brave men who served the Empire overseas in the Great War. *And who returned home.*'

Jack looks around, then leans towards the girl. 'Look, miss,' he begins. 'I've got something to tell thee. I think there's something else you ought to know.'

30

'Er . . .' Jack is struggling to find the right words. The girl could help him, of course, if she wanted to. Expensive private lessons, no doubt, with a governess at the Big House. But she's in no mood now for talking. '*Donnez-moi quelqu'un pour m'aider loger femme?*' The landlady looks at him briefly, then looks at Anna, then shuts the door in their faces.

'Bastard,' Jack spits. 'Sorry, love, it's just that—'

'Don't,' the girl frowns. 'I understand. And believe me, I've heard much worse.'

'Aye, happen.' But after trying most of the hotels in Poperinghe (all *complets*) and half-a-dozen lodging houses, Jack is starting to get desperate. 'Look, love, I suppose you could bunk down for the night at Toc H, but—'

'Bunk down? Oh Jack, I think not!'

'Well, it's either that or t'church hall,' he says. 'We can't have you sleeping on t'streets.'

The girl looks thoughtful. The few market traders in the town square are packing up. There are shouts in a foreign language. Someone shoos away a dog.

'Look, love,' Jack says, 'if you catch the last train from Poperinghe you'll probably just make it to St Omer in time for a connection to Dunkirk.'

'But could I catch the last boat home?' Suddenly the thought of home, of shaking the dirt of Belgium from her shoes and getting as far away as she can from this nightmare, is becoming more and more attractive. 'No,' she says suddenly. 'I can't. I'm not going back without—'

'Look, love,' Jack shakes his head. 'I'm not coming with thee. I can't!'

'Then at least let me take back home some proof that you're alive,' the girl says. 'For the committee. This is important, Jack. My mother—'

'Yer ma's dead,' Jack says quietly. 'God rest 'er soul.'

'I know,' the girl nods. 'But the memorial. The Lady Bowker monument. She worked so hard, Jack. She wanted it so much. I feel I owe it to her memory.'

'Aye, lass.'

'And you're, you're . . .'

Jack looks down and sighs. It's impossible to explain. He can't explain. Not here. Not now. And especially not to her.

'I just don't understand,' the girl says at last. 'I cannot see why anyone would not want to come back. To come home. Why would anyone want to stay here?'

'It's hard to explain, lass.' He reaches out to her but she pulls back her hands. 'So much has happened,' he says. 'I'm not the same ma—' He stops. They both laugh. 'Well, you know all about that, lass, don't you?'

'But Jack!'

'Whatever it says on yon slip of paper, whatever Army number I have on me shoulder, whatever badge they gimme to wear on me titfer, I'm just not the man I used to be. Don't reckon anyone is,' he says, 'who went through this.'

'Talk to me, Jack,' she says. 'I want to know.'

'It's a long story,' Jack sighs.

'Well you'd better get on with it then,' the girl says. 'Come on,' she puts her arm in his. 'There must be somewhere else we can try. Let's find some shelter before it starts to rain.'

'Well,' Jack hesitates. 'I suppose there is just one more place that might have a bed.'

'Then what are we waiting for?'

A few minutes later they are walking down the Chaussée Brussels. The sign says 'Fermé' but the door of the café is unlocked.

'Monsieur Steenvan?' Jack calls. 'Katia?' The bar is empty. Then the cellar boy appears. 'Anyone about, lad? Oh, hang on. I mean, er . . . *Is er hier iemand?*'

'*Nee, alleen ik,*' the boy replies.

'Where is everybody, then?' Jack looks puzzled.

'*Ik weet waar Katia is,*' the cellar boy smiles. '*Ze is op Ieper naar jou!*'

'She's gone to Wipers?' Jack says. 'What the bloody hell for?'

The boy shrugs, then says something Jack cannot translate, but understands only too well.

'Come here, yer little—'

The boy ducks but not before Jack's hand connects. 'Hey!' he rubs his forehead. '*Je doet me pijn!*'

'I'll do more than gi' thee a clip round the ear, lad,' Jack hisses, 'if tha doesn't show a bit more respect.'

'What's going on, Jack?'

'Nowt, lass. Sit down for a while. I'll just go out t'back to get some coal. I won't be a moment. Michel here . . . Michel?' The scowling boy wanders to the table where Anna is now sitting. 'Michel'll get you something to eat. *Haal voor de dame wat brood en kaas,*' Jack says to the boy. 'And you' – he turns the minute he hears the door opening and Margreet's heels clip-clopping on the wooden floor – 'you make yourself useful for once. Go and make up the bed in the small back bedroom, will you?'

'You mean—'

'Aye, lass. I mean Françoise's old room.'

The woman looks at Jack then at Anna and her face changes, suddenly. She nods quickly, and then disappears upstairs.

'I'm tired, Jack.' Anna appears in the doorway that leads through to the back room, a blanket draped around her shoulders.

'Aye, lass, I know. It's been a long day. Been a bit of a shock for me an' all, truth to tell. Come on.' He gently ushers her upstairs. 'Let's get you to bed.'

A short time later Katia hurries through the door out of the rain. 'Jacques?' she shouts. 'Jacques?' before turning to Margreet. 'Has Jacques been here?'

The woman smiles, then nods, then raises her eyes and points to the ceiling.

'He is here?' Katia is puzzled. 'In the bedroom?' Passing the discarded blanket on the floor, she turns and makes for the stairs.

'Katia?' Jack calls, hearing her footsteps. 'Sit here a minute, lass.' He shows Anna to the small bedroom at the back of the house. 'Katia?' Jack calls out again as he picks up the bucket of coal he left on the landing. Hearing no reply, he turns back into the room to light the fire.

Anna is holding her stomach and rocking slowly back and forth on the edge of the bed. Her head is spinning. She has come such a long way, searched so hard. And she has found more than she could possibly have bargained for.

Suddenly the door opens and Katia bursts in, wiping her hands down the side of her skirt. She stares at the girl for a long time, unable to believe what she is seeing. Anna gets to her feet unsteadily, places her bag on the bed and puts out her hand. Jack drops the twisted paper he has lit into the grate and gets to his feet.

'I'm . . .'

'I know who you are,' Katia takes a step back. '*Mon Dieu*! I know.'

'I'm sorry, love,' he says to Katia. 'There was nowhere else we could go.' He puts out a blackened hand in an attempt to touch her arm. Katia pulls away.

'Aye, well.' Jack kneels down at the hearth. 'I'll just set this going. We'll all feel a lot better with a bit o' warmth around us.' An orange glow soon fills the room, casting flickering shadows on the women's faces. But the fire isn't giving out much heat.

'So,' Jack says, getting up from his knees, 'Katia – this is Anna. Anna Bowker.'

Katia sniffs and wipes away a tear.

'Love.' Jack reaches out to take her hand but Katia turns away again. 'Love,' he says again. 'Sit down. This is going to come as quite a shock.'

An hour later, and the girl is sleeping soundly.

'It's been a hell of a day for her,' Jack says, as they sit watching the tiny, birdlike figure gently breathing beneath the heaped blankets.

'I'm sorry, Jacques,' Katia takes his hand. 'It was such a shock.'

'I know, lass. I know. Believe me I never planned any o' this.'

The fire settles in the hearth. Jack adds more coal as quietly as he can. But Anna will not be woken. Even the noise from the bar downstairs does not disturb her.

'How much does she know?' Katia looks at the girl's face, seeing the obvious resemblance. 'Surely she—'

Jack looks down at the floor and shakes his head.

'Jacques? But, Jacques, you must tell her. You have to tell her. She has a right to know.'

'If I tell 'er,' Jack's hands begin to tremble, 'it's the end, y'know.' He looks at Katia. 'It'll be the end of everything.'

New coals catch and crack. Sparks flare like fish as they flicker and flash before they vanish in the draught of the flue.

'So what do you intend to do, Jacques? You can't let her go home to England thinking—'

'What? That she's the daughter of the Lady of t'Manor?'

'But she is!'

'By adoption, aye.'

'And she knows that?'

'Aye, she does. I told her. I had to. It was a shock, o' course. But, you know, I reckon she already knew, deep down. Well, suspected, anyway. I reckon that's partly why her mother sent her.'

'But not—'

'No!' Jack shakes his head. 'That's not the only reason.'

'She sent her here to find you, Jacques.'

'Aye, lass. I know.'

They sit in silence. Words form on their lips but remain unspoken. Both are afraid of triggering the inevitable detonation.

'So, what happens now?' asks Katia at last.

'You'll put her on t'train,' Jack says. 'In t'morning. She's got what she came for. Now send her home. Please?'

Katia nods, knowing that nothing will ever be the same again.

31

'Come on, fellas, final night – let's make sure it's a good 'un.'

'Aye, come on, Jack, stop moping. At least let's go and say our farewells to the locals. Does Katia even know you're leaving tomorrow?'

'Don't even know if she's speaking to me any more.' Jack shakes his head. 'After what happened t'other day.'

'What? Turn you down at last did she, Jacko?'

'I cannae believe that,' says Mac. 'The lassie's all over him like fleas on a dog.'

'Maybe that's the trouble,' Ocker smiles. 'Haven't given her a dose, have you, Jacko?'

Ocker ducks and Jack's boot misses him and thuds into the door of the hut, scattering flakes of dried mud over the floor. 'Reckon we've hit a raw nerve there, Mac old son!'

Mac is sitting on his bunk, polishing his rifle for the last time. 'Who was yon mystery woman, then, Jack?'

'I'd . . . it's . . . it's a long story,' Jack says.

'Didn't look like you two was exactly strangers,' Ocker says. 'What with you arranging for her to bunk up in Françoise's old bed for the night.'

'Pretty wee lassie, from the little I could see.'

'Fancy a bit o' jelly roll with 'em both together, Jacko?'

'Poor taste lad.' Jack stands up and takes a step towards Ocker's bunk. 'Poor bloody taste, lad – even for thee.'

Jack nods a greeting to the small crowd of evening regulars, shakes the odd hand, exchanges pleasantries in the vernacular and, reaching the bar, orders the men's beer. Katia has recovered slightly – familiar dimples forming as she smiles at Jack – but still can't quite believe what she's been told. Upstairs, the bed that Anna slept in has been stripped.

'You are quiet tonight, Jacques,' she says eventually, after slowly filling the jug, then half-filling each of the glasses, then going back along the line, topping up each drink in turn.

Jack turns, looking round the small *estaminet* as if seeing it again for the first time. Clean glasses sparkle on neat, wooden shelves behind the counter. On the walls, etched mirrors reflect the flickering light of candles on each table or throw the dim glow of gas lamps back into the room. Small bowls of flowers sit in the middle of each of the tables. Her touch, he thinks.

Katia concentrates on measuring out the beer. Her father's daughter. Not a drop spilt. The slow, deliberate action – well practised – is hypnotic. Jack closes his eyes and shakes his head.

'No Pa tonight?' he asks the girl. She shakes her head, but Jack already knows why Monsieur Steenvan now spends almost all his time in Ieper. This tiny temporary *estaminet* in Poperinghe has become Katia's sole responsibility. As has her sick mother in the bed upstairs.

A few miles down the road in Station Straat, the British Tavern sheds its skin like a snake. Each successive wave of building and rebuilding sees the place grow larger, stronger, grander. And there is now a renewed urgency in this small act of reconstruction. Because with each new phase the British Tavern is transforming itself back into the pre-war hotel where Katia and her sister Françoise once played in the small rear yard under the protective shadow of the cathedral. Monsieur Steenvan is turning back the clock. Or trying to.

'Don't see him much these days.' Jack is thinking of another conversation with Katia's father that he has, until the last few days, been planning.

'He is happy for me to be here,' the girl says at last. 'Keeping things going for a little longer.'

'You do a grand job, love.'

'I do my best,' she says, looking up at him. 'It won't be for much longer. As soon as the hotel in Ypres is ready . . .'

Jack nods. 'Aye, o' course. No more British Tavern, eh?'

She smiles. 'You know, Jacques, that my father would—'

'I know,' Jack nods, holding up a hand. She must not say any more.

Katia continues carefully measuring out the beer. Looking at her in the half-light, the concentration on her face, the tired look in her eyes, the strands of auburn hair escaping from their pins, Jack is seized almost physically by the realisation that this – here, now – is the moment. Or would have been the moment. Until just three short days ago, with release papers from the Army in his pocket and a future opening up before him, this would have been the moment when he popped the question. His fingers twist and spin the cheap gold ring that has been buttoned securely in the pocket of his breeches for a week.

'You know I'm going . . .' he starts, then looks down at the floor. How can he possibly tell her? How could she possibly understand? He looks at the gentle contours of her face, the bottom lip already trembling slightly in anticipation.

'Home?'

'Aye, lass – home.' He shakes his head. 'If you can call it that.'

'You don't want to go?' She looks down at her hands and grips the handle of the jug she's holding even tighter.

'I . . . I don't rightly know,' Jack shakes his head. 'Not now. Oh, I thought I did. I thought I knew. It was all so clear. But since the other day . . .'

Katia suddenly starts pouring furiously, carelessly. The beer mushrooms over the rims of the glasses in a spurt of froth. All along the line of glasses, foam erupts.

'Steady on, lass.'

The heavy weight of the piled hair strains at the loose pins holding it in place, and the harder she mops up the spills, the more loose strands escape to fall across her flushed face. When she looks up again, Jack sees that there are tears in her eyes.

'Do you want to leave me?'

Jack shakes his head, slowly, looking at the girl all the time, looking into her dark brown eyes, looking into her face so intently that it starts to make his own eyes hurt with the memory.

'Then why?' she says. 'Why must you go there, to her? Is it work, Jacques? Is it the money? There is still so much to do here . . .' She breaks off and puts her hands over her face.

'Aye,' he says quietly 'There's plenty o' work. But not for t'British Army. Not for me. Not any more. We're finished here. Buried all the horror.' He looks at her. 'Tidied it all up and swept it all away, hidden it, smartened it all up and made it right again. At least, that's what I thought.'

'I know, Jacques. I know that.'

'And now,' he says, 'it needs skilled men – men who can

plant flowers and trees and rake lawns and make the places pretty. And men who can make better sense of things than I can.'

'You could do that.' She looks up desperately. 'You could do that, Jack. You could do anything. I could help. Anna, she could—'

'She wouldn't want to,' Jack says.

'Please, Jack. Please!'

'Aye, well . . . happen I could apply for a Commission job,' he says. 'But then, they're bringing men over from England all the time. There's over a thousand of them already here.'

'But the graveyards are still, how do you say? . . . a tip.'

Jack laughs. 'Aye, lass, they are. Truth is, they haven't enough men to take care of 'em all. One of the caretakers has to take on eight cemeteries on his tod.'

'His . . . tod?'

'On his own,' Jack says. 'That's too much for anyone.'

'Then they should employ more—'

'They are, lass, they are – there's twenty more coming out on t'boat from Folkestone every week.'

'They should employ you!'

'Ah've told thee, lass . . .' His voice trails off. 'I would, but . . .'

'Then forget the graves, Jacques. You know there is work for you – for us – here.' Tears are running silently down Katia's dimpled cheeks, even as she tries to smile.

'I know,' Jack sighs. 'Happen three days ago, things'd have been different. But now . . .'

'It is all because of her!'

'I have to go back, don't I? What choice have I got?' He looks down at the floor, suddenly noticing how thick with mud are his breeches, how the puttees he still wears are moth-eaten, frayed, torn, and how his bootlaces have as many knots as there are eyeholes in the worn brown leather of his boots. The Army, for him, is over. The war is over. His uniform is over.

'Shall I see you later?'

The girl smiles.

'For old time's sake? To say goodbye?'

'You never give up, Jacques, do you?'

'You know,' Ocker is saying as Jack hands round the beers, 'I reckon we must've buried nigh on five hundred coves since we started doing this job three years ago.'

'Aye, and every one of them somebody's son or sweetheart, someone's brother, someone's father.'

'What's that?' Jack says.

'I was just saying,' Mac replies, 'each one of them is someone's brother, son . . . father.'

'Not me,' Ocker smacks his lips. 'Not that anyone's ever told me, anyway.'

'I thought you said you were only transferred because your mother was English?'

'Ocker has a mother?'

'God rest her soul,' says Ocker. 'Must've done. But that wasn't what I meant.' He looks at Jack. 'Jeez, will you take a look at your face, Jacko? We're going home tomorrow, mate.' He claps a hand down on Jack's back. 'Home!'

'Well, some leaving do this is,' Mac grumbles. 'More like a wake. Drink up, will ye, chaps? I need another.'

'I'll go,' says Jack.

'What? And take half the evening like you did the last time? No thank you, you sit right there. We don't want to die of thirst.'

'Come on, Jacko, why the long face?' Ocker rests a hand on Jack's shoulder. 'Is it the missus?'

Jack sighs.

'Plenty more fish in the sea, mate. Plenty more English fish, an' all. It's not like you'll go short, Jacko. Not like you don't get your fair share of attention from the ladies, is it?'

'More than his fair share, I'd say.' Mac puts down another tray of drinks. 'Wish I knew the secret.'

'I reckon you've been given short measures there, Mac old son.'

'Away with you, laddie, they're whiskies. The beer's on its way. Katia . . .' He stops and looks at Jack. 'Katia says she'll bring it over in a moment.'

> *I ain't got nobody*
> *Nobody cares for me, nobody*
> *Nobody cares for me.*
>
> *I'm so sad and lonely*
> *Sad and lonely, sad and lonely*
> *Won't some sweet mama come*
> *And take a chance with me.*

'Shut up, Ocker!'

By the time the men leave three hours later, the bar is deserted. The door is locked. Most of the candles have been extinguished. Mac is asleep in his chair.

'Well, fellas,' Ocker says. 'Early start tomorrow. Come on.' He puts a hand on Mac's shoulder. 'Shake a leg, grandad. We've got a train to catch.'

Mac stands, a little unsteadily, then takes Katia's hand and kisses it softly. 'It's been a pleasure, lassie. A real pleasure.'

'. . though a little more for some of us than others,' Ocker murmurs.

Jack has struggled to his feet and she gives him a hug. Skerritt cries; only Blake, who is stone-cold sober, shakes hands stiffly and stays completely in control. As they step outside the cool summer night air stuns them all into sobriety, and they trudge down the road back to camp with heavy steps.

'Hang on a minute, will you,' Jack says suddenly. Turning on his heels he starts sprinting back along the Rekhof. 'Actually,' he calls out, waving. 'Don't wait – go back to camp. I'll see you later.' When he gets back to the bar, the door is bolted.

He lifts his hand and pauses, before knocking, softly at first then harder, faster, louder – loud enough to wake the dead. 'I'm sorry, lass,' he says when Katia appears at the door at last. 'Just came to say . . .'

'Goodbye?' she says.

'Aye, lass. Properly.'

As soon as he steps inside she opens her arms and holds onto him tight, afraid that the earth might open up beneath her feet, afraid that the world is ending, afraid ever to let go of him. Eventually, prising himself from her arms, Jack fetches a bottle of whisky and two glasses.

'You don't have to go, Jacques,' the girl says suddenly. 'Not tonight, anyway.'

Jack kisses the top of her head, softly, closes his eyes and breathes in the delicate, lavender fragrance of her hair.

'What about your pa?' he says, already knowing the answer.

'Papa is in Ieper. He will stay there this evening.' She shrugs. 'Nobody will ever know.'

'You'll have me shot.' Jack leans forward, looking at the

amber reflection in his whisky glass. 'And what about your ma?'

'She sleeps all the time these days.' The girl looks down. 'When I am not having to apply the poultice. She does not ever leave her bed. She is not well, Jacques.'

'Aye, lass,' Jack says. 'I know. I'm sorry.'

By the time they reach the bedroom, the only sound is the heavy hall clock tick-tock, tick-tocking away the time to midnight. Somewhere nearby, shortly afterwards, a church bell chimes. Katia sits on the bed, heavy hair still piled high above her hot, tired eyes. The chaste, buttoned blouse is soft to his touch. Moonlight, like a torch beam, shines through the gaps in the shuttered window. Jack watches as she reaches up and finally unpins the mass of long, dark hair, its colour as rich and brown as plump horse chestnuts.

She turns her back to him and slowly, clumsily, Jack unpicks the laces of her stays. At the same time, she shakes her head and Jack's hands are suddenly covered in cascades of soft, sweet-smelling curls. He cups great handfuls of her hair in his palms, bringing the strands up to his lips and breathing deeply, drinking the fragrance as if he were drinking the sweetest, purest spring water. He presses it against his mouth and nose and is lost in a world where nothing but this moment matters. The girl sits motionless, eyes closed, feeling his breath on the nape of her neck. The clock ticks.

An hour later, when the moment finally arrives it is both quick and utterly overwhelming. Great heaving sobs convulse Jack's body, rising in strength with each desperate gulp for air and growing louder and louder.

'Shhh . . .' the girl whispers. 'Somebody will hear.'

Jack does not hear. He chokes back each wave of tears, but they return stronger, louder than before, until the storm of his emotions, of release, is a torrent no man could possibly resist.

Katia isn't sure what to do. She lies on the bed, underneath him, then at his side. She holds him tight, then lets his taut, convulsing body go. She strokes him softly and then finds that she is gently stroking the side of her own face in the darkness, quietly biting her bottom lip as she does.

The storm passes. The energy of the tidal surge of tears slowly ebbs away and all she can eventually hear is Jack's breathing – slowly, quietly, rhythmically – and the clock ticking, loudly. Sometime later she falls into a fitful sleep. And in the morning, when she wakes, her bed is empty.

Oh mademoiselle from Armentières, parlez-vous?
Mademoiselle from Armentières, parlez-vous?
Just blow your nose, and dry your tears,
We'll all be back in a few short years,
Hinky, dinky, parlez-vous.

32

A sergeant opens the door and swings a hurricane lamp inside the hut. 'Five o'clock,' he shouts into the thinning darkness. 'Transport leaves in one hour.'

Only when the men get up, when the electric light is turned on, do they realise that Jack's bunk is empty. They look at each other but no one says a word.

Mac's kit is packed and ready; Ocker is whistling 'Waltzing Matilda' while picking up anything and everything he can lay hands on – whether it belongs to him or not. Skerritt hums his own strange, high-pitched whine of a tune as he carefully packs up the last of his kit.

'Weapons? Any more weapons? Ammunition?' comes a cry from the parade ground. The men double-check pockets for spare rounds, search bags for ammunition belts and anything else that might delay their long-awaited departure. Only Blake, Labour Corps and never armed, has nothing to declare.

'Transport parade, ten minutes!' comes another order as the sergeant major bangs on the hut with his swagger stick. The men haul bags onto their shoulders, stop, then look at one another.

'This is it, then.'

'Aye, laddie, this is it.'

A bugle sounds from across the parade ground. Suddenly the door is flung open and Jack sprints across the floor.

'What the—'

'One step further and you'd have been wearing that door, Mac old fella,' says Ocker.

'Sorry, lads!'

'Christ almighty, Jacko, cutting it a bit fine, aren't you?'

'How the devil did you get past the guards?'

'Ask no questions, get told no lies.'

'Handed in your rifle yesterday, Jacko, didn't you?'

'Aye, aye.' Jack is frantically stuffing everything he can lay his hands on into his Army haversack. The others put their own bags down to help him.

'Five minutes,' comes the call from the sergeant major. A bugle calls. Outside, in the sidings, there is a sudden loud hiss as the troop train gets steam up ready for the journey.

'Come on, Jack, we don't want to miss it.'

'Not after waiting all this time!'

'You go on ahead, lads,' Jack says. 'I'll see you on board. Save us a space in the omms-n-chevoos . . . if there's any left.'

'Right you are.' Mac picks up his bag. 'Well, so long, Ocker ol' son,' he pats him on the back. 'Shame you're not on this one with the rest of us.'

'No offence, Mac, but I'd rather not be going in your direction.'

A whistle blows. Metal scrapes as loosened wheels settle on the rails.

'Right, I'm done,' Jack makes for the door. 'I'll see thee,' he puts a hand on Ocker's shoulder.

'Still don't understand a word o' this fella,' Ocker says to the others. 'Now bugger off home the lot of you, before you miss the train.'

'Come on, lads,' Jack shoulders his haversack. 'Last on t'train buys the teas.'

In the sidings, soldiers are crowding round the carriages. Troops from neighbouring camps gather at one end of the small station under the watchful eye of an NCO. Slowly the men embark. The carriages fill. A whistle blows. The train moves.

'Hey, this is a bit of all right, isn't it?'

'What is? Seats?'

'Aye and warmth and windows.' Mac takes his sleeve and rubs the glass. 'Bit mucky, mind.'

'Complain to t'guard, Mac. Tell him you want your money back.'

'I would do if I'd paid for my ticket myself,' Mac laughs. 'But this journey's on the King!'

Soon the warmth, the deep springs and clean carriage cloth together with the steady motion of the train lull the excited men to sleep. Familiar brown fields and ruins recede as the train slowly travels farther behind the old front lines. Soon there are trees, their branches thick with the dark green leaves of high summer, autumn little more than a vague idea. Within an hour they have crossed the border and are in France. More troops board the train at each stop, and soon there are men sitting in the corridors, or standing in each of the compartments holding on to luggage racks as the carriages sway. The air is thick with smoke. Blake edges closer to an open window. Two hours and a change of train later, they finally reach the ferry.

'That's that, then.' Jack looks at the silhouette of the coast of France and shakes his head. 'That's that.'

*

Early next morning, England emerges from the mist, the white cliffs glowing salmon pink in the rising sun. Doors slam at Folkestone station. Words in a familiar language echo on the platform. A third-class carriage has a few spare seats. Mac and Skerritt are asleep within minutes. Blake opts to stand guard – he smiles at the thought – by the door. Soon afterwards, the train is moving – slowly at first, struggling against the weight of a cargo of men who have been so far away and so far below ground for so long: men of the trenches, saps, dugouts, funk holes – and the graves that they have dug, lives made heavy by the weight of Flanders mud that still sticks to them like clay. Gradually, as the sun strengthens, a weight seems to lift and the train gathers speed and they are heading, headlong – a long, dark arrow – for the capital.

'What's that?' A boy, sitting on his mother's lap on the seat opposite, is looking at Jack's sleeve.

'These, you mean, lad?' He lifts up his arm, pointing to a row of small brass bars pinned to his cuff.

'Yes,' the boy says. 'Those little bars. What are they for?'

'Wounds,' Jack tells him. 'They're wound stripes.'

'You were wounded,' the boy nods. It is a statement rather than a question. 'You're a wounded soldier.'

Jack smiles.

'My mummy says that I'm a wounded soldier' – he turns to see if she is listening – 'don't you, Mummy? When I fall down and hurt myself.' He looks at Jack. 'Poor wounded soldier, Mummy says. That's what you say to me, isn't it, Mummy?'

The woman smiles, and carries on reading.

'Why haven't you got any?' The boy shifts his attention to Blake. 'Why haven't you got any wound stripes?' the boy asks again. 'Aren't you a wounded soldier too?'

'Actually,' Blake smiles, sliding his book back into his tunic pocket, 'I'm not a soldier at all.'

'You're not a soldier?' the boy's screws up his eyes. 'But you're in a soldier's uniform. Are you a pretend soldier, then?'

Jack stifles a laugh.

'Is he a pretend soldier?'

'Nay, lad. He's a . . .'

'I chose not to fight,' says Blake. 'I don't believe in violence.'

'So why were you there?' the boy asks.

'I was sent,' Blake says. 'I was sent to France to help . . . in other ways.' He looks out at the trees and ripening fields of Kent. Oast houses, tucked into folds in the hills, the whole garden of England as seen through the grubby, soot-stained carriage window.

'Didn't you believe it was worth fighting?' the boy says.

'There's a lot more to war than fighting, lad.' Jack looks at Blake.

'Is there?' the boy says. 'Is there any more to war than fighting? Where are your guns?'

'Had to hand 'em back, lad. Now that the war's over.'

'The war's been over a-g-e-s,' the boys says, stretching out the final syllable. 'Why are you only just coming home? Were you taken prisoner?'

'Like he said' – Jack smiles at Blake – 'we've been busy . . . in other ways.'

The boy looks at the double reflection of his face in the carriage window for a while. 'Where are you from?' he asks eventually.

'Freddie, leave the men alone,' the woman tells him. 'Stop asking so many questions.'

'It's fine,' Jack smiles at her. 'It's no bother.'

'We've just been to France,' the boy announces. Blake

346

suddenly looks up – a glance at Jack. The two men nod almost imperceptibly at one another.

'We went to see my daddy. My daddy was a soldier,' the boy goes on. 'Daddy was a soldier, wasn't he, Mummy? He was a real soldier, too.' He frowns at Blake. 'He was a wounded soldier,' the boy says, eyes fixed on Jack's sleeve. 'He was wounded to death,' he adds quietly. 'He was wounded to death so he could never come home. Isn't that right, Mummy? We went to see where they had buried him.'

The woman looks down, hiding her eyes as her shoulders silently begin to shake.

'Well.' Blake grasps Jack's hand amidst the smoke and steam of King's Cross station. 'Good luck!'

Doors slam. A whistle blows. 'Go on,' Blake says. 'Miss this train and you'll be in for a long wait for another.'

'Sure you won't come with me,' Jack smiles. 'For the ride?'

Blake looks at his travel warrant. 'It's quite clear,' he says. 'Transport to London, no farther. I've got to make my own way back from here.'

'Sorry, lad. Hell of a journey for you.'

'I've got a good book,' Blake says, patting the tattered copy of the Bible in his tunic pocket.

'Come on, son,' Mac says impatiently.

'Blakey?'

'Yes, Jack.'

'If you do go back . . .'

'Back?'

'Aye. To Toc H, like you was saying.'

'It's a possibility,' Blake says. 'If Reverend Clayton plans to buy the place and keep it going.'

'Aye, well . . . if you do go back, say hello to Katia for me will you? If you see her?'

Blake smiles. 'Get on the train, Jack.'

'Yes, man. Come on. Get on the train.'

'Please, Blakey?'

'Never mind Katia,' Blake says. 'Get on your train. And when you get to Yorkshire make sure you go and see Anna. Sort it all out with her.'

'Aye.'

Ripon, when he finally arrives almost a day and a half later, looks exactly as Jack remembers it. The camp is quieter, the parade ground smaller, but in every other respect things could not have changed less than when he was last here, six long years ago. It is as if the war had never happened. Marched alone to the gate on the morning of his discharge, Jack immediately turns left, taking the road to Pateley Bridge, and keeps up the same brisk pace until he is as far away from the camp as he thinks is safe. Slipping from the road into Limekiln Woods for a smoke, he allows himself to look back towards camp for the first time. There is no one following.

After lunch he heads south for a while, feeling conspicuous as his footsteps crunch on the dirt track through the village of Studley Roger. He manages to beg a screw of tea from a sympathetic cottager and seeks the shade of the trees in the afternoon heat, sleeping on his pack as pigeons clatter in the branches overhead and pheasants dart and peck among the dry leaves. By the time he wanders down the hill through the trees to Fountains Abbey, hours later, the light is already starting to fade.

Sitting on the floor in the gloom of the crypt, he lights a cigarette. The sudden flame attracts a dozen pairs of eyes, like moths. From deep within the shadows, the vaulted undercroft is suddenly alive with men, with what remains of men, old soldiers slowly rising like the dead from an afternoon sleeping off their hangovers on damp earth, men yawning and stretching and scratching in the dark depths of the ruined abbey.

Too weary by now to move, Jack leans his head on his bag and drifts into a fitful, restless slumber. Now and then the sudden flare of matches pierces the darkness, punctuating the night as he attempts to sleep. An owl's screech is a sharp stab of pain pulling him back from the threshold of insensibility. The gentle, soothing, soft *whoo-hoo*ing answer from the bird's mate, perched high in the abbey's hollow tower, settles his nerves and calms his breathing. And somewhere, in the blackest depths of his dreams, an Irish voice is softly swelling to a song.

> *My young love said to me,*
> *My mother won't mind*
> *And my father won't slight you*
> *For your lack of kind.*
> *And she stepped away from me*
> *And this she did say:*
> *It will not be long, love,*
> *'Til our wedding day.*

The hard, damp earth beneath Jack's hips is suddenly, sharply, desperately uncomfortable. He wakes and turns, slowly. A hundred orange cigarette ends flicker in the darkness like a sudden swarm of glow-worms.

> *She stepped away from me*
> *And she moved through the fair*

And fondly I watched her
Move here and move there.
And then she made her way homeward,
With one star awake,
As the swan in the evening
Moved over the lake.

Now fully awake, Jack rolls a cigarette, adjusts the haversack behind his head and lies back, smoking, listening, thinking.

The people were saying,
No two e'er were wed
But one had a sorrow
That never was said.
And I smiled as she passed
With her goods and her gear,
And that was the last
That I saw of my dear.

The sound of someone coughing echoes round the stone walls. Farther off, a man snores. Jack's eyelids are suddenly once more very, very heavy.

Last night she came to me,
My dead love came in.
So softly she came
That her feet made no din.
As she laid her hand on me,
And this she did say:
It will not be long, love,
'Til our wedding day.

33

The next morning Jack is up and off before the mist has cleared. Crossing the road, he wanders north, across fields, skirting hedgerows. By lunchtime he has reached Masham, stopping in the main square as the smell of malt and barley from the brewery fills his nose and the clamour of children in the schoolyard fills his ears. He arrives on the outskirts of Edgham later that same day, shunning the centre of the village to turn down Low Lane towards the Backs. His mother's cottage, a ruin when he last saw it years ago, now has a new roof. Children play with a ball in the road outside; a young woman standing in the open doorway watches while a pig grunts from a sty in the backyard.

'How do?'

The woman stares. The children stop playing for a moment. Birds fill the sudden silence. 'My mother . . .' Jack nods. 'This used to be hers.'

The woman doesn't answer.

'Aye, well. That were years ago,' he says. He ruffles the hair of the youngest boy, who wrinkles his nose and smiles.

'I can spare you some tea,' the woman says. 'But I've got no brass so don't ask me.'

'Thank you,' Jack smiles. 'That'd be grand.' The stone flags of the kitchen floor are cracked, but scrubbed. 'Oh.' Jack looks down at his boots. 'I'm sorry, lass.'

'You're worse than t'children,' she scolds, then smiles. 'Walked far?'

'From Ripon,' he says, unshouldering the heavy canvas haversack from his back.

'You a soldier?' the woman asks, looking at the stencilled number on the canvas bag.

'Aye,' Jack says. 'Well, used to be.'

'Sit down then. I'll mash you some tea.'

'Thank you,' he says, pulling out a chair.

'Save you having to light a fire in t'woods at any rate,' the woman says, putting a kettle on the plate by the stove.

'Aye,' he nods. 'Wouldn't want to attract attention from the estate.' His hands ache as they close round the hot tin mug. He closes his eyes and drinks.

'You from t'village, then?'

'Actually, no. Officially, I'm from t'next parish. That's where I enlisted,' he says. 'Although I had plenty o' pals here.'

'Thought I didn't recognise you,' the woman smiles. The cries of the children in the road outside come and go as games begin, stall, break up and then begin again.

'Sounds like war out there,' Jack smiles. 'Did your husband . . . ?'

The woman shakes her head. 'He were never released,' she says. 'Tried. Wanted to. Bloody desperate to get away, he was. But the estate wouldn't sign to let him go.'

'Aye,' Jack nods. The estate. The big house. Anna. Her late mother.

'Aye, well.' Jack pushes back the chair. The woman watches as he makes his way to the door. It is already dark when he steps outside, but he knows which barns will be empty, where the best straw will be kept. Climbing the steep hill and ignoring signs and fences, scaling the drystone walls and jumping across near-dry streams, he finds a place to sleep. And in the morning, he knows where he will find her.

He knows better than to go to the kitchens of the big house, unannounced. A friendly escort, that's what is needed. But the keeper's cottage is empty. Going back to the woods, Jack soon comes across the pheasant hatchery, but the birds have already been fed. The keeper could be anywhere, and time is running out. Staying close to the hedges and ducking down behind stone walls, he skirts the edge of the estate and ends up at Home Farm. The dogs, on chains, bark fiercely at first – but then tails wag and wet tongues loll. Hens scatter. Pigs rear their fat heads above the side of pens before flopping back into the cool mud.

'You're not wanted here, Patterson.' The shotgun is broken, resting across the man's forearm, but loaded – both barrels. Sun glints off the brass caps of the cartridges.

'Oh, aye?'

'No. Got long memories, people here, tha knows.'

'Was I ever welcome here?'

'Probably not. But there's no one left alive now with a good word for thee, nor ever had.'

'I can believe that.' Jack laughs. But it is anything but funny. 'So how did they find out?' he asks.

'Well, Miss Anna's mother . . .' the man checks himself. 'Lady Agnes, I mean – God rest her soul. Not the whore . . .'

Jack suddenly takes two big strides towards the man. He steps away quickly, cocking the gun.

'If yer think I'm frightened o' that thing,' Jack nods.

'It's loaded.'

'I know.'

'I'll use it.'

'You won't.'

A cock crows from the other side of the farmyard.

'Her mother . . .' Jack says quietly. 'Don't talk of her like that.'

The man spits on the farmyard floor, a green-brown gobbet of phlegm stained with the tobacco he's been chewing. 'At least Lady Agnes made something of the girl.' He wipes his mouth. 'More than your whore would ever have done. More'n you would ever have done an' all,' the man says. 'Not that you hung around long enough to find out.'

'I'm telling you.' Jack stares at the man, unblinking. 'Don't talk of her like that.'

'Why's that then?' a voice calls from the other side of the yard. 'Wrong to speak ill of the dead, is it?'

'Harrison!' Jack turns, keeping both men in his sight and an eye on the only exit.

'Welcome home, Jack,' the man grins. 'After all these years.'

'Aye, it's certainly been a while. Well, lads,' Jack raises his hands. 'It's been grand, but I'll not keep you two any longer. I know how busy you've been. Why, so busy you couldn't even spare a couple o' years abroad, fighting for the King.'

'We all know why you left in such a hurry, Patterson.'

'Yeah, now fuck off out of it again,' says the man with the gun.

'An' don't fucking well come back.'

Next morning, before dawn, Jack sets off on foot for York. His travel warrant has just three more days to run. Twenty-four hours later he is on the London train.

Dear Anna.

The station café at King's Cross is almost empty. Jack sits at a grubby table with his back to the counter, covering the words with his arm as he writes. He moves the ashtray to the windowsill. His mug of tea sits next to a single sheet of paper.

I was discharged from the army on the 3rd of September. It nearly didn't happen after the mix-up over the grave you came to Belgium hoping to find. My grave, that is.

Jack takes the fag from the ashtray, puts it to his lips and inhales deeply, blue-grey smoke suspended in thin, swirling layers above his head.

Funny, up to then I'd have been quite happy to be someone safely six feet under. There's plenty better than me out there that is! There was such a lot of trouble in the village after you was born. I reckon I had almost as many enemies in Edgham as I did in Belgium. It seemed easier not to bother putting the record straight. The Battalion lost so many wickets on day one of the Somme that there was next to nobody left alive who knew who I was. It seemed like a stroke of luck, being 'killed' like that and coming back as someone else.

Jack lifts the mug and holds it midway between the table and his mouth as he goes over what he's written. Satisfied, he drains the tea. Picking up his pencil, he goes on.

355

I should've known that I could never pull it off, should've known that one day someone would come looking. Only I never dreamt that someone would be you. I had it all planned, in me head. New life, new country, marry a local girl. Even learning bits and bobs of the language, I was. I had it all mapped out. After all, there was nowt for me to come home to. They wouldn't let me near you when you was born and now, well – as Lady of the Manor it's better that the secret stays that way, if you ask me.

Anyhow, the army sent me back to Ripon, so naturally I tried to see you. There was such a lot I should have told you when we met. I know it was a shock. It was a shock for me, too. I realise now why Lady Agnes sent you. I think you knew that, too. I reckon she knew that I was the only one who could tell you what you had a right to know.

Jack looks through the steamed-up window. A train grunts then screeches like a greased pig as the brakes of the huge black locomotive bring it to a jarring halt just a few feet from the buffers. Doors open. Instantly the previously empty platform is alive with people. Hundreds of identical shapes step down from carriages, a few hurrying down the platform to be the first to hail a cab, others checking their luggage and summoning porters while the younger, fitter travellers run into the open arms of waiting lovers. A group of women gathers at the platform gates, straightening hats and replacing pins. A man comes up, speaks to them and ticks off their names on a list. They follow him out of the station, onto the concourse. The women all wear black.

Your mam – your real mam, that is – was a grand girl. She weren't much more than eighteen – your age now. And I was about a year younger than her, I reckon. Both of us was employed on the estate. Me, I were a poacher turned gamekeeper – well, 'keeper's apprentice – and your mother, she was Lady Agnes' favourite. A proper surrogate daughter to her, she was. Even called her 'Auntie'. Lady Agnes insisted!

That's what probably made it harder, when Lily found out she were expecting. There was a bit of trouble. You can probably imagine. I lost me position. Lily was to be kept on during her confinement but then . . . ? Nobody knew what was going to happen. So your mam did a flit. She upped and left in the middle of winter. Half the estate was out searching for her. But they didn't find her. Not before I did. And not until you was born. But the strain had been too much. She died, while I held you in my arms.

I hope they don't speak badly of her. She would have been so proud of you. It weren't her fault she got into trouble. And it was kind of Lady Agnes to take you in and to bring you up as her own. They always used to say she longed for a daughter. Well, she got one didn't she? And the most beautiful, adorable, wonderful daughter any one could ever wish for, I reckon. I know I'm biased, but . . .

Outside the café window, the station is deserted. Black gates close off the ends of platforms. Carriages stand empty, their locomotives up the line taking on coal and water.

I'm going to see if I can get a job back in
Flanders. There's nothing for me here. I've tried,
believe me I've tried. There's nowhere to live,
no job, and no family. Well, apart from you, that is.
If I'm allowed to call you 'family' of course. I'm
hoping I might be able to pick up things again
with Mademoiselle Steenvan – Katia. Do you
remember her? I might get some work with the
War Graves Commission. There's still plenty needs
doing out there. But I won't be far away. You
found me once and it'll not take as much effort
next time. If there is a next time. I hope there
will be a next time, once you've settled down,
once it all makes sense to you, once you
understand what happened, why I did what I
did. You're the spitting image of your mam, you
know – your real mam. But you wouldn't know that,
would you?

Jack puts down the pencil, reads what he has written, makes a few corrections, orders another mug of tea and lifts the ash-tray from the windowsill and places it back on the table. He squints at the station clock through the smoke of his cigarette. The café, he reckons, will be closing shortly. He wonders if it's still raining outside.

Anyhow, I'd better sign off now. Please don't think
of this as my interfering. You've had a lot to come to
terms with and I know it'll take time to get things
straight, in your head. I'm not going to ask you for
anything. I just want you to know that I'm here if

you want me. I'll always be here. And I want to tell
you that I'm sorry.
    Yours,

    Yours? Jack chews the pencil. *Yours* . . . He puts the pencil down, picks up the smouldering Woodbine, drags, balances the stub on the ashtray and picks up his pencil again. He crosses out the 's' of 'yours', changing it quickly to,

    Your ever-loving,
    Pa.

34

'So you've been working at the cemeteries already?' the man is asking. 'In one of the Labour Companies?'

'Aye,' Jack says, fiddling with his cap. His ribs ache after another night sleeping on a hard, damp bench in the park. His greatcoat is so badly stained from sleeping rough that only the arrival of the chairman of the interview panel prevented the top-hatted doorman at the entrance to the Cavendish Hotel in Jermyn Street from turning him away.

'We was attached to them, sir. When t'war was over and they was trying to find some bits and bobs for us to do. I weren't able to bear arms after the Armistice, sir, so I weren't eligible for other duties – army of occupation, prisoner escort, peace conference . . .'

'Why was that, Corporal?'

'I was downgraded, sir. After being gassed.'

'But you could still dig?'

'Dig like the very devil, so I hear,' one of the other panel members interrupts. 'Drive too, I see.'

'Aye, sir.' Jack sits a little higher in the chair. The three men behind the wooden desk look down at their papers, look at one another, then look back at him.

'You say . . .' The chairman picks up a small piece of paper.

'You say here' – he pushes a pair of spectacles further up his nose and reads the short note to himself – 'it says here in your application that you will only accept a position in or around Ypres. Is that correct?'

'Yes, sir. That's right, sir.' Jack runs the rim of his tattered cap through his fingers, wheeling it backwards and forwards, over and over, round and round, again and again.

The man tosses the scrap of paper down, raises his eyebrows and lets out a sigh. The bald man on his left shakes his head.

'We cannot possibly guarantee a man a specific placement,' the red-faced man on the right says. 'It's out of the question, simply out of the question.'

'If we offered you a position,' the chairman of the panel goes on, 'you would I'm afraid have to be prepared to work wherever the Commission were to send you.'

'Yes – wherever there is work to be done,' says the other man.

Jack looks at each of the three of them in turn, unsure whether they expect him to respond or not.

'Do you wish to proceed with your application on that basis?' the chairman asks.

Jack isn't sure what to say. He opens his mouth for a moment, then closes it again, shaking his head and looking down at the floor.

'We're wasting our time here,' the red-faced man mutters. 'There are plenty more men to see.'

The chairman holds up a hand, looking down again at the papers in front of him, searching for something.

'Why Ypres?' he looks up, suddenly. 'Why Ypres, in particular?'

'Almost everybody served in the Salient, sir,' Jack says. 'It's the place I know best.'

'You've served in other sectors, too,' the red-faced man says.

'"Served on the Somme", it says here. Conducted searches and salvage operations around Loos too, I see,' the bald man adds.

'Aye, sir, that's right, sir,' says Jack.

'Well then, Corporal, I think under the circumstances that's about all there is to say on the matter. If we find we are in a position to offer you employment then you must understand that you will have to decide for yourself whether you are able to accept. But if you do choose to accept it will be whatever position we offer you, in whatever location we choose. Do I make myself clear?'

'In a position, sir?' Jack shakes his head. 'In a position to offer me employment? Pardon me, sir, but you're hardly flooded out wi' applications, are you?'

'Thank you, Corporal, that will be all.'

'No sir, but that won't be all. I've been out there for six years – three years fighting and nigh on three years digging. And I want to go back. I don't want to stay here. I have a job to do and I want to see it through.'

'Corporal?'

Jack is now pulling his cap through his hands like rope, the heat from the friction burning through even his thick calluses. He gets to his feet.

'There's things I have to do, sir. It has to be there. It has to be Wipers.'

The red-faced man leans across and points to something on the application form. The man in the middle looks more closely.

'Sit down, soldier,' the other man says.

'It says here . . .' The chairman pushes the spectacles up onto the bridge of his nose. 'It says here that you were . . . you are. Hang on, yes – 22198 Lance-Corporal Patterson, J. . . . yes, here it is . . .'

'What's all this about?' asks the bald-headed man.

Jack sighs. 'There was a mix-up, sir.'

'What kind of mix-up?'

'I, er . . . Mistaken identity, sir. I was listed as missing. Missing, presumed killed, sir.'

'But you are clearly neither.'

'No, sir.'

'So why wasn't the record altered?'

'Well, sir,' Jack sighs. 'I, er . . . I didn't . . . I don't rightly know.'

'You don't know?' The red-faced man splutters theatrically.

'Not really, sir. No. Seemed best not to, er . . . cause any trouble. Kick up a fuss.'

'Man's as good as a deserter,' the red-faced man is saying. Jack hears the words 'court martial' muttered darkly from across the table.

'So how—'

'Well, sir, it turns out I were dead an' buried and lying in the very cemetery whose graves I'd just been digging.'

'Vlamertinghe?'

'Yes, sir.'

'But the grave was someone else's?'

'Aye, sir.' A horse whinnies as a hansom passes on the street outside. The ruddy-faced man throws down his pen, but the chairman of the panel smiles and passes him a piece of paper, pointing at something with his finger.

'You were highly decorated, Jack. In your former incarnation, that is.'

'Aye, sir.'

'Can't be many men on the exhumation teams entitled to wear a VC ribbon.'

'No, sir.'

'But yours of course, your medals . . . well. You can hardly wear them if you're dead, I suppose?'

'No, sir.'

'Rescuing a fallen comrade under heavy fire,' the man reads, 'returning time and again in the face of hostile action . . .'

'You're a brave man, Patterson.'

'I weren't brave, sir. Not really. Just glad to take t'risk I suppose. Didn't care much about coming home, if I'm honest. If you can call this country home.'

'What's that supposed to mean, soldier?'

'Well, I er . . .' Jack stammers. The man on the right glares at him above bristling whiskers, face ruddied by brandy downed in the safety of the Officers' Mess rather than days and nights in all weathers in the trenches with a tot of rum, Jack thinks. Or still less, sleeping under the stars for a couple of months in the centre of London.

'I'll tell thee what that means, sir.' Jack is suddenly on his feet again. 'It means I fought for this country for nigh on three years, stayed on burying them that fought but didn't make it for another three – spent getting on for six years in France and Belgium, sir, I did.'

'Get to the point, man.'

'The point is, sir, that I come back six years later and to what? To fellas wi' one arm missing selling trinkets on street corners from a tray slung around their necks. To fellas – aye, sir, an' not just fellas like me, neither – fellas like you, officers, too – sleeping on t'benches in Hyde Park because they can't afford no better. D'you want to know where I slept last night, sir? Do you?'

'Hyde Park?' the man sighs.

'St James's Park, actually. Tha gets a better class o' vagrant there, what wi' it being so close to royalty. I had a major sharing t'bench wi' me. Aye! An' an MC he were, an' all.'

'That's . . . that's outrageous,' the red-faced man splutters.

'True, though,' the chairman answers. 'Sadly, only too true.'

'Land fit for heroes?' Jack says. 'Well, sir, let me tell thee something. There are no heroes here no more. And this country in't worthy of 'em anyway.'

'But . . .'

'No!' Angry tears begin to prickle at the corners of his eyes. 'I buried 'em.' He jabs a finger at his chest. 'They're all six feet under in fuckin' Flanders wi' flowers growing out o' their faces.'

'Now, look here—'

'Land fit for heroes?' Jack trembles. 'I know all about a land fit for heroes.' He shakes his head. 'Land fit for heroes? I'll tell you what a land fit for heroes is . . . it's . . .'

'Steady on, old man.'

'It's a fuckin' graveyard!'

35

Six months after Jack's departure, and growing visibly – her belly swelling almost daily – the time has come for Katia, too, to leave and to go on a journey of her own. During the war such things seemed not to matter, or at least not matter quite as much. People understood, or if they didn't understand they didn't have the time or energy or opportunity to judge. Now, in peacetime, things are different. Life is slowly returning to normal. A new life is growing. And people are noticing. They see that Katia can no longer manage to change the barrels or lift the heaviest crates; they know why she is getting tired more often; why she cries more easily.

The *estaminet* in Poperinghe is now deserted. In Ieper, meanwhile, the cobbles of the Grote Markt have been relaid. The walls of the Cloth Hall are rising from the rubble. And the British Tavern is a family hotel again, run by a father and his daughter, *with hot running water and with central heating.*

The broken stone of St Martin's Cathedral has been cleared, and plans are in hand to raise the mighty nave roof once again, for it to swell and billow like the great ship of Christian souls that it has been for over seven centuries. Her own ship, her soul, is bound for a more distant port. In St Omer, almost nine months after Jack's departure, Katia gives birth to a baby girl, a daughter, who will in time grow up to be the very image of her father. For a few precious hours Katia stares, astonished, at the girl's blue eyes. Then the nuns return. The girl is taken. And a few days later Katia's bags are packed and she returns to Ieper.

It is only then, as the bus is pulling out of the French town, that she catches sight of him, or what she thinks is him, with six other men lining up beside an ex-Army transport wagon and being spoken to by someone in a dark suit and stiff wing collar.

'Jacques!' She bangs on the window of the bus, then suddenly notices everyone else on the bus has stopped talking. Women are turning and staring; men are peering over the tops of newspapers. Somebody at the back of the bus is tut-tutting. Katia rubs her head and curses quietly, hoping to fool them into thinking that she's been thrown against the glass as the vehicle bumps along the cobbled road. She tries desperately to look back, but by now they have turned a corner. Staring straight ahead, she thinks of nothing else until she arrives back that afternoon in Ieper.

The wagon lurches, coming to a halt at the south-west corner of the Grosse Markt at the end of Rijsel Straat. Jack jumps out, slings the huge haversack across his shoulders and walks round to the cab.

'OK,' the driver says, 'straight up along, er . . .'

'Vandenpeereboomplein?'

'That's the one. People here will insist on using Flemish now instead of French,' the man explains. 'An assertion of their regional identity, I suppose. You'll find a lot of places being referred to in Flemish these days.'

'Aye,' Jack says. 'I know that. I just didn't think that it was called Vandenpeereboomplein the last time I were here.'

The driver shrugs. 'So anyway, it's past the cathedral, left into Elverdingestraat, and the IWG office is on the right just before Haiglaan.'

'I hope they've gone and got themselves a Plumer Straat an' all,' Jack smiles.

'Well, they're planning to as a matter of fact. You certainly know your stuff!'

'Aye, sir. I know me way around.'

'Jolly good. Remember when you get there to report to Captain Grady. He's in charge of the cemeteries around Nieppe and he'll be your supervisor – got it?'

'Got it, sir.' Jack tips his cap. 'Thank you, sir.'

'Good luck!'

Jack waits until the truck has driven back down the Menen Straat towards what Jack can just make out is the cleared gap in the ramparts where, it is said, a new memorial arch is to be built. But instead of walking on in the direction he's been given, he turns and crosses the Grosse Markt in front of the rising, scaffolded walls of the Lakenhalle and, with the Gerechstot on his right, turns and strides out purposefully down Boter Straat.

The hotel now has an impressive stone façade. How can so much have changed in little under a year? All over the town buildings have begun to rise, phoenix-like, from the ashes of war. Only the fresh white mortar and newly chiselled stone give the game away. Opening the door of the small hotel, he walks straight to the bar and looks around for her.

'*Kan ik u helpen?*'

'Er ... I'm looking for ..?' The bar has changed so much, but the space is still familiar, like a remembered dream. 'I'm sorry ... *Ik spreek niet goed Vlaams,*' Jack stutters. '*Spreekt u Engels? Mag ik een pintje, alstublieft.*'

The woman starts pulling at a decorated hand-pump. '*Ik spreek geen Engels,*' she is saying.

'Aye, but I bet you know someone who can . . .' Jack mutters under his breath. 'I'll call back,' he says, when he finishes his beer. 'Tell her I'll come back. I'll see her later.'

The small Imperial War Graves Commission Office in Elverdingestraat, no more than five minutes' walk away from what was once the British Tavern, is empty when Jack finally walks in.

'Hello? Hallo?'

After a few moments Jack hears footsteps on the stairs and a small, bespectacled man appears in the office. 'Patterson, sir. Jack Patterson.'

The man squints at him for a moment.

'Er, Patterson, sir. Albert Jack Patterson. I've been taken on by t'War Graves Commission. They said to . . .'

'Yes, yes,' the man is saying. 'Yes, yes, I know.'

'Sorry,' Jack says. 'Didn't think that you'd heard.'

'Oh yes,' the man smiles. 'I heard all right.'

'So?'

'So, Lance-Corporal "Jack-the-lad" Patterson – or should that be *monsieur le patron*? Whose medals are you going to be wearing at the church parade on Sunday morning? Or are you here to don your kitchen apron?'

'Bloody hell,' Jack stares at the man, open-mouthed, then starts grinning broadly. 'Bloody hell!'

'The gardening teams are already out,' Jim says eventually, once the two of them have recovered from the initial, mutual surprise and have finished reminiscing.

'No longer out gardening yourself then, over Lijssenthoek way?'

'No. Too old for all that.'

'Never!'

'Yes. They've given me a job here now. Filing bits o' paper.'

'Really,' Jack raises his eyebrows. 'That could be handy.'

'Anyway,' Jim goes on, 'I'd come back tomorrow if I were you. You'll have had a long journey. Let me take you to your lodgings. We've booked you in with a family in Chaussée de Bruges.'

'Chaussée de Bruges?'

'Aye,' Jim Ashbury nods. 'I hadn't realised when the order came through that, well . . . you know! But now I suppose you'll be staying at Mr Steenvan's new place, will you?'

'Well I don't know about that,' says Jack. 'It were all a long time ago.'

'I know,' Jim nods. 'I was there when they buried the girl. Remember?'

'Helped me dig the grave, if I recall.'

'You're right,' Jim nods. 'It was a long time ago.'

'Aye, well . . . If it's all t'same to you,' Jack says, 'I wouldn't mind a bit o' fresh air. As you say, it's been a long journey, and for most of it I've been cooped up inside one sort of wagon or another.'

'Of course,' Jim nods. 'And it's a lovely afternoon. You leave your stuff here, then. Have a wander round the town. Changed a bit since the last time you were here, no doubt?'

'Aye,' Jack says. 'And not just the town, neither.'

'Very well then,' Jim says, turning to go. 'I usually close up here at five o'clock.'

'Before I go.' Jack takes a folded slip of paper from his inside pocket and opens it out. 'I was wondering.' He hesitates. 'There's something I ought to do. Would you mind?'

He hands over the scrap of paper. Jim reads, then listens,

then disappears back up the stairs. A few minutes later he is in the office holding several typed forms.

'You're right,' he says, 'there's a grave in Motor Car Cemetery. The records certainly show some ambiguity . . . Yes, here you are. You're in Plot C, Row 12, 12, 12 – f. Here you are!' He hands Jack one of the typed sheets. At the bottom there is a familiar signature.

'Well, well.' Jack shakes his head. 'Ingham was certainly thorough with t'paperwork, I'll say that for him.'

'What's that?'

'Oh, nowt. The officer who used to be in charge of our little section . . . Let's just say he was an officer,' Jack pauses. 'But not a gentleman.'

'So anyway, about this empty grave . . .'

'This one, you mean?' Jack hands back the piece of paper. 'He were meant to be shipped back to Blighty.'

The War Graves man continues leafing through a sheaf of different forms, licking his thumb: 'What did you just say?'

'He were supposed to be shipped back to Blighty.'

'But that's . . .'

'Illegal, I know. Didn't stop it happening though!'

'So this plot here, the one at Vlamertinghe. The one that should've had—'

'Aye, lad!' Jack smiles. Outside, in the street, a wagon passes.

'That's quite a story,' the man says at last.

'Oh aye,' Jack sighs, shaking his head. 'Reckon could write a book!'

Leaving the beer behind the bar to settle, the woman goes through the door that leads into the enlarged back room, through to what Jack takes to be the hotel kitchen. He strains his eyes into the darkness after her, but sees nothing. 'Katia!' he hears the woman call.

And then, suddenly, like the dawn chorus, like the sunrise, like Reveille, there is the unmistakable sound of her, of Katia, of her voice, raised in conversation with this other woman, speaking fast, too fast for him to have any chance of translating whatever she is saying. Then, at last, he sees her, hands first, rubbing a towel as she walks through the door and into the bar to see for herself what the woman has just told her, to see if it could possibly be true. Then her eyes – huge, brown eyes – startled at first, then briefly pleased, and then suddenly angry. As she meets Jack's gaze and as slowly, slowly, slowly, the rising tide of relief in her heart begins overwhelming every other swirling and confused and tormented emotion, she smiles – but without intending to. She lets out a nervous little laugh as Jack smiles back – then throws the tea towel she is holding hard into his face.

Acknowledgements

My thanks go to the staff at the Commonwealth War Graves Commission for their patience and courtesy in answering my many requests for information, and to staff at the Imperial War Museum for their invaluable assistance. I would like to thank Diederik Vandenbilcke for his help with the nuances and accuracy of the Flemish language as spoken in Ypres, and Mike Hodgson for advice on the historical accuracy of the events and locations described. Any mistakes, however, are entirely my responsibility! My good friend Nick Fitton read and commented on early drafts, as did my father, and I am indebted to them both for their advice and encouragement. I am extremely grateful to Scott Pack, my editor, and to Imogen Denny and all the staff at Unbound for making this book what it is. Finally I would like to thank my wife, Sarah, for her patience, support and advice throughout the process of researching and writing this book – without you it would not happen!

Further reading:

Readers who would like to know more about the events described will find the following books and sources, all of which are highly recommended, invaluable:

Max Arthur, *Forgotten Voices of the Great War,* London, Ebury Press, 2002

——, *We Will Remember Them,* London, Weidenfeld & Nicolson, 2010

Franky Bostyn, *Passchendaele 1917,* Barnsley, Pen and Sword, 2007

David Crane, *Empires of the Dead,* London, Collins, 2013

Wayne Evans, Pierre Vandervelden & Luc Corremans, *Silent Cities in Flanders Fields: Ypres Salient and West Flanders WWI Cemeteries,* Houten, Lannoo, 2013

T.A. Edwin Gibson and G. Kingsley Ward, *Courage Remembered,* London, HMSO, 1989

Tonie and Valmai Holt, *Battlefield Guide to the Ypres Salient,* Barnsley, Pen and Sword, 1997

——, *My Boy Jack,* Barnsley, Pen and Sword, 1998

Philip Longworth, *The Unending Vigil,* Barnsley, Pen and Sword, 1967

E.P.F. Lynch, *Somme Mud,* London, Bantam, 2008

Martin Middlebrook, *The First Day on the Somme*, London, Penguin, 1984

Alan Palmer, *The Salient - Ypres 1914–18*, London, Constable, 2007

Sidney Rogerson, *Twelve Days on the Somme*, London, Greenhill Books, 2006

Tim Skelton and Gerald Gliddon, *Lutyens and the Great War*, London, Frances Lincoln, 2008

John Starling & Ivor Lee, *No Labour, No Battle: Military Labour During the First World War*, Stroud, History Press, 2014

Glossary

Alleyman – a German soldier, from the French '*allemand*', for German.

ASC – Army Service Corps (from 1918 Royal Army Service Corps) – responsible for supplies and logistics, as well as a labour force in support of front-line fighting troops.

base rat – soldier based behind the lines, either at HQ (headquarters) or a supply base, out of the range of enemy guns.

Battle Police – Military Police, the Army's police force charged with maintaining discipline and – in battle – ensuring that men didn't linger in the trenches. There are reports of summary executions on the front lines (see Middlebrook, p. 221), but no official reports exist.

Blighty – name derived from the Hindi term for foreign country – 'Bilayati' – used widely by the British in India and arriving in the trenches as slang for Britain.

Blighty one/Blighty wound – an injury serious enough for a soldier to be evacuated back to Britain for treatment.

Bull Ring – the parade ground at Étaples, notorious for the harsh discipline imposed by NCOs on troops arriving in France for the first time.

bum brusher – an officer's servant (or someone unduly subservient to authority).

canary – an instructor, so called because of the yellow armband worn.

cold meat ticket – one of a pair of identity discs. Discs carried the name, number, unit and religion of the wearer, and from 1915 the British Army issued two official tags made of compressed fibre, strung together. One was removed if a man was killed; the other (the cold meat ticket) remained on the body.

cooler – slang for prison.

coolie – Chinese labourer. Members of the Chinese Labour Corps were recruited to free front-line troops for fighting.

devil dodger – slang term for an Army chaplain (see also 'sky pilot' and 'holy Joe' below).

Eat Apples – Étaples, a small fishing port on the French coast where imperial troops trained on first arriving in France and from where many casualties were evacuated.

estaminet – a small café.

Fritz – slang for German (see also 'Jerry' and 'Hun' below).

Graves Registration Unit – British Army unit responsible for recording battlefield burials.

holy Joe – nickname for an Army chaplain.

German Flandern Stellung – Reserve position behind German front-line trenches at the start of the Battle of Passchendaele, July 1917. Prince Rupprecht of Bavaria proposed withdrawing to these lines when it became clear the Allies were going to attack but the defences had only been under construction for about a month.

Hun – slang for German soldier, or the German Army, often referred to as 'The Hun'.

Imperial War Graves Commission (IWGC) – the body responsible for recording burials and commemorating all those killed in war. It evolved from a Red Cross Mobile Unit founded (on his own initiative) by Fabian Ware. In 1915 it became the Graves Registration Commission under the auspices of the Army before being chartered in 1917 as the Imperial (now Commonwealth) War Graves Commission.

Jerry – slang for German.

King's Regulations – Army manual of rules and regulations, governing conduct as well as battle tactics.

landowner – the buried dead.

Lee Enfield – standard-issue .303 bolt-action rifle used by the British Army.

minnie-woofer – German mine thrower (Minenwerfer) used to fire small calibre shells at Allied trenches.

omms-n-chevoos – French railway carriages marked with the maximum occupancy for men (*hommes*) and horses (*chevaux*) and used to transport troops to and from the Front.

Pickelhaube – traditional German spiked helmet.

pillbox – small concrete fortification with fire holes, often spaced along German defensive lines.

RAMC – Royal Army Medical Corps, or 'Rob All My Comrades', thanks to the myth that orderlies would routinely remove personal effects including money from the wounded for 'safekeeping'. The RAMC was the Army's medical division.

redcaps – Battle Police (see above).

rest camp – slang for a military cemetery.

sky pilot – nickname for an Army chaplain (see also 'devil dodger' and 'holy Joe' above).

SIW – self-inflicted wound.

wooden cross or 'WC', order of – another way of referring to a
  soldier who is dead, in this case buried and with a grave
  marked with a wooden cross.

A Note on the Author

Tim Atkinson is a teacher, author and award-winning blogger. He was born in Colchester, brought up in Yorkshire and now lives in Lincolnshire.

www.timatkinson.info

Unbound
Liberating ideas

Unbound is the world's first crowdfunding publisher, established in 2011.

We believe that wonderful things can happen when you clear a path for people who share a passion. That's why we've built a platform that brings together readers and authors to crowdfund books they believe in – and give fresh ideas which don't fit the traditional mould the chance they deserve.

This book is in your hands because readers made it possible. Everyone who pledged their support is listed below. Join them by visiting unbound.com and supporting a book today.

Jolene Abbey
Louise Abson
Neil Achary
Andy Acheson
David Acheson
Sarah Acheson
Scott Addington
Angela Airey
John Allum
Richard Anderson
Catherine Ann
Andy Annett
Sandra Armor
Cheryl Arnold
John Arnold
Mike Atherton

Charles Atkinson
David & Janet Atkinson
Eloise Atkinson
Gail Atkinson
Janet Atkinson
Nicola Atkinson
Sally Atkinson
John Auckland
Cetin Bahadir
Daniel Bainbridge
Joanne Baird
Neil Balderson
Jason Ballinger
Vic Bannister
Robert Barclay
Mandy Barker

Matthew Barnes
Hayley Bashford
Emily Bassin
John Bayne
Paul Beard
Chris Beasley
Danny Beattie
Faye Bellfield
David Benjamin
Francesca Bennett
Matthew Berry
Ella Best
Philip Biggs
Ivan Boeing757
Nick Bowman
Mike Bradley
Natalie Bradley
Peter Brady
Richard W H Bray
Alice Broadribb
Ross Brooks
Tizzy Brown
Andy Bryan
Elizabeth Buccleuch
Stuart Bull
Alison & Tony Burns
Liz Burton
Jon Bush
Marcus Butcher
Karen Cannard
Micki Carey
Lee Carnihan

Sarah Carr
Linda Carradice
Cazzikstan
George Challis
David Chant
Fred Chant
Helen Chant
Jonathan Chant
Robert Chant
Sarah Chant
Francis Chantree
Zac Chapman
John Charlesworth
Colin Cheer
John G Chester
Michael Clarke
Jamie Clarricoates
Janet Clifford
Katy Clifford
Andrew Coburn
Adam Cock
Darren Cohen
Richard Coles
Stevyn Colgan
Diane Collingridge
Lawrence Collins
Victoria Connolly
Antoinette Cook
Sue Cook
Carol Cooper
Abigail Couchman
Gillian Couchman

Peter Couchman
Sarah Cowling
Tristan Cullen
Alice Cullerne Bown
To Dan from Margit xxx
Barry Davis
Rachael de Moravia
Neil Dickens
Bryan Dixon
Carol Dixon-Smith
Lucas Doig
Jenny Doughty
Simon Duff
Robert Dumelow
Alex Dunmore
Robert Eardley
Steve Easter
Ben Edwards
Daniel Elkington
James Ellis
Jeannette Ellwood
Ben Evans
Lyndsey Evans
Will Eves
Abigail Fenton
Claire Ferry
Kerry Fielding
Philippe Fierens
Andrew Finch
Nicholas Fitton
Chris Ford
Richard Foster

Sarah Foster
Sue Foster
Jordan Fox
June Frantzen
Caroline Gale
Edwina Galloway
Michaela Garbett
Nicholas William Garforth
Sam Gascoyne
Jack Gavaghan
Hazel Gaynor
Ted Gee
Ian Gibson
Chris Gillings
David Goddard
Becky Goddard-Hill
Martin Grahame-Dunn
Antonella Gramola-Sands
Abi Gray
Hannah Gray
Liz Grayson
Jeremy Green
Rachel Green
Vanalyne Green
Joanne Greenway
Rosalind and David Grice
Emma Grossmith
Sue Guiney
Mary Hague
Sarah Hague
Rubab Haider
Pete Hall

Helen Halliday
Jon Halliday
Lee Hampson
Phil Hancock
Jason Hanger
Linda Harbin
Jill Hardy
Kate Harmond
Charles Harrison
Ben Harwood
Stephen Herrick-Blake
Lee Hextall
Adam Hildred
Fay Hilton
Lisa Hilton
Martin Hodgson
Paul Holbrook
Lucy-Anne Holmes
William Hudson
John Hughes
Kate Hughes
Margaret Hughes
Warren Humphries
Simon Hyland
Allyson Issitt
Daryl Jackson
Andrew Jarvis
Catherine Jarvis
Celia Johns
Stephen Johnston
Alice Jolly
Angela Jones

Karin Joyce
Liam Joyce
Bryce Keane
Dain Keating
Jane Keightley
Kathryn Kelly
Graeme Kent
Kelvin Kent
Ryan Kevelighan
Kidz Drama
Dan Kieran
Patrick Kincaid
Ian King
Shona Kinsella
Stephen Kinsella
Claire Kirk
Penelope Kirkham
Ben Kirkman
Ronald Kirkpatrick
Harish Kurup
Audrey Lancashire
Samantha Leake
Richard Leatherdale
Mark Leech
Brenda Leonard
Philip Leonard
Oli Lill
Kerry Lister
Amanda Lloyd Jennings
John Loane
Billie Lowe
Jonathan Lowe

Rachael Lucas
David Luck
John Lyon
Ian MacDonald
Seonaid Mackenzie
Gautam Malkani
William Mallett
Vincent Maltby
Sabina Mangosi
Susan Mann
Carl Manning
Shaun Manning
Ryan Mason
Ron Mattocks
Marina Maxwell
Lynda McCraw
Richard McCready
John McGarel
Ian McMillan
John Meddick
Vicky Meddick
Erinna Mettler
Jo Middleton
J Millington
Ned Millington
John Mitchinson
Virginia Moffatt
Peter Mortimer
Heather Moulson
Danger Mouncer
Sarah Murphy
Marc Murray

Tamsyn Murray
Rosie Murray-West
Ernest Napier
Carlo Navato
Alex Needham
Richard Nice
Elna Nilsson
Bruno Noble
Kevin O'Connor
Jenny O'Gorman
Dominic O'Reilly
Scott Pack
Kenneth Park
Stephen Parry
Jane Parsons
Geoff Patterson
Michael Paul
Clare Pear
Jill Pepper
Tony Pepper
Alison Percival
Simon Pereira
Jo Perks
Mark Phillips
Martin Phillips
Karon Phoenix-Hollis
Jennifer Pierce
Justin Pollard
Bridgett Posey
Arthur Prior
Francis Pryor
John Pudsey

Leon Pycock
Waheed Rabbani
Alan Radcliffe
Alan Rainsforth
Andy Randle
Andrew Richley
Steve & Mandy Ridding
Annie Robb
Ian Rogers
Lee Rooke
SJ Ross
Tracey Scoot
Joan Seagroatt
Julie Seagroatt
Julie Seales
Melody Shanahan-Kluth
Laura Shelley
Trudy Shephard
Adam Shergold
Abhinav Singh
Vimal Sivasanker
Aiden Skinner
Emily Skinner
Michael Skinner
Mark Sleaford
Rowena Smalley
Toni Smerdon
Chas Smith
Helen Smith
Ray Smith
Thomas Smith
Liam Solomon

Martyn Soulsby
Richard Soundy
Thomas Spillane
Alex Spittal
Wendy Springett
Sue Sproats
Janice Staines
Iain Standen
Rohan Stewart-MacDonald
Mike Stokes
George Storry
Liz Stothard-Chew
Sue Stott
Ciaran Sundstrem
Nathan Talbot
Mike Tarran
Carol Taylor
Ian & Wendy Taylor
Alex Tilley
Bev Toogood
Dianne Tranmer
Melanie Trevelyan
Christopher Tubb
Genny Tunbridge
Heba Turki
Gill Turner
Joseph Turner
Kelly Turner
Tom Tweddle
Nicole Vandenbosch
Laura Vaughan
Bob Wagstaff

Emma Leigh Waite
Jen Walshaw
James Ward
Lee Ward
Christopher Watson
Richard Watte
Michelle Watts
Eric Wayman
Miki Weaver
Karyne Whalen
Peter Wharmby
Jo Wheatley

Katy Wheatley
Terry Whenham
Rev'd Alan White
Robin Whitehead
Chris Willerton
Conor Wilson
Moira Wilson
Catharine Withenay
Stephen Wood
Peter Worrall
Chris Yeates
Tom Young